TECHNICAL WRITING

for

READERS

and

WRITERS

TECHNICAL WRITING

for

READERS

and

WRITERS

Brenda R. Sims

University of North Texas

Houghton Mifflin Company   Boston   New York

To my parents, to Patrick,
and especially to Bill

Sponsoring Editor: Jayne Fargnoli
Senior Associate Editor: Janet Edmonds
Senior Project Editor: Christina M. Horn
Senior Production/Design Coordinator: Jennifer Waddell
Senior Manufacturing Coordinator: Priscilla J. Abreu
Marketing Manager: Nancy Lyman

Cover design: Walter Kopec
Cover image: Jim Krantz/Tony Stone Images

Printed in the U.S.A.

Library of Congress Catalog Card Number: 97-72548

ISBN: 0-395-63328-1

1 2 3 4 5 6 7 8 9-QH-02 01 00 99 98

Brief Contents

Contents

Chapter 9   Using Reader-Oriented Language

Preface

*T*echnical Writing for Readers and Writers has two goals: to prepare students for the many writing tasks they will encounter in the workplace and to provide technical communication instructors with a flexible, comprehensive teaching tool. Beneath these two goals lies the foundation of this book—the belief that writing is more than simply putting words on paper or a computer screen and that students learn best to write by understanding their readers and by writing and revising. This book, therefore, contains numerous samples of student and workplace writing and dozens of exercises by which students can apply the principles of technical writing.

Technical writing, of course, goes far beyond reporting facts. Technical writing is a series of deliberate problem-solving activities—activities that require critical thinking. Before writers can effectively put words on a computer screen or report facts, they need to understand why they are writing, who is reading, and why the readers are reading. Without this information, a document will most likely fail to achieve its desired purpose. When writers know for what purpose and for whom they're writing, they have a better chance of communicating effectively.

Technical Writing for Readers and Writers presents principles designed to give students the tools and practice they need to respond effectively to varied writing situations. With these principles, students can determine the organization, layout, and content that will best meet the needs of readers.

ORGANIZATION OF THIS BOOK

In addition to a brief introduction to technical writing in Chapter 1, *Technical Writing for Readers and Writers* contains four major sections and three appendixes.

Part I: Understanding the Role of the Writer

Part I helps students to understand their roles as writers in the workplace. Chapter 2, "Understanding the Writing Process," treats technical writing as a problem-solving, analytical process. Students learn that the writing process is a dynamic, recursive process. Many students have trouble getting started writing, and Chapter 2 provides strategies to help them begin. In Chapter 3, "Understanding and Writing for Your Readers," students learn principles for examining workplace writing from several vantage points: that of the writer, the readers, and the workplace. In Chapter 4, "Readers, Writers, and Ethical Communication," students learn to consider the ethical dimensions of their communications. In Chapter 5, "Collaborating and the Writing Process," students see how to adapt to the interpersonal challenges and opportunities of collaborative writing. This chapter also suggests ways for students to use electronic media to facilitate collaborative writing.

Part II: Knowing the Tools of the Writer

Part II presents principles students need to create effective, reader-oriented documents. In Chapter 6, "Gathering Information for Your Documents," students learn strategies for formulating research questions and exploring primary and secondary sources—including using research tools on the Internet and World Wide Web. This chapter includes information on documenting sources using APA style and MLA style. Chapter 7, "Structuring Information for Your Readers," presents techniques for organizing documents that readers can understand and use. In Chapter 8, "Writing Reader-Oriented Sentences and Paragraphs," and Chapter 9, "Using Reader-Oriented Language," students learn and practice style principles at the sentence, paragraph, and word levels. These principles provide students with strategies they can use to write clear, concise, reader-oriented documents. Chapter 10, "Designing Documents for Your Readers," and Chapter 11, "Creating Effective Visual Aids for Your Readers," demonstrate the rhetorical implications of document design and visual aids. These chapters give students "how-to" information that they can easily apply to their own documents and information. Finally, Chapter 12, "Preparing Front and End Matter," shows students how to prepare the elements required for formal reports—elements such as covers, title pages, tables of contents, and appendixes.

Part III: Producing Effective Documents for Your Readers

Part III applies earlier principles and tools to planning and writing various types of technical documents. Students learn to apply these principles and tools to proposals (Chapter 13), progress reports (Chapter 14), completion reports (Chapter 15), and instructions and manuals (Chapter 16). Students examine sample documents written by other students and workplace professionals. These documents include annotations that point out how the documents demonstrate the principles presented in the chapters.

Part IV: Writing Effective Correspondence for Your Readers

Part IV applies the text's principles and tools to letters, memos, e-mail, and job correspondence. In Chapter 17, "Writing Reader-Oriented Letters, Memos, and E-Mail," students learn rhetorical strategies, principles, and formats for writing correspondence that conveys what they intend and that meets the needs of the readers. In Chapter 18, "Writing Reader-Oriented Job Correspondence," students learn strategies for looking for jobs and for writing résumés, letters of application, and follow-up letters.

Appendixes

Appendix A, "Creating Reader-Oriented Web Sites," provides guidelines to help students build an effective Web site. Appendix B, "Creating Listener-Oriented Oral Presentations," presents information on planning oral presentations and suggests strategies for delivering the presentations. Appendix C, "Review of Common Sentence Errors, Punctuation, and Mechanics," provides a convenient, brief handbook.

FEATURES

Technical Writing for Readers and Writers offers students five recurring features: computer technology icon, Worksheets, Case Studies, *The Readers' Corner* boxes, and *Issues in Context* boxes. The technology icon signals tips and information that help students use computer technology to streamline the writing process. The Worksheets appear at the end of each chapter and present questions that students can use as they write. The Case Studies allow students to apply the principles of a particular chapter in extended workplace scenarios. Several of these Case Studies give students the opportunity to practice collaborative writing. *The Readers' Corner* boxes present anecdotal information about technical writing—past, present, and future—and suggestions for students to follow when writing. *Issues in Context* boxes report on current research on the topics raised in each chapter or provide a bibliography for more in-depth information.

ANCILLARIES FOR TECHNICAL WRITING FOR READERS AND WRITERS

The following ancillaries accompany *Technical Writing for Readers and Writers*:

- **Instructor's Resource Manual,** which includes guidelines for teaching technical writing, transparency masters, and quizzes
- **Instructor's Resource Disk,** which includes an alternative table of contents, syllabi, and additional Case Studies

ACKNOWLEDGMENTS

Several reviewers helped to shape and reshape this book. They have enriched this book, and I am grateful to them: **Rita J. Bova,** Columbus State University; **Norbert Elliot,** Institute of Technology, Newark, New Jersey; **Joanna Freeman,** Pittsburgh State University; **Peter H. Goodrich,** Northern Michigan University; **D'Wayne Hodgin,** University of Idaho; **Johndan Johnson-Eilola,** Purdue University; **Dan Jones,** University of Central Florida; **Rebecca Kamm,** Northeast Iowa Community College; **Olivia Mason,** Milwaukee School of Engineering; **Mary Massirer,** Baylor University; **Carolyn R. Miller,** North

Carolina State University; **Ronald J. Nelson,** James Madison University; **Fiore Pugliano,** University of Pittsburgh; **Mark E. Rollins,** Ohio University; **Scott P. Sanders,** University of New Mexico; **Patrick M. Scanlon,** Rochester Institute of Technology; **Charles R. Stratton,** University of Idaho; **Eva M. Thury,** Drexel University; **Nirmala Varmha,** Oklahoma City College.

I have also worked with an excellent—and friendly—team at Houghton Mifflin: Jayne Fargnoli, Janet Edmonds, Christina Horn, Terri Teleen, Nancy Lyman, and Jennifer Marsella. They have guided my hand, encouraged me, and shown extraordinary patience.

At the University of North Texas, I have had the privilege to work with talented graduate students and faculty members who have provided a creative, innovative workplace. I want to thank all of you.

Most of all, I want to thank my husband, Bill, and my son, Patrick, for their patience, guidance, and—always valued—ideas.

SUGGESTIONS

If you have any comments or suggestions for improving this book, I'd enjoy hearing them. Please contact me at the Department of English at the University of North Texas, Denton, TX 76203. My phone number is (940) 565-2171, and my e-mail is sims@unt.edu. I look forward to hearing from you.

Brenda R. Sims

Chapter 1

Writing, the Workplace, and This Book

As you begin reading this book, you may be asking: "Why should I take a technical writing course? I came to college to learn about my major, not writing." Indeed, many of you reading this book probably came to college to study engineering, computer science, biology, chemistry, or other technical fields. You probably didn't come to college solely to learn to write. However, in any of these fields, you will communicate your ideas and your progress to your managers, your clients, or your peers primarily through writing. As a professional, you may communicate by writing at the beginning of a project, during a project, and perhaps at the end of a project. In fact, you may write during every phase of a project.

Let's consider a mechanical engineer, Ernie Chavez, who works as a piping specialist for an electrical generating company. Ernie spends an average of 40 percent of his time writing. He begins most of his piping analysis projects with a written proposal to a plant manager. If the manager approves the project, Ernie reports his progress and possible changes in written progress reports to the plant manager. Ernie usually closes a project with a final report of his work and the cost of the completed project. Like you, Ernie went to college not to learn to write but to learn his profession; yet writing, he now realizes, is vital to succeeding as a professional engineer.

Let's also consider Jennifer Nowakowski, a computer programmer in the research and development division of a company specializing in software applications for the hotel and restaurant industries. Jennifer and her team have developed a prototype of a software application for inventorying food and supplies in restaurants. Before they can test the prototype, they write a proposal for company executives, introducing the prototype and asking for the funds they need to test it. If they write persuasively, the proposal may convince the executives to fund the test.

In this chapter, you will learn why writing is important to your career and how your workplace may affect your writing. You also will learn how this book will help you prepare to write in your career.

HOW WILL WRITING IMPACT YOUR CAREER?

Like Ernie and Jennifer, you will have to communicate your ideas effectively to perform your job and succeed in your career. You can't assume that others will see your work and approve it. Instead, you must effectively communicate your work, ideas, and progress to those with the power to implement your ideas or those who supervise you (Barabas). The better able you are to communicate your ideas and your work, the better is your chance of receiving rewards for your ideas and work. Your managers may even evaluate you indirectly and possibly directly on how well you communicate in writing. Your writing skills can even help you to receive promotions (Barnum and Fischer).

If you are like the typical college graduate, writing will fill about 20 percent of your time as a professional (Anderson). This percentage is likely to rise as individuals and organizations communicate more over the Internet and the

World Wide Web. Many companies are using electronic written communication such as electronic mail (e-mail) and the World Wide Web instead of voice communication and other traditional media (Halpern; Perry; Perry and Adam). This percentage also may rise as more companies trim their work force and professionals follow their written documents through to the production stage rather than relying on clerical staff (Dautermann). Instead of sketching out only a handwritten or printed draft of a document or correspondence for a secretary or administrative assistant, many professionals now prepare final or nearly final drafts of documents without the aid of clerical staff—but, instead, with the aid of computer software.

As a professional, you not only will spend much of your time writing; but you will need to write effectively to succeed in your career. Surveys tell us that 94 percent of college graduates believe that writing well is important for success in their workplace—42 percent believe it is of great importance (Anderson). Although writing well does not solely lead to success in the workplace, it is an important contributing factor. You may find that you can enhance your reputation with your managers, your peers, and your company through your writing. Whether you are writing to propose a new idea to your manager or to record a project's history for the permanent files, clear writing gives you visibility and credibility with your manager, your peers, and, ultimately, your company. Poor writing, too, gives you visibility—but without credibility. If you write poorly, other people may have difficulty understanding your ideas; and your ideas and your work may fail to receive the recognition they deserve.

HOW DOES THE WORKPLACE AFFECT WHAT AND HOW YOU WRITE?

Several workplace factors will affect you and your writing tasks. These factors include

- Your company's and your manager's expectations
- Your readers' expectations
- Time and budget limitations
- Ethical considerations
- Collaborative writing

Expectations of Your Company and Manager

When you become a professional, your company and your manager may have certain expectations about your documents. They may state or write their expectations explicitly, or they may imply their expectations. Your company or manager may expect the format, organization, or style of a document to meet certain criteria or established guidelines; or a manager may have certain preferences about format and style. For example, many companies have a standard format for progress or status reports; some even have forms. Some companies have a standard cover page and a standard layout for letters and

ISSUES IN CONTEXT

Are You Ready to Be an Information Broker?

In the post-industrial age, information is becoming the primary product for many companies. Companies still manufacture and purchase products, but many companies deal primarily in information (Johnson Eilola 245). For example, traditionally hardware drove the computer industry; software and technical assistance were clearly secondary. Now, software companies, such as Microsoft, drive the computer hardware industry. With this shift to an information-driven age, we will see a new class of service work intertwined with information. Former U.S. Secretary of Labor Robert B. Reich suggests three new classes of this work:

- Routine production: These workers perform repetitive tasks. They might be line managers or clerical supervisors—those who repetitively oversee subordinates' work and ensure that workers follow standard operating procedures (Reich 174).
- In-person service workers: These workers perform the tasks of routine production combined with the ability to work with people. Reich says these workers must be "courteous and helpful, even to the most obnoxious of patrons" (176).
- Symbolic-analytic: These workers identify, rearrange, distribute, abstract, and "broker" information. Their tools are information and symbols, and their products are "reports, plans, and proposals" (Johnson-Eilola 255). Symbolic-analytic workers might be research scientists, engineers, computer programmers, strategic planners, architects, lawyers, or other information brokers.

Post-industrial work inverts the traditional relationship between product and product knowledge: Knowledge and information have attained "primary value" (Johnson-Eilola 256). The more valued workers in this environment will be able to manipulate, revise, and rearrange information (Johnson-Eilola 256): They will be information brokers.

memos. Many companies also have a style sheet that dictates style and grammar rules that the company expects you to follow when writing documents for internal readers or for readers outside the company. Find out whether your company or manager has certain expectations about style and layout, and then meet those expectations to the best of your ability.

This book suggests some general formats and guidelines for many workplace documents. If your company or manager does not have implicit written guidelines, you can use the example documents and the style guidelines presented here. The examples and style guidelines given in this book will help you to become familiar with the types of documents and style that you may encounter in the workplace. To supplement these examples and guidelines, once you begin your career you can gather samples of effective documents written by your coworkers and then use those documents as models. Your company and your manager will appreciate that you are trying to create documents that fit with other documents the company produces—that you are being a team player.

Expectations of Your Readers

As a student, you generally know your reader—your instructor—and what he or she expects. In the workplace, however, you may or may not know your readers. They may be your manager or your peers. They may be company executives whom you've never met. They may be clients or potential customers. You may never meet your readers.

The readers for many of your documents may be more than one person or group, and each individual or group may have different expectations of your documents. Your readers may include men and women who live and work in countries and cultures other than yours. Their expectations of you and your document may differ from the expectations of those who work in your own country. As a professional, you will want to account for these differences to write effective, successful documents.

This book will help you learn how to determine what your readers expect and then how to meet those expectations. It also will help you begin to consider what international readers will expect from your documents and then how to write for these readers.

Time and Budget Limitations

As in college, the workplace will limit the amount of time you can spend on writing documents. Your manager and your company will expect you to write quickly and efficiently. They will expect you to finish documents on time and within the budget. Deadlines and budget limitations may force you to spend extra hours at work or to submit a document before you are ready. For example, your manager may ask you to write the documentation for a new software application that your company is marketing. He or she may require you to have the document ready for user testing within a month even though you normally would need two months. Time and budget limitations may also affect your writing. You may have to adapt an idea or a document to meet budget requirements. Every professional must contend with time and budget limitations; but, like other successful professionals in your field, you can learn to write effective documents despite these constraints. This book suggests ways to streamline your writing process, to prioritize format and design decisions, and to use computer technology to help you submit documents on time and within the budget.

Ethical Considerations

As a professional, you may face ethical considerations about the language or the information that you or your coworkers use in workplace documents. For example, how will you report the results of tests on a new airbag design when the testing shows some serious design flaws and redesigning the airbags would delay the production of a new car model? The language you use could affect how your readers perceive the design problem and ultimately how they decide to act. The language you choose could force the company to spend thousands of dollars correcting the design flaws. Your decision could also cause the company to lose sales to a competitor or to install the flawed airbag in automobiles—possibly endangering consumers.

As a professional, you may face similar ethical predicaments. This book does not dictate values or tell you how you should act, but it does help you to analyze the ethical implications of the language you select for your writing and to understand how language can affect readers' perceptions.

Collaborative Writing

When writing in the workplace, you frequently will work with others to produce a document. In fact, 87 percent of the college graduates surveyed by Lisa Ede and Andrea Lunsford said that they sometimes collaborated with others to produce documents (60). In conversations with professionals in various fields, I discovered that they collaborate on most of the documents they write—except short letters, memos, and e-mail. They reported collaborating in these ways:

- Planning a document with others either in their company or outside their company
- Coauthoring or writing as part of a team
- Reviewing and revising documents

Planning Documents with Others

Before a large writing project, most companies create a team to determine the document's purpose, readers, schedule, and organization. The team may contain only writers; however, in most cases, the team consists of members from different areas of the company. A company might select team members according to the function they will perform in the production of the document; the team might have a subject-matter expert, a writer, a graphics expert, and an editor. The company might select team members according to their knowledge of the product, including members from engineering, computer programming, manufacturing, marketing, or other technical areas.

Collaborative planning can help team members identify global issues early in the document cycle. They can answer important questions about these issues before writing begins. In these planning sessions, team members establish a schedule for producing the document and agree about areas of responsi-

THE READER'S CORNER

Reading Time

Recent Gallup polls show that people today are working roughly four weeks more per year than they worked in 1970. They spend much of this time reading. The average management employee probably spends about half of his or her time reading. You can reduce this time and boost productivity with two simple techniques: eliminating bad reading habits and developing new reading skills. The reading eye leaps from point to point in a sentence, fixating only momentarily on specific words or phrases along the way. Many readers, though, fixate too long on single words. Similarly, although readers normally reread on occasion, too much rereading slows the reader down. Another bad habit is subvocalization—saying the words silently to yourself as you read. For strong readers subvocalization unnecessarily slows the reading. You can also increase reading speed by developing these new skills:

- Learn when 50 or even 25 percent comprehension is enough. Your reading comprehension doesn't always need to be 100 percent.
- Skim over redundant details or visual elements.
- Learn to focus on the key words in a paragraph (nouns, verbs) to discover the main point.
- Scan the page for transitional words such as *yet* or *finally* to locate crucial sentences or paragraphs.

When you develop these simple reading skills, you will have more time for other tasks—at work and at home.

bility. Once the team has planned the document, set the schedule, and assigned areas of responsibility, one or more persons may actually write the document. In some collaborative situations, the team may plan the document but only one person actually writes (Raign and Sims).

Coauthoring or Writing as Part of a Team

In some organizations and writing situations, several people write a document. These people collaborate in one of two ways:

- Each person is responsible for writing a particular section of the document, and then usually one team member serves as a final editor (Raign and Sims).
- Team members write the document together—word by word.

Most teams find the first method of collaborating is more efficient. Regardless of the method, the more successful teams decide on the style, design, and tone of the document early in the writing process.

Reviewing and Revising Documents Collaboratively

Even if you don't work as part of a team to write a document, you probably will collaborate with others when reviewing and revising most documents. You may even collaborate with others by reviewing their documents—documents that you didn't help plan or write. The review can be a formal process in which the writers and other interested parties meet to review the document—often suggesting revisions. These people may meet more than once before formally approving the document. Even if you are not writing as part of a team, you may take part in a formal review of your documents. William Sims, a mechanical engineer, reports that before he sends to others some of the documents that he has written, other engineers must review them. He also reports that newly hired and unlicensed engineers write under the signature of a licensed engineer; so a senior or licensed engineer must review many documents. Collaboration in this instance does not involve the teamwork mentioned earlier; instead, collaboration takes place at the reviewing or revising stage rather than at the planning or drafting stage.

The review process may be informal. When it is, coauthors and interested parties receive a copy of a document to review. Often, these reviewers make comments and suggestions through e-mail or in a shared file accessible to all reviewers. The authors then use this file for revising. This book will help you to develop techniques for successfully collaborating with others to create effective documents.

WHAT'S AHEAD IN THIS BOOK?

Technical Writing for Readers and Writers will help you to write effectively as a professional. Part I explains your role as a writer in the workplace and introduces some issues that you may face as a technical professional. The chapters in Part I focus on

- Understanding the writing process in the workplace
- Understanding how to analyze and write for readers
- Considering the ethical issues of writing and language
- Understanding how to collaborate effectively

Part II discusses the various "tools" that a writer needs to create effective technical documents. You may have learned how to use some of these tools in other writing courses; some, however, may be new to you. In Part II you will learn about tools for the following tasks:

- Gathering information for your readers
- Arranging information for your readers
- Writing reader-oriented sentences and paragraphs
- Using reader-oriented language
- Designing reader-oriented pages and documents

- Creating effective visual aids
- Creating front and end matter

Once you understand the role of the writer and have the tools you need to write effectively, you can begin writing specific technical documents. In Part III you will learn about the types of documents that you are likely to write in the workplace. You will learn about writing

- Proposals
- Progress reports
- Feasibility and research reports
- Instructions and manuals

In Part IV you will learn how to write effective correspondence. Part IV has two chapters. One presents specific guidelines for writing effective letters, memos, and e-mail. The other explains how to write effective job-hunting correspondence—specifically, résumés, letters of application, and follow-up letters. This chapter also suggests some techniques for looking for jobs when you graduate.

Throughout this book, you will see three features:

- An icon for using computer technology
- *The Reader's Corner*
- *Issues in Context*

The icon for using computer technology (shown at left) appears in many of the chapters. This icon points to tips and information to help you use computer technology to streamline the writing process. *The Reader's Corner* appears in every chapter. It presents an opportunity for you to consider how technical writing—past, current, and future—affects you, your readers, and the workplace. This feature also presents anecdotal information about the chapter's topic and tips for you to consider as you write. *Issues in Context* appears in every chapter, too. It reports on research about topics raised in the chapter and sometimes provides a bibliography for more in-depth information. Along with these topics, the book includes examples of student and professional writing. It also includes exercises that will let you practice and improve your writing and editing skills, including some exercises where you will work with a team.

PART I

UNDERSTANDING THE ROLE OF THE WRITER

Chapter 2

Understanding the Writing Process

CHAPTER OUTLINE

Some people believe that writing is as simple as putting ideas on the computer screen and then printing them. *Effective* writing, however, is more than just putting words on a computer screen or sheet of paper. The writing process actually begins before you commit words to a computer screen or page. The complexity of the document and the workplace influence the process. You may write documents as simple as routine e-mail messages or as complex as feasibility reports. The requirements of your workplace, your coworkers, and the purpose of the document itself also influence your writing process. In this chapter, you will learn how the workplace influences the writing process. You also will learn about the various stages of the writing process. At the end of the chapter, we will examine several strategies that you can use to begin the writing process.

THE WORKPLACE AND THE WRITING PROCESS

As a student, you write most documents for one person—an instructor. Your primary purpose for writing is to meet the requirements of the instructor and to complete the course successfully. As a professional, you will write for various readers—your managers, your company, your coworkers, and your clients or customers. The various expectations, needs, or requirements of these individuals or groups will influence your writing. At times, you may collaborate as part of a team to write various documents; and you and other team members will work to meet the expectations and requirements of your company and managers.

In the workplace, you may interact with others to produce your documents. For example, until you gain experience or move ahead in a company, you may write documents under a manager's signature. Your manager may ask you to plan and write a report or a letter for which another person is ultimately responsible. Therefore, your manager may want to see the document at several stages of the writing process and may ask you to revise it before he or she approves it.

Even if you're not writing under a manager's signature, your company may require you to submit your drafts and plans to a coworker or manager before you can continue with or complete a document. Your company may require your manager to approve the final document before you send it to others in the organization or to customers. These coworkers and managers can give you valuable feedback and information to improve your documents. You also can gather feedback and information from other people directly and indirectly involved with your writing task. For example, if you are writing a procedures manual for an environmental control system, you might ask sample users to test your manual for readability and accuracy. These users can give you valuable feedback about the clarity and accuracy of the procedures and about the design and organization of the manual. You can gather helpful information by talking with individuals in your company who have written similar documents. These coworkers may give you sample documents to examine, or they may give you some insight into the readers' needs or the company's expectations.

The requirements of your company may influence your writing process. Some companies have specific style or design guidelines that they expect employees to follow. Check with your supervisor or coworkers to find out whether your company has such guidelines. If it does *not*, it may have a technical writing, design, or graphics staff that prescribes style or design guidelines. For example, the public information staff at my university must approve any brochure or flyer sent to readers outside the university. Before I send these materials to readers outside the university, I take a draft to this staff. The public information staff helps me to meet the university's guidelines. Likewise, people in your company can help you to meet established guidelines and expectations.

Sometimes, you may write documents with a coworker or a team. In this collaborative writing environment, you may be part of a formal team. As a team member your role may vary. In one instance, team members together may decide on an organization for the document and then decide among themselves who will write specific parts of it. In another instance, you may be the primary writer on the team and be responsible for much of the writing while other team members serve as content experts. For example, you may be part of a team producing a new product. Some members of the team design and test the product, and others write the documentation to accompany the product.

You may collaborate informally. Suppose you are writing a proposal to renovate your building to better accommodate wheelchair users. You gather the needed information and write a first draft of the proposal. As you write, you work with architects to help you plan and produce blueline drawings showing the proposed renovations. You also ask the facilities manager for his or her opinion of your proposed renovations; the facilities manager advises based on previous projects that the company has completed to accommodate the disabled. You then ask a coworker who is familiar with your project or with the people who will be reading the proposal to read and respond to the draft. Each of these coworkers gives you valuable advice to help you produce an effective document.

Your writing process in your workplace is more interactive than your writing process as a student. In the workplace, you may interact with a team, a coworker, or other departments, and you consider more than the expectations of an individual instructor and your goal to complete a course successfully. Instead, you consider your company's and your manager's needs, expectations, and deadlines. In the next section, we will discuss the stages of the writing process and selecting strategies most appropriate for your workplace and your writing.

THE STAGES OF THE WRITING PROCESS

Although many factors can affect the writing process in the workplace, effective writers generally pass through these stages (see Figure 2.1):

- Analyzing the writing situation
- Creating and gathering information

Figure 2.1
The Writing Process

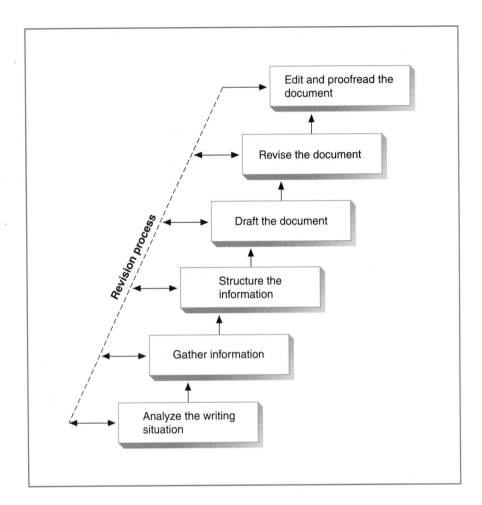

- Structuring the information (including design and visual aids)
- Drafting the document
- Revising the document
- Editing and proofreading the document

They may complete one stage and move on to the next, or, more likely, they move back and forth from one stage to another.

In the workplace, you may begin drafting a document and discover that you don't have enough information; so you return to the information-gathering stage. While you are revising a document, you may decide that you have not logically arranged the sections; so you return to the structuring stage and reorganize. Writing is rarely a linear activity. Most writers return to early stages of the process until they are satisfied with a document or run out of time.

Analyzing the Writing Situation

Before you begin putting words on a sheet of paper or screen, consider analyzing the writing situation and creating and gathering information. These two activities provide the foundation for the later stages. Many writers analyze the writing situation before they create and gather information; however, this stage and the creating and gathering stage often occur simultaneously, or sometimes you may analyze the writing situation after you have gathered and created information. These two stages complement each other: you need information about the purpose and readers of a document as you gather and create information, but often you need to know what information to include before you can define your purpose or specifically identify your readers.

Whether you analyze the writing situation before or after you gather and create information, spend some time thinking about the purpose of your document—what you want your document to accomplish. Find out about the readers and their reasons for reading the document and about the needs and expectations of your company. Your company may have a previously defined purpose for your document or may have specific requirements for organization, style, and design. Your company also may have secondary readers or a secondary purpose that you will need to consider as you plan the document. You may also think about how the company has written similar documents and the relative importance of your document in the context of the company's mission. You might consider your position in the company and the resources available to you. Then you can balance all these considerations and expectations with those of your readers. This information about your readers, your company, and the purpose of your document will help you to plan, structure, and revise effectively.

Because of all the factors involved with planning a document, you may find yourself revisiting this stage several times to reanalyze the writing situation. As you begin structuring and drafting, new ideas may occur to you, and you may revise your purpose to better meet the needs of your readers or the expectations of your company and its deadline. This stage is dynamic; it fluctuates as you develop your document.

Creating and Gathering Information

Whether you initiate or are assigned a writing project, you will create or gather information. During this stage, you create information by brainstorming, outlining, or writing a start draft. Using these techniques (described in detail later in this chapter), you begin to flesh out your ideas and decide what types of information to gather. You might simply write or type all the ideas that come to mind about the project, or you might informally sketch your ideas in the form of a diagram or chart.

Be sure to consider all ideas and methods of organization. You probably won't use them all in the final draft, but you may miss some excellent ideas or

THE READER'S CORNER

Writing the Declaration of Independence

Resolved to proclaim American independence to the British and the world, the revolutionary Continental Congress appointed five delegates on June 11, 1776, to draft a formal declaration. As a member of this "committee of five" would remember later, "they unanimously pressed on myself alone to undertake the draught." That member was Thomas Jefferson, who wrote feverishly for several days. Unfortunately, his first drafts are lost, but Jefferson clearly relied on the Virginia Declaration, which ran in part: "that all men are by nature equally free and independent and have certain inherent rights . . . namely, the enjoyment of life and liberty, with the means of acquiring and possessing property, and pursuing and obtaining happiness and safety." Jefferson's revision is notably more compelling: "that all men are created equal; that they are endowed by their Creator with inherent and inalienable rights; that among these are life, liberty, and the pursuit of happiness."

Before presenting the draft to the committee, Jefferson privately sought the advice of two older committee members, John Adams and Ben Franklin, who, with the rest of the committee, eventually revised Jefferson's draft forty-seven times (including changing "inherent and inalienable rights" to "certain unalienable rights"). Receiving the document on June 28, Congress made thirty-nine more changes. Approved on the morning of July 4, the Declaration of Independence was available as a broadside that afternoon. On July 9, General George Washington, stationed in New York City, read the text aloud to the ragtag but proud American army.

a good organization if you don't consider even the most unlikely. At this stage of the writing process, you can begin to

- Describe your readers and their needs
- Anticipate the organization of the project
- Identify the types of information you will need for the project
- Estimate the time you will need for the project

If you are working with a team or even informally with a coworker, this stage will help you to determine each team member's or coworker's role. You also can allow team members and coworkers to help define the project, giving each person the opportunity to feel a part of it from the beginning.

After you have begun structuring or drafting the document, you may need to return to this stage. For example, you may decide on a method of organization and then discover that you lack information for a particular section of the planned document. You then return to the information-gathering stage. You might brainstorm about possible information to include in that section and then plan some interviews to gather the needed information.

Structuring the Information

As you analyze the writing situation and gather information, you also will be thinking about ways to structure your document. You might consider how to organize the information or how to put the information into the document. Some writers even consider elements such as the table of contents, index, appendixes, and headings that they will include. As writers design the page layout, they may draw a sketch of several potential layouts and visual aids. During this stage of the writing process, you determine

- How you will organize the information
- How you will lay out the information
- What visual aids, if any, your readers will need

As you consider the organization, you may complete an informal outline of the information that you will include. You might want to ask your coworkers to give you feedback about your outline before you begin drafting the document. If you are working with a team, team members may work on an outline together, and then various team members write different sections of the document that correspond with the outline. Some teams and writers create an outline after they have completed one or more drafts of a document; they use this outline to check for sections that they've not developed adequately or for sections that may be out of order. Your company or the group requesting the document may specify an overall organization for the document. For example, the instructions for preparing many requests for proposals or requests for bids may specify the sections that the proposal or bid must include and the order in which these sections must appear.

Before you begin drafting your document, design your page layout and your visuals. You can save yourself and your team time and frustration by designing both at this stage. If you wait until you have drafted the document, you may not have enough time to create the layout or visuals that will make your document most effective, and you may not have the space, funds, or time to create the appropriate visuals. If you are working with word-processing or desktop publishing software, you or your team can easily decide on the layout and visuals early in the process. Each team member can then use the same electronic layout or style sheet; the process of putting the document together from each member's disk or file will be relatively simple because you will have made the most important formatting decisions early.

As you begin drafting the document and perhaps after you finish the first draft, you may find that you need to reorganize some or all parts of the draft.

You may decide that the page layout won't work for your readers. You may revisit the structuring stage of the writing process after you've drafted the document and even while you are revising the document. Like the activities of the previous stages, structuring may occur throughout the writing process. Often you will recognize the best structure only after you've drafted the document.

Drafting the Document

When you have analyzed the writing situation, gathered information, and structured the document, you are ready to put words on paper or on a computer screen. If you have effectively analyzed the writing situation and planned the document, you can more easily and quickly write the first draft. Writers who begin with the drafting stage of the writing process rather than with the planning stages often find that they have trouble knowing where to begin or what to write.

To ease your way into the drafting stage, you might start not at the beginning of the document but with the section with which you are most familiar. You never have to begin with the introduction. Instead, you might write the introduction after you've drafted the body of the document. Writing the introduction for a document that you have not yet written can be difficult—it's like introducing someone you don't know well.

As you draft the document for the first time, avoid revising and editing your work, especially if you are having trouble getting words on the page or screen. Many writers find that their writing goes more quickly and smoothly when they separate their composer from their editor (Elbow). These writers try to put all their words on the page or screen before they revise or edit. When they have completed the draft, they then begin the revising and editing tasks. This technique allows writers to get all their information, ideas, and notes into the draft before they are distracted by revising and editing. You, however, may realize as you draft some documents that the organization that you devised or the information that you generated is not appropriate. When that happens, you may have to return to the planning stages before you can effectively complete the draft.

The amount of time and energy you spend on drafting will depend on how well you write and on how well you have planned. Some writers compose quickly and try to complete one draft before moving to another task. Other writers start and stop, moving to other tasks and then back to composing. Some writers write drafts with a pen or pencil and then type the drafts using word-processing software. Other writers compose at the computer. Composing at the computer generally is more efficient because you combine the writing and typing tasks. Along with your composing style, several other factors may affect the amount of time and energy you spend drafting a document:

- The time constraints of your job, organization, or readers
- The availability of the information that you need and your familiarity with the information and the topic

ISSUES IN CONTEXT

Staying Fit at the Keyboard

As you sit at your computer, consider the design of your workplace. If the design is not ergonomically correct, your posture will not be correct, and you could injure your neck, wrist, and lower back. Irene Harris, an occupational therapist, suggests these "Seven Commandments" for staying fit at the keyboard (16–17):

1. "Mind the Spine." Make sure your chair fits your body. Your chair should support the curve of your lower back. If not, you'll slouch. This improper posture can make you look hunched when walking or standing.
2. "Beware of the Chair." Make sure that you plant your feet firmly on the floor. They should never dangle. Also, check to see that your chair is high enough so the crease in the front of your elbow is the same height as your keyboard.
3. "Assist the Wrist." Keep your wrists straight and support them with a wrist pad.
4. "Align the Arms." Place your keyboard so you can type while your elbows are bent directly beside your body.
5. "Check your Chin." Put your chin directly over your sternal notch (the curve at the top of your breastbone), parallel to the floor.
6. "Center the Nose." Position your keyboard so your nose lines up between the *g* and *h* on the keyboard. Position your keyboard so that it lines up with the center of the monitor.
7. "Take a Break." Take a break every hour when you are working at the computer for long periods.

- The length and importance of the document
- Whether you are writing alone or with a team or coworker

Revising the Document

After you have drafted a document, carefully read it, noting problems in organization and style. Look for areas that you have not adequately developed or areas where you have included too much or inappropriate information. Read your document critically, looking for problems in content, style, or page layout. Don't be afraid to make major as well as minor revisions. The first drafts written by even the best writers often look little like the final draft.

You can use several techniques for revising your document. You might ask a manager or a coworker to read your document and suggest revisions. If you are working alone, you can read the document and note problems and potential changes on the document. If you select this technique, use a pen or pencil with a color other than black, so you can easily see your notations. If you edit using a word-processing program, put your notations in the margins or in another color, or use the strikeout function available in most programs. This function draws a line through words you want to delete and underscores or highlights words you want to add. This function is especially useful when you are working with a team or coworker.

After you have carefully read the document, you or your coworkers can decide what changes you want to make. You may have to rearrange paragraphs, delete paragraphs, and write new ones. You may want to rearrange or combine whole sections, using the cut-and-paste feature of a word-processing program. After you have made the changes, read the draft again. You may discover new problems or find that you have forgotten to make changes that you noted earlier. After you make the changes that you or your coworkers have noted, compare the new draft with the marked-up earlier draft to make sure you have made all the changes.

Editing and Proofreading the Document

To edit and proofread, look at the words on the page or screen and try to put yourself in the position of a reader encountering your document for the first time. Look to see that the style is reader-friendly and that the sentences are clear and concise. Look for punctuation errors, misspelled words, missing words, and doubled words. Also look for inconsistent spacing, incorrect margins, and layout problems such as inconsistent formats for headings, lists, and figures. When you edit and proofread, systematically examine each of the following:

- Spelling
- Style
- Grammar and usage
- Spacing, margins, and page layout

Careful and systematic editing and proofreading help to ensure that your document will reflect positively on you and your company.

STRATEGIES TO HELP YOU GET STARTED

If you are like many writers, you find getting started to be the most difficult part of the writing process, but once you begin, the writing goes relatively smoothly and quickly. If you have a tried-and-true technique or ritual that you use when beginning to write, use it. However, if you have difficulty starting a document, try one or more of these strategies:

- Brainstorming
- Outlining
- A start draft

Brainstorming

Brainstorming helps people get their ideas on paper or on a computer screen. It is a technique used by writers and by other people who want to discover all the available ideas about a particular topic or project. To brainstorm, write or type all the ideas that come to mind about the topic or project. Your goal is to get all possible ideas about the project on paper or on screen.

Some writers brainstorm in categories. Suppose, for example, that you need to write a résumé. If you already know the major categories that appear in most résumés, you can brainstorm about information to put into the education section or the work experience section. You might also brainstorm about the skills, honors, and activities to include. If you don't know what major sections or categories to include, you can brainstorm for five or ten minutes about the major sections that you will create. Then you can brainstorm about the information to include in each one. You may not use all the ideas that you write down; however, brainstorming will give you ideas to select from and help you to think of information that you might otherwise forget.

Let's look at some brainstorming for procedures for testing a new fire protection system at a gas-powered electricity-generating plant (see Figure 2.2).

Figure 2.2

Sample Brainstorming About Testing a New Fire Prevention System

> **Description of the New System**
> how it differs from the old, manually operated system
> description of the control panels
> description of the equipment
> pictures/drawing of the control panels and the equipment
> how the system works
> include only enough information to help the technicians—they won't be interested
>   in an overly detailed description of the system and how it works
>
> **Testing the System**
> schedule for testing—monthly or quarterly? Check with the plant manager and
>   OSHA
> training requirements for testing
> procedures for testing:
>   announce the test—after alarm sounds
>   position personnel at various places in plant—each person should have a radio
>   begin test
>   personnel stationed at various places verify whether the system works as it
>   should
>   stop the test
>   reset the system
> include pictures of the control panels and equipment to clarify the procedures
> possible checklist for the testing procedure
> reporting after using the system—who? how?

The writer has brainstormed in categories, but the information in each category does not follow any particular structure or sequence.

Brainstorming is especially useful in collaborative writing situations. Brainstorming helps teams to hear ideas from all members, to get more ideas on the table, and to get started on projects. By brainstorming, teams also can ensure that each member has the same view of the readers and purpose of a document or project. A team can spend ten or fifteen minutes brainstorming about the readers and purpose before brainstorming about the information to include in a document or about the methodology for completing a project. Often a team has a vague, open-ended task, so the team may need to brainstorm to clearly define the task.

During a brainstorming session, all ideas are welcome, even ideas that seem farfetched. One team member writes all the ideas on a board or a computer screen, so that the team has many ideas to select from when organizing and drafting the document.

Outlining

Outlining may help you to begin a writing project. Outlining is a valuable tool for organizing the information you have gathered through research or brainstorming—especially when the writing project is extensive. Outlines can especially benefit collaborative writing projects. An outline lets each team member know what sections will appear in the document. You and your team can use one of the outlining software packages available to create and then share your outline. Creating an outline electronically will allow you and your team to quickly and efficiently revise the outline before and while you draft the document.

Outlining can be informal. You don't have to use the traditional format for formal outlines—Roman numerals and letters. Instead, an outline can be informal and dynamic, constantly evolving as you gather more information or as you begin to write. An outline in the early stages of the writing process may be incomplete but will develop as the process continues.

To work with an outline, follow these tips:

- List the major sections of your document. You might think about the order of the sections. Try rearranging the sections to determine the most effective order.
- After listing the major sections, list the types of information that you will include in each one. Be as specific and detailed as possible. If you put specific, detailed information in the outline, you can more easily and quickly draft the document.
- List any subsections that you can identify at this stage. Again, use specific, detailed information to help you when drafting.
- Try rearranging the information in the sections and subsections. Move the sections and subsections until you arrive at a logical sequence.

Don't worry if your outline at this stage is incomplete. You may need to gather more information before or as you draft the document. Don't be afraid to change the order of the sections or subsections as you draft the document. Your outline is merely a guide (for information about the format of formal outlines, see Chapter 7, "Arranging Information for Your Readers").

A Start Draft

Another technique that you can use early in the writing process is a start draft (see Figure 2.3). In a start draft, you write a detailed description of the document that you are planning to write. Much of the information that you include

Figure 2.3
A Start Draft

Title:	Procedures for Testing the Valley Fire Protection System at a Gas-Powered Electricity-Generating Plant
Purpose:	The purpose of this guide is to describe the Valley fire protection system and how it works and to present step-by-step procedures for testing and operating the system. This computerized system replaces a manually controlled one.
Objectives:	• To describe the fire protection system and briefly how it works • To give step-by-step procedures and a schedule for testing the system • To give step-by-step procedures for reporting after testing and after a fire • To present a troubleshooting guide for problems that may occur when testing the system
Preview of the Document:	These procedures have three major sections: **Section 1:** The Valley Fire Protection System and How It Works This section will explain the fire protection system and how it works. This section will describe the equipment and computerized control panels used when operating and testing the equipment and will include diagrams of the equipment and panels. **Section 2:** Testing the Valley Fire Protection System This section will give step-by-step procedures and a quarterly schedule for testing the system. This section will include a troubleshooting guide for problems and error messages that may occur during testing. **Section 3:** Reporting After Testing the Valley Fire Protection System or After a Fire This section will give step-by-step procedures for reporting after testing the fire protection system or after a fire. This section will include sample reports.
Locating Tools:	Table of Contents Index

in the start draft is likely to appear in the introduction of your finished document. A start draft can include these elements:

- **A title for the document:** A title helps you to focus on the topic and purpose of the document.
- **The purpose of the document:** A specific statement of the purpose or problem that the document will address.
- **The objectives of the document:** A list of the objectives that you or readers expect the document to accomplish.
- **A preview of what the document will contain:** A statement or list of the information that will appear in the document after the introduction. This statement should present the organization of that information. This statement or list is also called an *advance organizer.*
- **A description of any visual aids and locating tools that the document will include:** This description might include a tentative list of visual aids that you will prepare for the final version of the document. This description also might mention the locating tools that will appear in the final document, such as an index, a table of contents, quick-reference cards, or chapter divider pages. Knowing about these visual aids and tools will help as you plan the document and organize your time.
- **A prototype of the page design:** The prototype shows the position of the headings, subheadings, page numbers, and perhaps visual aids. It also shows the style and size of type that you will use (see Figure 2.4). Deciding on the page design early in the writing process can help you as you begin to draft the document. A prototype of the page design helps you to visualize where information will appear on the page—where to locate headings, visual aids, and text. Many writers find that visualizing the document helps them to draft the words that go on the page. If you postpone page design until after you have drafted the entire document, you may have to spend hours—even days—reformatting the document, especially if you are using word-processing instead of desktop publishing software.

CONCLUSION

This chapter surveys the entire writing process and examines three strategies to help you or your team start the process. You will learn about analyzing the writing situation in the rest of Part I, "Understanding the Role of the Writer," and about creating and gathering information in Chapter 6, "Gathering Information for Your Documents." You will learn about structuring information in two areas of the book: the basics of organization in Chapter 7, "Structuring Information for Your Readers," and the foundations of page design in Chapter 10, "Designing Documents for Your Readers." You will discover how to structure specific types of documents in the chapters in Part III, "Producing Effective Documents for Your Readers," and in Part IV, "Writing

Figure 2.4 A Prototype Page

Chapter Heading   22

LEVEL-ONE HEADING

Dolor sit amet, consectetuer adipiscing elit, sed diam nonummy nibh euismod tincidunt ut laoreet dolore magna aliquam erat volutpat. Ut wisi enim ad minim veniam, quis nostrud exerci tation ullamcorper suscipit lobortis nisl ut aliquip ex ea commodo consequat. Duis autem vel eum iriure dolor in hendrerit in vulputate velit esse molestie consequat, vel illum dolore eu feugiat nulla facilisis at vero eros et accumsan et iusto odio dignissim qui blandit praesent luptatum zzril delenit augue duis dolore te feugait nulla facilisi.

Level-Two Heading

Lorem ipsum dolor sit amet, consectetuer adipiscing elit, sed diam nonummy nibh euismod tincidunt ut laoreet dolore magna aliquam erat volutpat. Duis autem vel eum iriure dolor in hendrerit in vulputate velit esse molestie consequat, vel illum dolore eu feugiat nulla facilisis at vero eros et accumsan et iusto odio dignissim qui blandit praesent luptatum zzril delenit augue duis dolore te feugait nulla facilisi.

Level-Three Heading

Lorem ipsum dolor sit amet, consectetuer adipiscing elit, sed diam nonummy nibh euismod tincidunt ut laoreet dolore magna aliquam erat volutpat. Ut wisi enim ad minim veniam, quis nostrud exerci tation ullamcorper suscipit lobortis nisl ut aliquip ex ea commodo consequat.

Figure 1. Title of a Graphic or Table

Effective Correspondence for Your Readers." You will learn and practice the skills you will need to draft, revise, edit, and proofread your documents in Chapter 8, "Writing Reader-Oriented Sentences and Paragraphs," and Chapter 9, "Using Reader-Oriented Language." The chapters in Part III will help you to draft, revise, edit, and proofread specific types of documents.

WORKSHEET for Understanding the Writing Process

Analyze the Writing Situation

- Who will read your document?
- What is the purpose of your document?
- What is the readers' purpose for reading your document?

Create and Gather Information

- What are your readers' needs and expectations?
- What organization best fits the information and the readers' needs?
- What information will you need?
- How much time will you need to complete the document?

Structure the Information

- How will you organize the information?
- How will you lay out the information? Have you created a prototype of the layout?
- What visual aids, if any, will you include?

Draft the Document

- Do you have all the information you need to begin your first draft?
- Do you have a strategy (such as brainstorming, outlining, or a start draft) to help yourself get started?
- Have you avoided revising and editing as you draft?

Revise the Document

- Does the document have organization and style problems?
- Are there sections in which you have included too much, too little, or inappropriate information?
- Does the document have style or layout problems?

- Have others, such as a manager or coworker, read the document and given you appropriate feedback?
- After revising, did you compare the revised draft to the marked-up earlier draft?

Editing and Proofreading

- Have you systematically examined the spelling, style, grammar, and usage?
- Have you systematically examined the spacing, margins, and page layout?
- Does the document reflect positively on you and your company?

EXERCISES

1. Find two professionals working in your major field of study. (For example, if your major field is computer science, find two computer programmers or systems analysts.) Set up an interview to discuss how these professionals write. At the interview, ask them to discuss the following:

   - Techniques they use to begin writing
   - Steps they take when writing a short document
   - Steps they take when writing a longer document such as a manual, a proposal, or a feasibility report
   - When and how they revise and edit their documents (Do they edit as they revise? Do they draft as they edit? Do they revise as they draft?)
   - Computer software they use when they write

   You may also develop some questions of your own. You may want to ask them to give you some samples of their writing at different stages of the process.

2. After the interviews, write a memo to your classmates about what you learned. If possible, send this memo to them by means of e-mail.

3. To help you identify your personal writing process and compare it with the process described in this chapter, record the steps that you take to complete two documents. As you work on the documents, keep careful notes about what you do as you plan and draft. To make these notes, you can use pen and paper, word-processing software, or a tape recorder. When you have recorded your notes, do the following:

   - Identify the stages of your writing process.
   - Compare the stages of your writing process with those described in this chapter. (Look at the order of the stages. Determine whether you revisit earlier stages of the process as you write. If the documents differed in purpose or length, think about whether those differences affected your writing process.)
   - Identify the strengths and weaknesses of your writing process.

4. Write a memo or e-mail message to your instructor describing the stages of your writing process, its strengths and weaknesses, and how you can improve it.

CASE STUDY Boosting Attendance at Red Apple Days

Background

John Rameriz, a staff engineer for Colorado Cooperative Electric, is the chair of the company's annual "Red Apple Days—A Festival of Fitness." The festival is a health fair for all employees and their families. John is responsible for getting a larger number of employees and their families to attend the festival. During the past two festivals, only 40 percent of the employees attended; and of this 40 percent, only 20 percent brought their families. The low turnout disappointed not only the company volunteers working at the festival booths; but also the representatives from the local hospitals, fitness centers, manufacturers, and health-care organizations. If the turnout does not improve this year, the company may cancel the festival. Since the festival began five years ago, the company has negotiated a credit for preventive medical care based on the festival. If the company cancels the festival, the employees could lose this preventive care credit and see their monthly medical insurance premiums increase.

To encourage employees to come to the festival, John decides to draft a memo for all employees (see Figure 2.5). After writing the memo, John copies it for the other members of the festival committee. He attaches a cover letter explaining that he wants each member to read the memo before a meeting the next day. John also explains that although they may be uncomfortable commenting on his writing, he wants them to help with the memo.

At the committee meeting, John and the others decide to revise and expand the memo and to change the format. They begin by reanalyzing the writing situation, focusing primarily on the readers. The committee decides on the following list of reader characteristics:

- Various educational levels from high-school graduates to college graduates
- Varying degrees of interest in health-related matters (Some readers will be highly motivated to come; the committee must persuade others.)
- Various ages and health-care interests and needs
- Busy (Many readers will not want to spend either work or leisure time to attend the festival.)

Looking at the draft in light of these reader characteristics, committee members decide to select a format more interesting than a memo. They also decide to expand the memo to include specific information that they hope will persuade more employees to attend the festival. They brainstorm and come up with a list of items that they might mention about the festival (see Figure 2.6).

Assignment

You and your team assume the role of the festival committee and revise John's memo, selecting a format other than a memo for your document. To complete your assignment, your team completes the steps in Parts I, II, and III.

Part I

1. Write a purpose statement for the document. A purpose statement will help to ensure that all members understand the purpose of the document.

2. Examine the list of items that John's committee prepared during their brainstorming session (see Figure 2.6), and identify items that seem likely to persuade employees to attend the festival.

Figure 2.5
John's Memo

COLORADO COOPERATIVE ELECTRIC

Office Memo

Date: September 17, 1998
To: All employees
From: Red Apple Days Staff

During the first week of October, 1998, we will conduct our sixth annual health fair, "Red Apple Days – A Festival of Fitness." This health fair is for you and your families. It promises to offer health checks, information, fun activities, and more. These events should help you assess your wellness status and learn how and where to change your lifestyle if necessary.

As an expanded event this year, the festival will also offer seminars each hour, on the hour, during the festival. Health-care professionals will speak on important and timely health topics. A schedule of the seminars is attached. We hope that you find these programs beneficial and that you will be able to work one or more into your schedule.

So mark your calendar for Thursday, October 3, from 10:00 AM to 8:00 PM, and Friday, October 4, from 8:00 AM to 8:00 PM, for our festival. All activities will occur at Skyway Tower on the fourteenth floor.

See you there!

3. Using the items that you identified in step 2, either outline the document or write a start draft. During this step, determine the most appropriate format (other than a memo) for the document.

Part II

1. Each team member drafts the new document using the outline or the start draft as a guide. Each member should use a word-processing program to draft the document.

2. Each team member brings a paper and a disk copy to the next team session, attaches a copy to an e-mail message sent to the team, or saves the electronic file in a public directory that all team members can access it.

- Free blood-pressure checks by trained health-care professionals who will then counsel employees about their blood pressure
- Free cholesterol screening followed by counseling from trained health-care professionals
- Height and weight check followed by counseling from a trained health-care professional and dietitian (if desired)
- Computerized analysis of total health and wellness, based on the employee's height, weight, blood pressure, age, and answers to various health-related questions
- Health-related seminars on topics such as nutritional cooking, preventive health care, choosing a managed-care company, aging parents, cancer risk, dealing with stress
- Free products from health-care and food companies
- A children's area where children can play, have their hearing and eyesight screened, and get fingerprinted (the fingerprinting done by the local police department as part of a Kids' Watch program).
- Free babysitting in the children's area so parents can attend the festival
- Door prizes
- Festival hours until 8:00 P.M. so employees can easily bring their families or can attend without taking time away from their work
- Location close to offices so employees can easily attend during working hours or lunch without taking long hours away from their work
- Free hearing screening and eye exams for all adults
- Free body-fat measurement by Weight Loss Clinic
- Free lemonade and popcorn

Figure 2.6 The Committee's Brainstorming List

Part III

1. Each team member reads the documents drafted by all team members.

2. Each team member answers the following questions for each document:

   - Does the document give specific, detailed information about the festival? If it does, is the information persuasive? If it does not, what information should the writer include? Where should the writer include the information?

   - Is the document organized effectively? If it is not, how can the writer improve the organization?

   - Is the document reader-friendly? If it is not, what can the writer do to make the document more reader friendly?

   - Does the writer need to improve the style or appearance of the document? If so, how?

3. Using the answers to the questions in step 2 and the "background" information for this case, your team creates a persuasive, reader-oriented document—a document that will persuade readers to come to the festival.

4. After your team has revised, edited, and proofread the document, submit it to your instructor.

Chapter 3

Understanding and Writing for Your Readers

Have you ever read a report or a letter in which you didn't understand many of the words the writer used? Have you ever been unable to complete a task because the manual didn't give you the instructions you needed? In each situation, the writer—not you, the reader—was responsible for your not understanding the report or letter and for your not completing the task. The writer assumed that you knew more about the subject than you did—that you had a higher level of technical knowledge than you did. Such misguided assumptions can frustrate a reader and undermine a document's effectiveness.

The words and sentences that a writer selects for a document may not mean the same to readers as they do to the writer. Readers—not the writer—derive meaning from a document through their familiarity with the subject, their interpretation of the words, their experiences, and their attitudes. When readers are familiar with the subject, they can more easily understand the document and any new information in it.

Writers are responsible for readers' understanding of a document. As a writer, you need to spend time anticipating how your readers are likely to respond to a document, even to particular words you use. You need to find out what your readers know about the subject of your document and predict how they will respond to you, your company, and the document. This information about your readers will influence all aspects of a document—its purpose, organization, design, tone, and content. This chapter presents four principles to help you determine the purpose of your documents and to develop a profile of your readers.

PRINCIPLE 1: DETERMINE YOUR PURPOSE FOR WRITING

Before you begin writing, think about why you are writing and what you want the document to accomplish. For example, Randy, a mechanical engineer, is writing a feasibility report about repairing a turbine that has been vibrating excessively. The vibration is damaging surrounding equipment and reducing productivity. The purpose of Randy's report is to present three options for repairing the turbine and then to persuade the plant manager and the home office to choose the third option, a million-dollar plan to perform a high-speed balance of the turbine rotor. The first option is to operate the turbine in its current condition and to minimize the vibration damage by increasing the overhaul frequency of the affected equipment. This option will increase maintenance costs and will not permanently solve the problem. The second option is to limit the turbine load to reduce the damage from vibration. This option will cause the company to lose revenue.

Randy will send his report to the home office and to his supervisor. Randy has worked in the home office but has recently been promoted and transferred to the plant where the vibrating turbine is located. He wants to make a good impression on his superiors at the home office and on his coworkers at the plant. He also wants to begin to establish a good working relationship with his

Figure 3.1
The Purpose of
Randy's Report

The Purpose of My Document

- **What is the purpose of the document?**
  To present three options for repairing the turbine and to persuade readers
  to fund the third option: performing a high-speed balance of the turbine
  rotor at a cost of $1 million.

- **Does this document have a long-term goal? If so, what is that goal?**
  To convince the home office and the plant manager that I can solve
  problems and that I am capable of doing my new job; to establish a good
  working relationship with the plant manager and with the home office.

---

readers and show them that he is capable of solving problems in a timely, reasonable manner. Figure 3.1 shows Randy's summary of this purpose.

You will face writing situations where you will have to ask similar questions to determine the purpose of a document. For some documents, the purpose will be clear from the beginning; but for other documents, the purpose will be apparent only after you have asked questions about your readers and about the writing situation. Sometimes, the purpose that you identified at the beginning of the writing process changes as you gather information about readers' needs. When this situation happens, you may discover that the document has a long-term goal—such as maintaining the goodwill of the reader or establishing a positive working relationship.

PRINCIPLE 2: IDENTIFY YOUR READERS

As you determine your purpose for writing, you can begin to identify your readers. Identifying the intended readers is one of your most important tasks. Documents can accomplish their purpose only when they meet the needs and expectations of intended readers. The time you spend identifying your readers and understanding their purpose for reading may vary from one writing situation to another. For example, if you are writing for readers whom you know well or have worked with before, you will need to spend little time identifying readers and their purpose for reading. However, if you have never met your readers, plan to spend some time finding out about them and their purpose for reading your document. This section poses three questions to help you identify your readers:

- Are your readers internal or external?
- What do your readers know about the subject?
- Will more than one person or group read your document?

Are Your Readers Internal or External?

Internal readers work for your company. **External readers** work outside your company. Whether you are writing to internal or external readers will affect the information, formality, and language that you use. When writing to internal readers, you first may want to determine how they relate to you in the organization's hierarchy—both horizontally and vertically. When you know the horizontal relationship, you have information about the organizational roles of readers on the same level in the hierarchy. These readers may have the same level of authority but perform different duties.

Let's consider the organizational hierarchy at Randy's plant (see Figure 3.2). Below the plant manager, the organization has four areas: environmental staff, production superintendent, support superintendent, and administrative staff. The technical expertise of the people in the production and support groups varies, based on their roles, experience, and educational background. Individuals at the same horizontal level in production have the same level of expertise and similar educational backgrounds. However, the plant operators in this group have a different level of expertise and education. They are technicians who have high-school diplomas and extensive on-the-job experience. They don't have the technical expertise of the engineers and production supervisors, who have engineering degrees.

Your readers' vertical level in the organizational hierarchy will tell you whether the readers have more authority in the organization than you. If you know where they are in the hierarchy, you can better determine the appropriate tone for a document. If you and your readers are at the same level, you probably can use an informal, friendly tone; but if your readers are several levels above you, you may want to use a more formal, less familiar tone. Because

Figure 3.2 Excerpt from an Organizational Chart for a Power Plant

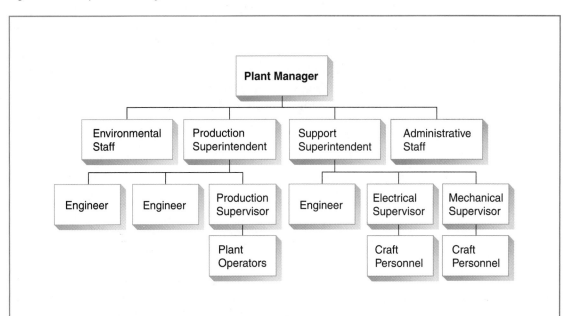

these readers may know little about the specific project that you are writing about, you might provide background information for them.

External readers may be customers, consultants, or other professionals. They probably won't have the information that internal readers have, such as the background of a project or document. When writing for most external readers, use a relatively formal tone and format. For example, companies generally use informal memos when corresponding with internal readers; but when corresponding with external readers, they use a more formal, letter format. This convention, however, is changing as more companies use e-mail and the World Wide Web to communicate with external readers. With e-mail, many writers use a memo format instead of the traditional letter, or they combine parts of the two formats. When using e-mail, most writers also use a relatively informal tone with external readers.

In traditional paper documents, companies generally use different formats for internal and external readers. For example, if you are writing a proposal for someone within the company, you might use a one-color memo format with the pages stapled together. However, if you are sending a proposal to a customer outside your company, you might use a two-color layout, a table of contents, tabs between the sections, and an attractive, well-designed cover.

What Do Your Readers Know About the Subject?

Will your readers understand the technical terms that you use? Will they understand the concepts that you present? Readers of technical documents have varying levels of technical expertise. Some of them may have the same level of technical expertise as you; others may know little about your technical field. Your job as a writer is to determine readers' levels of technical expertise and then use terms and concepts that they will understand or define the terms and concepts that they are likely to find unfamiliar.

Think of expertise as having three levels: high, mid, and low (see Figure 3.3). Readers with a **high level of technical expertise** are generally experts or technicians with a broad and deep knowledge of their field based on many years of practical experience or study. These readers

- Understand technical terms and information in their fields
- Understand and often even expect abbreviations and technical jargon
- Expect few—if any—explanations of technical terms or information
- Want a direct presentation of the information
- Are interested in theory

For these readers, explain only concepts and terms that you think will be unfamiliar to them. If you explain familiar terms and concepts, you may frustrate these readers.

Figure 3.4 presents the opening of a document for readers with a high level of technical expertise. The document uses technical terms, such as "open-pollinated seedling of W-26," "polycrossed," and "medium internodes," and the Latin name *(Ipomoea batatas)* for the sweet potato that is the writer's

Figure 3.3
Levels of Technical
Expertise

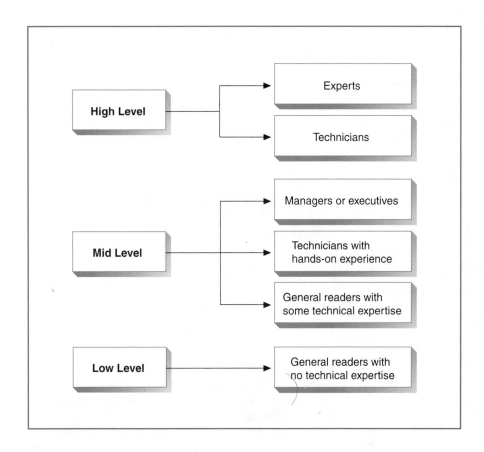

subject. Most readers with a high level of expertise will be familiar with these terms and expect to see Latin names.

Readers with **mid-level technical expertise** are technicians with hands-on experience and managers, executives, and general readers with some technical expertise. The technicians have practical experience in the field and also may have some theoretical expertise. Technicians generally have less formal education than readers with a high level of technical expertise but have extensive hands-on experience. Technicians

- Understand some terms and concepts in the field because of their practical experience
- Are interested more in practical, how-to information than in theory
- May need explanations of some technical terms and information

For technicians, explain only the most advanced or obscure terms and concepts.

Let's consider the instructions for constructing a chase for a woodburning fireplace (see Figure 3.5). The instructions define *chase* but assume that readers have some hands-on construction experience. The instructions recommend to "insulate the chase floor using batt type insulation between the floor joists."

Figure 3.4
A Document for
Readers with a High
Level of Technical
Expertise

'TOPAZ' SWEET POTATO
D. R. Paterson, D. R. Earhart, and T. E. Boswell

The 'Topaz' sweet potato [*Ipomoea batatas* (L.) Lam.] developed by The Texas Agricultural Experiment Station combines high yield, good sprout production, and excellent baking and canning quality.

Origin
'Topaz', previously tested as 8W2641, originated as an open-pollinated seedling of W-26 polycrossed at the U.S. Vegetable Laboratory in 1973 with other parental types developed for multiple disease and soil insect resistances. W-26 was from the 5th generation of mass-selection population I. The authors evaluated the seedlings from which 'Topaz' was selected.

Description
The vines of this entry are trailing with medium internodes. The stems and leaves are green. The leaves are medium in size and heart-shaped. The roots are chunky and slightly tapered at each end. They have an orange flesh color and a smooth, bronze skin color. . . .

Source: Texas Agricultural Extension Service, College Station, Texas. Used by permission.

The writer assumes that readers know what "batt type insulation" and "floor joists" are even though they may have never before constructed a chase.

Managers or executives read technical material to make decisions. They may have backgrounds related to your field, or they may have earned a degree in your field, but their knowledge is not up-to-date. For example, the vice president of a computer manufacturer might have a degree in business administration and on-the-job knowledge of computers but does not program or design hardware. Generally, managers and executives

- Read to gather information for decision making
- Expect conclusions, recommendations, and implications to appear near the beginning of the document or in an executive summary
- Read selectively or scan documents for the information they need to make decisions
- Need definitions and explanations of most technical terms and information
- Want practical information
- Like simple graphics that quickly summarize information

General readers with mid-level expertise (see Figure 3.3) may be interested but not formally educated in your field. They may have degrees in related areas—for example, a reader interested in engineering might have a degree in industrial technology. General readers with mid-level expertise have read widely in your field and understand basic terms and concepts. You might think of them as *sophisticated* general readers.

Readers with a **low level of technical expertise** have little if any knowledge of your field. Examples include a high-school student reading a brochure

Figure 3.5
A Document for Readers with Mid-Level Technical Expertise

CONSTRUCTING A CHASE

A chase is a vertical box-like enclosure built around the chimney and firebox. You can construct a chase for the fireplace *and* chimney or for the chimney only. The chase is most commonly constructed on an outside wall. In cold climates, insulate the chase floor using batt type insulation between the floor joists.

Three examples of chase applications are shown in Figure 20.

1. Fireplace and chimney enclosed in an exterior chase.

2. Chimney offset through exterior wall and enclosed in chase.

3. Chase constructed on roof.

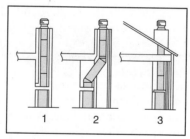

Figure 20
Chase Constructions

Materials for the Chase

To construct the chase, use framing materials much the same as the walls in your home. You can use a variety of materials, including brick, stone, veneer brick, or standard siding materials.

In constructing the chase, follow these guidelines:

• Maintain a 1/2" minimum air space around the firebox.

• Maintain a 2" air space around the chimney.

• Use a noncombustible material to construct the top chase.

• In cold climates, install a firestop spacer in an insulated false ceiling at the 8-foot level above the firebox assembly. This prevents heat loss through the fireplace.

• In cold climates, insulate the walls of the chase to the level of the false ceiling as shown in Figure 21. This will help prevent heat loss from the home around and through the fireplace.

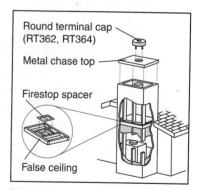

Figure 21
Chase Assembly

Source: Adapted from *E36, E39, E42: Woodburning Fireplace Installation and Operating Instructions for Residential Use* (Mt. Pleasant, Iowa: Heatilator, Inc., n.d.) 18–19. Used by permission of Heatilator, Inc.

about the dangers of blood clots, a journalism professor reading a newspaper article about macroeconomics, and a computer programmer reading tax-filing instructions. We are all general readers when we are reading technical information outside our fields of expertise. General readers

- Do not understand basic terms and concepts in your field
- Need simple definitions of most concepts and terms
- Expect examples and analogies
- Expect a simple, direct presentation
- Learn from simple graphics

Writing for general readers with a low level of technical expertise is often difficult because determining what they already know and understand is tricky. Your job as the writer is to gather as much information as possible about these readers. The more you know about their background, education, reading ability, and attitudes, the better you can anticipate what they will understand and the type of vocabulary you can use.

Let's look at a document for the owners of a new bicycle (see Figure 3.6). Compare the simple language and the friendly tone used in these instructions with the language and tone of the sweet potato document aimed at readers with a high level of technical expertise (see Figure 3.4).

Once you have some sense of your readers' level of technical expertise, you can choose words, concepts, and information that your readers will understand. Once you have determined what your readers know about your subject, don't waste time by giving them information that they already have. If, for example, they are familiar with the background of the project that you are reporting on, give them only a brief summary of the background.

You may have to write a document for readers with different levels of technical expertise. When you do, use the following techniques:

- **Divide the document into distinct sections so that readers can read only the sections that apply to them.** For example, you might have a "Getting Started" section for novice users and an "Advanced Techniques" section for readers with technical expertise.

- **Use devices that help readers find different information in the document.** These devices include indexes, tables of contents, executive summaries, headings, and page tabs that indicate sections (Holland, Charrow, and Wright 38).

- **Put the definitions of technical words, explanations of technical information, and other technical details in footnotes, appendixes, or other special sections that readers can easily find** (Holland, Charrow, and Wright 38).

- **Direct the language and presentation of a single document to readers with the lowest level of technical expertise.** This technique works especially well for instruction manuals.

- **Write separate documents for each group of readers if you have the time and the budget.**

Figure 3.6

A Document for Readers with a Low Level of Technical Expertise

USING THE BRAKES ON YOUR NEW BICYCLE

Your bicycle has caliper brakes. These brakes have brake shoes that are squeezed against a wheel rim much like disc brakes on an automobile. You have a caliper brake for the front and the rear wheels. To operate the brakes, use the brake levers mounted on the handlebars (see the illustration below). The left-hand lever controls the front brake and the right-hand lever operates the rear brake.

To slow your bicycle,

- Squeeze **both** levers to slow your bicycle, beginning with the right-hand lever (or rear brake).

  Be sure to use both brakes. If you use only your front brake, you can lock the front wheel and lose control of the bicycle.

Follow these braking tips for a safe and fun ride:

- When turning, brake slowly to avoid skidding.

- When the ground or pavement is wet, sandy, or covered with gravel, start braking sooner and brake slowly to avoid skidding.

- If the brake shoes or wheel rims are wet, start braking sooner as you will need more distance than normal to stop. As the shoes or rims dry during braking, the efficiency of your brakes may rapidly increase. Be prepared to stop quickly.

- Control your speed going downhill: the faster the speed, the longer the stopping distance.

- Check your brakes and adjust them (if necessary) the first time they don't stop your bicycle quickly and smoothly or don't stop your bicycle as well as they did in the past. (See pages 33-35 to learn how to adjust the brakes or take your bicycle to an authorized dealer.)

- Adjust your brakes when you can squeeze the brake levers to within one inch of your handlebars. (See pages 33-35 to learn how to adjust the brakes or take your bicycle to an authorized dealer.)

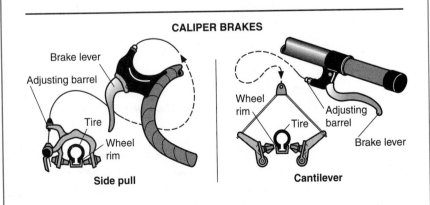

CALIPER BRAKES

Side pull

Cantilever

Source: Adapted from *Raleigh Owner's Manual* (Kent, Wash: Raleigh USA Bicycle Company, n.d.) 30–31. Courtesy of Raleigh USA Bicycle Company.

ISSUES IN CONTEXT

How Do Readers Read?

Readers read either to learn or to do (Sticht et al; Duin). When readers read *to learn*, they store information in their long-term memories, so that they can then use it later. (Sticht et al; Duin). However, when reading *to do*, readers typically have a well-defined purpose for reading before they begin reading. In other words, they might need information to solve a software problem or to install equipment (Brockmann). Unlike readers who read to learn, these readers typically use the information immediately and don't store it in their long-term memory (Sticht et al; Duin). Readers who read to do retain the information only long enough to complete the related task. These readers primarily use three reading strategies to locate specific pieces of information: skimming, scanning, and search reading (Digital; Pugh; Thomas). These readers don't begin a document at the beginning and read until they locate a specific piece of information—instead, they read documents in a "random access method" (Brockmann 192). In other words, these readers turn to the information they need without necessarily reading the information before or after it (Brockmann). Readers who read to do become more important as we consider the Web. Web readers don't always access a site through the front or home page. Instead, they may access the document internally through a link from another site. To accommodate the Web readers and readers who read to do, consider all the strategies you can employ in a document to help these readers skim, scan, and randomly access information.

- Put the document online so you can compartmentalize it for readers with various levels of knowledge. Be sure to include good navigational tools, so readers can easily find the sections they need.

Will More Than One Person or Group Read Your Document?

Often more than one person or group will read your documents. **Initial readers,** such as an administrative assistant or even the head of a department, may skim the document to determine who in their organization should receive it. Judging from the summary, cover letter, title, or introduction of the document, the initial reader sends the document to the primary reader. The **primary reader** is the intended reader—that is, the technician who will use the instructions, the executive who will decide to implement the proposal, and so on. The primary reader will use the document to complete a task, to gather information, or to make a decision. Some primary readers may use the document to make a decision but read only certain sections and then send the document to a **secondary reader,** who has only a minor interest in the document as a whole. The secondary reader might be a technical adviser whose opinion the decision maker is seeking. Such a reader assumes the role of *primary* reader of the sections that draw on his or her area of expertise. For example, the primary reader of a proposal might be a manager, and the secondary reader might be a technical expert whose views of the "Problems" section the manager requests. The technical expert, however, is the primary reader of the "Problems" section.

PRINCIPLE 3: DETERMINE YOUR READERS' PURPOSE, NEEDS, AND PREFERENCES

Just as you have a purpose for writing your document, your readers have a purpose for reading it. They approach your document with specific questions and expectations about the information and perhaps the style of the document. They have specific needs that you can consider when designing your document. How can you determine your readers' expectations and needs? One of the best ways would be to talk to each of your readers. This method, however, may not always be possible because of the number of readers, their geographic location, or your relationship with them. You may not know them, or they may not be expecting the document, so gathering information directly from them might not be feasible or appropriate. If you are writing to a large group, you can find out about your readers by talking with a representative sample. You also can contact people who know your readers or have previously written for or worked with them.

Let's consider Randy and his feasibility study for repairing the turbine. Randy knows the secondary readers at the home office, but he doesn't know the plant manager well. How can he determine the manager's needs and preferences? He can ask both the plant manager and coworkers who have worked with the plant manager. He can also look at reports previously prepared for the plant manager.

The following paragraphs give you some guidelines and questions to help you meet your readers' purpose, needs, and preferences.

Think About Readers' Purpose for Reading

Your readers will have one or more of these purposes for reading a technical document:

- To gather information
- To answer a specific question
- To make a decision
- To perform a task or specific action

To determine readers' purposes, you can consider some of the questions that they might ask.

Let's consider Randy's readers. His primary reader is the plant manager; his secondary reader is the vice president of production in the home office. Figure 3.7 lists the questions that Randy thinks these readers will ask. Randy thinks that Thomas, the plant manager (the primary reader), is concerned with three aspects of the recommendation: the cost of the recommended option in time and personnel, whether the recommended option will solve the problem, and why Randy thinks option 3 is the most feasible. Sarah, the vice president (the secondary reader), is most concerned with the financial impact of the solution on the plant and home office budgets, the impact of the shutdown of the turbine on other plants, and the effect of the chosen option on the production of electricity.

Consider Readers' Physical Surroundings and Time Constraints

Some readers work in noisy, distracting areas; others work in environments where documents are likely to get dirty and the pages bent and torn. By considering readers' surroundings, you can design and organize the document to meet their needs. For example, if you know your readers will use your instructions in a warehouse, you might put the instructions in a sturdy binding or

Figure 3.7 Excerpt from Randy's Worksheet for Identifying His Readers

---

What Questions Might My Readers Ask While Reading My Document?

Primary Reader: Plant Manager
What are the three options?
What is the cost of each option?
How much time and personnel will each option take?
What are the criteria for evaluating each option?
What are the advantages and disadvantages of each option?
How much downtime, if any, will each option cause?
Which option is most feasible and cost-effective?
Which option is the best long-term solution?
How and why is option 3 better than the other options?
Is option 3 cost-effective?
Is option 3 technically sound? Will it repair the turbine and solve the vibration problem?
Can our plant personnel conduct the high-speed balance, or will we have to hire consultants?

Secondary Reader: Vice President of Production
What impact will option 3 have on the production of electricity in the northern region?
Will the other plants have to pick up the load while the turbine is being repaired? If so, for how long?
How much does option 3 cost?
Is the cost within the plant's budget?
Is option 3 cost-effective?
Has the plant looked at all possible options?
Is option 3 a long-term solution?

notebook and laminate the pages so readers can easily clean the pages. If you know your readers will use your reference manual at a small computer workstation, you might use a relatively small page size that will fit next to the computer and put the manual in a three-ring binder that will lie flat. Readers' physical surroundings can influence your choice of cover, binding, headings, page size, line length, paragraph divisions, and type size.

Also consider constraints on your readers' time. Most readers receive many documents each week and have little time to read them all. Organize and design your document to help readers locate information quickly. If you know your readers are busy executives who receive many proposals, include tabs for each of the major sections, so readers can quickly flip to the sections they are interested in. You could also include an executive summary that briefly states your proposal.

You can use several devices to help busy readers to find information in your document:

- Headings and subheadings
- Tabs that separate the major sections
- Table of contents and index for longer, formal documents
- Page designs with ample white space
- Visual aids that summarize information quickly
- Summaries at the beginning of documents and major sections
- Overviews at the beginning of documents and major sections that tell readers what follows

When you keep in mind readers' time constraints and physical surroundings, you can better design and organize documents that meet their needs.

Consider Readers' Preferences

Your readers will have certain preferences about style, format, design, and media (paper, e-mail, other electronic forms). For example, some people like to receive documents by way of e-mail, and others prefer paper copy. Companies also have "preferences." Some want their logo to appear on every cover page and in particular colors. Some expect all documents to be printed in a specific typeface. Find out as much as possible about your readers' and your company's preferences, so you can meet their expectations and make a good impression.

How can you find out about these preferences? You can

- Talk to your readers when possible
- Talk with others who have written for or worked with your readers
- Look at some of the documents that your readers or their companies have written

As you talk with readers and their coworkers and examine their documents, look for their preferences in style, format, design, and media. You may discover other preferences, but these four areas give you a place to start.

Once you have identified preferences, decide whether you can accommodate them. When possible, try to accommodate them all. Unfortunately, if you are writing to more than one person or group, these preferences may be incompatible. They may contradict with your company's policies for technical documents, or they may be inconsistent in style.

PRINCIPLE 4: ANALYZE YOUR READERS' ATTITUDES

If you understand your readers' attitudes, you can select the appropriate tone and organization to make your document persuasive or appealing. You can easily determine the attitudes of readers whom you or your coworkers know personally; but when you or your coworkers don't know your readers, analyzing their attitudes is more difficult. You probably won't be able to analyze their attitudes toward you or your company, so try imagining yourself in their place to determine how interested they may be in the subject or how they may react to your document. The following sections suggest some techniques for analyzing your readers' attitudes about the subject of your document and about you and your company.

Analyze Readers' Attitudes About the Subject

Readers' attitudes about your subject may be negative, positive, neutral, skeptical, or enthusiastic. If their attitudes are positive or enthusiastic, writing your document will be relatively easy because you won't have to entice readers into your document or figure out how to convince them to read or use it. If their attitudes are negative, skeptical, or neutral, your writing task is difficult because you have to figure out how to motivate them to read your document or how to persuade them to accept your recommendations. For example, if you know readers will resist your recommendations, you might present the benefits or reasons for the recommendations before actually giving the recommendations. When readers have positive attitudes about your subject, you want to reinforce those feelings. When attitudes are negative, however, you want to change them.

To anticipate readers' attitudes toward a document, think about how they will feel about the topic. A computer software user with a question about how to install that software will need a manual and will be motivated to use the manual. In contrast, a company executive who receives an unsolicited letter from an unknown inventor requesting funding for a new way of measuring ozone in the atmosphere may be skeptical or unenthusiastic. Again, imagine yourself in your readers' place to analyze their attitudes toward your document. You can also

- Ask for help from people who have worked with your readers or who know them
- Talk with your readers about what information to include

THE READER'S CORNER

How We Read

Understanding how you read can help how you write. First, your reading eye hops across the page in what are called *saccades*. You pick up information during moments of rest, or *fixations*, when your *fovea centralis* (the point of sharpest vision on the back of your retina) focuses on the page. You then store this sensory information in your *sensory store* for a few hundred milliseconds (if you didn't pick up enough information the first time, you *regress* or reread). Your short-term memory processes the information in a variety of ways. Do you know the word by sound (*phonemically*) or by sight (*visually*)? Can you verify (or *parse*) the sentence structure and anticipate its direction? Your short-term memory can hold only about seven of these processed *chunks* before turning to your long-term memory for help verifying vocabulary and grammar.

As a writer, you can use these techniques to help your reader:

- Use type that contrasts with its background to facilitate your reader's saccades (rhymes with "what odds").
- Provide your reader with subtle phonemic cues (note the conclusion of the previous sentence): we remember words by sound as much as by sight.
- Use familiar sentence structures to let your reader know where you are going.
- Don't stack several nouns in a row or put too many items in a list; instead categorize the list items. Remember, your reader can hold only about seven such chunks in mind at a time.
- Choose your vocabulary wisely to save your reader's long-term memory some trouble.

- Read background documents and information related to the topic and find out what your readers thought of those documents and information

Let's again consider Randy's writing situation. In analyzing the attitudes of his readers, he begins with the plant manager, Thomas. Thomas is not happy about spending more money on the turbine because less than a year ago, the plant spent $750,000 to repair it. Those repairs caused the plant to be offline for more than six weeks. Thomas is nervous about spending more money and losing more production time. Randy works directly with Thomas but is new to the plant and still must prove himself to Thomas. He decides to meet with Thomas to get feedback about the three options. Randy also decides to talk to some friends in the home office who worked with Thomas for several years.

Randy's task with Sarah, the vice president of production, is easier. He reported directly to her for six years, so he decides to e-mail his recommendations to her to get her feedback. He believes that she is likely to agree with his recommended solution but will expect him to analyze all three options and present detailed explanations of their cost.

Analyze Readers' Attitudes Toward You and Your Company

Your readers' attitudes toward you and your company will influence their reaction to your document. These attitudes may reflect their previous experiences with you or your company. Readers who have had a good experience working with you will probably look favorably on your document even before they read it. Readers who have had a negative experience with you will pose a greater challenge. You will have to use part of your document to gain their confidence. If you don't know your readers, find out whether any of your coworkers have worked with them. If your coworkers have had positive experiences with your readers, you probably can safely assume that those readers will have a favorable attitude toward you and your organization. If the experience has been negative, you may have to design the document to gain the readers' confidence.

Even if your readers don't know you, they may have a preconceived attitude about your company. Think about your attitude toward the Internal Revenue Service (IRS). Would you be enthusiastic about receiving a letter from the IRS? Most of us would not be because correspondence from the IRS often is unwelcome information about filing tax forms or paying back taxes and penalties. Even though most of us don't know anyone at the IRS, we have a preconceived attitude about the organization and what it does. Likewise, your readers may have a preconceived attitude about your organization because of past experiences with it or because of its reputation.

Let's look at what Randy discovered about the plant manager's attitude toward him and the plant. Since Thomas is an internal reader, Randy knows that he will be interested in the future of the plant and in its reputation with the home office—both issues relate directly to Thomas's credibility and job performance. Randy knows that Thomas respects his abilities but will not accept his recommendation solely because of his abilities. Randy has been working at the plant for only two months, so Thomas will be looking for solid evidence to support Randy's recommendation.

CONCLUSION

Think about your readers throughout the writing process, not just at the beginning. They will react to your document section by section, paragraph by paragraph, sentence by sentence, word by word. Readers may not wait until they reach the end of the document to react to it. Instead, they may react to each part as they read it. Statements early in the document may determine a reader's reaction to the entire document, so think about your readers as you write every word, sentence, and paragraph. Spend time identifying your readers and anticipate as well as you can how they will react and respond to your document. After drafting a document, if possible ask one or more of the primary readers to read your draft and tell you unofficially how they would respond. If their response is not what you want, ask them for advice on how to change your document to get the response you want.

WORKSHEET for Identifying Your Readers

Principle 1: Determine Your Purpose for Writing

- What type of document are you writing?
- What is the purpose of the document?

Principle 2: Identify Your Readers

- Who are your primary readers? Are there secondary readers? If so, who?
- Are your readers internal or external to the company?
- What do your readers know about the topic and its related field?

Principle 3: Determine Your Readers' Purpose, Needs, and Preferences

- What questions might your readers ask while reading your document?
- How and where will your readers use your document?
- What time constraints are your readers under?
- What preferences about style, format, design, and media do your readers have?

Principle 4: Analyze Your Readers' Attitudes

- What are your readers' attitudes toward the subject of your document? How will they react to your document? Why?
- Have your readers worked with you or your company? Have the working relationships been positive or negative?
- What are your readers' attitudes toward you and your organization?

EXERCISES

1. Write two paragraphs about one of these topics or about a topic that you select:

   - A car accident that you were involved in
   - A grade that you received
   - A class that you have taken
   - The relationship between body fat and aerobic exercise
   - Functions of a new software package
   - The Windows environment for personal computers
   - The production of cheese
   - Sanitation standards for a meat-processing plant
   - Safety precautions for women walking alone at night
   - The World Wide Web and the future of written communication

   Write each paragraph for a different reader. The readers should have different purposes for reading and different levels of knowledge of the topic. Refer to the "Worksheet for Identifying Your Readers" as you analyze your readers and determine their needs, preferences, and attitudes.

2. Write a memo to your instructor explaining why the following paragraph about market value doesn't adequately respond to readers' needs and level of expertise. Comment on specific language that readers might not understand. This paragraph is from a pamphlet on property tax appraisals written for homeowners. These homeowners have different educational backgrounds and levels of expertise about property tax appraisals. Most of them have a low level of technical expertise and will read these paragraphs to help them understand their property appraisal, which determines its fair market value.

What Is Fair Market Value?

Section 1.04 of the Texas property tax code defines *market value* as follows:

Market value means the price at which a property would transfer for cash or its equivalent under prevailing market conditions if:

   a. Exposed for sale in the open market with a reasonable time for the seller to find a purchaser;

   b. Both the seller and the purchaser know of all uses and purposes to which the property is adapted and for which it is capable of being used and of the enforceable restrictions on its use; and

   c. Both the seller and the purchaser seek to maximize their gains and neither is in a position to take advantage of the exigencies of the other.

3. Find a short article on a topic related to your major field of study. The article should be for readers at a mid- to high level of technical expertise. Make sure that you understand the article; then do the following:

   a. Write a memo to your instructor describing the possible educational background of primary readers of the article, their level of technical expertise, and their purpose for reading the article.

   b. Select a 300- to 400-word passage that you find particularly interesting and rewrite it for readers with a low level of technical expertise.

   Attach a copy of the article to your memo and rewritten passage.

CASE STUDY Informing Students About Financial Aid

Background

Although this case is a team project, your instructor may modify it to be an individual assignment. Your team has received the following assignment from the scholarship and financial aid office at your college or university.

> Our school is losing many good students because they cannot afford the cost of tuition, books, and living expenses. Many of these students are unaware of the scholarships and other forms of financial aid that are available. Some scholarships are based on merit only, but others are based on merit as well as need. Some financial aid based solely on need is also available. Scholarships and other financial aid will help students to stay in school. Students, however, may be unaware of these scholarships and financial aid, may think that they don't qualify, or may think that applying for financial aid is too much trouble.

Your assignment is to write two documents:

- A memo to the director of the scholarship and financial aid office suggesting ways to inform students of available scholarships and financial aid

- A letter to all students informing them that scholarships and financial aid are available to qualifying students (Your letter should motivate students with financial difficulties to come to the scholarship and financial aid office for information.)

Assignment

Follow these steps to complete the assignment:

1. Answer the questions in the "Worksheet for Identifying Your Readers." Include information about the director of the scholarship and financial aid office and the students who will receive the letter. You may want to visit with the director of the scholarship and financial aid office at your college or university to gather information. If you cannot visit with the director, at least go to the office and find out what types of information are available for students.

2. Write a purpose statement for the memo to the director and for the letter to the students.

3. Brainstorm for information that you want to include in the memo and the letter.

4. Informally outline the memo and the letter.

5. Write and revise the memo and the letter.

Chapter 4

Readers, Writers, and Ethical Communication

CHAPTER OUTLINE

Susan works as a quality-control engineer for an automobile manufacturer.[1] She is responsible for testing a new design for a side-impact airbag. Company executives are eager to put these new airbags into next year's models because two other major automobile manufacturers have similar airbags in current models. However, Susan's tests of the new design have not been completely successful. In the tests, all the airbags inflated on impact, but 10 airbags out of every 100 tested inflated only 60 percent. The partially inflated airbags would protect passengers from most of a collision impact, but these passengers might receive more injuries than passengers whose airbags inflated fully. If the passengers with partially inflated airbags were small children, the injuries could be especially serious.

Before reporting the results, Susan tells her manager that she would like to test the airbags further to make sure that they are reliable and safe. Her manager explains that company executives want to get the airbags on the market as soon as possible—in fact, the marketing department is already working on the promotional material for the new airbags. The executives want the test results by the end of the week, so her manager can't authorize more tests. Susan now feels pressured to certify that the airbags are safe. Indeed, all the airbags inflated—at least partially.

Susan considers several ways in which she can report the test results. She might write that "all the airbags inflated," "none of the airbags failed to inflate," or "90 percent of the airbags inflated fully, and 10 percent inflated only 60 percent." Susan realizes that what she writes will affect the consumer and the company. Her choice of language could affect her role with the company and perhaps her relationship with her manager.

Susan's dilemma is not unusual. Professionals in the workplace frequently must consider the ethical ramifications of the language that they use in various technical documents. This chapter discusses ethics and presents three principles to help you deal with ethical dilemmas as they relate to language and communication in the workplace.

PRINCIPLE 1: DETERMINE WHAT COURSE OF ACTION THE ETHICAL VIEWPOINTS SUGGEST

Like Susan, you may face hard choices when communicating as a professional. You may feel pressured to compete at any cost, to save money, to get a product out quickly, and to turn over a clear profit. You may face pressures that test your ethics—your ability to act honestly and fairly and to fulfill your moral obligations and responsibilities to yourself, your fellow employees, your employer, or the public. You may not face potentially life-and-death situations such as the one facing Susan. The situations that you encounter may seem more "routine." They might include putting incomplete or inaccurate information on a job application, manipulating the language of an annual report,

---

1. I base this case and the analysis that follows on case study 1 in "Linking Ethics and Language in the Technical Communication Classroom" (Sims).

or manipulating statistical data to make the results of a study appear more favorable. Whether the ethical dilemma that you face is "routine" or life threatening, you will need a plan for dealing with it.

You can look at an ethical dilemma such as Susan's from three viewpoints:[2]

- The consequences of the action
- The morality of the action
- The impact of the action on the people involved

If you look solely at the consequences of an action, you are using what ethical theorists call the *standard of utility*. According to this standard, you select the course of action that produces the greatest good for the greatest number of people or the least amount of harm for the fewest number of people (Wicclair and Farkas 16). Regardless of whether an action is morally right or wrong, the principle of utility "prohibits actions that produce more bad than good" (Wicclair and Farkas 18).

If you look at the morality of an action, you consider whether it violates your moral duty. Instead of looking at the consequences of the action, you consider the action itself—to decide whether the action is morally wrong. Some actions are wrong "just for what they are and not because of their bad consequences" (Wicclair and Farkas 16). For example, we consider lying and stealing as morally wrong even if no one is harmed or if the lying and stealing produced positive consequences.

If you look at the impact of the action on others, you consider whether you are violating the rights of the people involved in the situation or the communication (Wicclair and Farkas 16). People have the right to be treated fairly, to receive "what is due or owed" and what they deserve or "can legitimately claim"; what they deserve, however, may be a "benefit or a burden" (Beauchamp and Bowie 40). People also have the right to be treated justly. They have the right to expect similar cases to be treated alike—equals to be treated equally and unequals unequally (Beauchamp and Bowie 41).

The following questions will help you to consider an ethical dilemma from each of the three viewpoints. They will help you to recognize the fundamental ethical responsibilities inherent in the communication tools of language and visuals.

- Is the communication honest and truthful?
- Are you acting in the company's best interest, in the public's best interest, in your own best interest?
- What if everybody acted or communicated in this way (Golen, Powers, and Titkemeyer 77)? If the action or communication is right now, is it right for everyone else in the same situation?
- Are you willing to take responsibility for the action or communication publicly and privately?

---

2. I base these viewpoints on the works of Mark Wicclair and David Farkas; Steven Golen, Celeste Powers, and M. Agnes Titkemeyer; and Tom Beauchamp and Norman Bowie.

- Does the action or communication violate the rights of any of the people involved?
- Are you treating similar situations similarly?

Let's consider how these questions will help Susan decide which language to use in her communication about the airbags.

Is the Communication Honest and Truthful?

You have a duty to be honest and truthful to your employer and to the public and to report problems and information that might negatively or positively influence your company, its employees, or its products and services. Likewise, the public expects you to use money, equipment, and supplies honestly and to give accurate, complete information. You will be dishonest and untruthful if you manipulate the language to hide facts, to make data say what you or your managers want, or to leave out unfavorable information. If Susan uses either of the statements "all the airbags inflated" or "none of the airbags failed to inflate," she will not be completely honest; she will be leaving out vital test results and creating false impressions. If she uses the statement "90 percent of the airbags inflated fully, and 10 percent inflated only 60 percent," she will be using honest, truthful language.

Are You Acting in the Best Interests of the Company, the Public, and Yourself?

Ideally, the company's, the public's, and your own best interests will coincide. However, you may be faced with a situation where these interests conflict. If so, you may have an ethical dilemma. For example, if Susan uses the statement "all the airbags inflated" or "none of the airbags failed to inflate," she will not be acting in the public's best interest because a consumer could be injured if an airbag failed to inflate fully. When Susan considers the company's and her own interests, the situation is less clear.

If she uses "all the airbags inflated" or "none of the airbags failed to inflate," she could argue that she is acting in her own best interest. She will get the test results to her manager in a timely manner, and she will not be "dishonest." She will not be claiming that all the airbags inflated fully or that none of the airbags failed to inflate fully. With either of these statements, she will— at least in the short term—please her manager and the company executives. However, she could also argue that using either of those phrases is not in her best interest. If one of the airbags injures a consumer and that consumer sues the company, Susan might be liable for not accurately reporting the results of the tests. Furthermore, if her manager or the company executives discover that only 90 percent of the airbags inflated fully and 10 percent inflated partially, they could view her actions as dishonest and untruthful. Susan could then lose their respect and confidence—or perhaps her job.

If Susan uses the statements "all the airbags inflated" or "none of the airbags failed to inflate," she could argue that she is acting in the company's best interest because the company will get the new airbags on the market

ISSUES IN CONTEXT

Don't Count on the Law to Guide You in Ethical Dilemmas

If you turn to the law to help you determine how to communicate or act ethically, you may or may not find answers. The law cannot always tell you how to communicate ethically. It can give you clearly defined legal restraints, but it can't give you ethical constraints that come only from the fine-tuning of your own judgment and conscience (Shimberg 11). In fact, legal and ethical considerations can conflict. The law often sets up only minimal legal restraints for behavior, whereas ethics implies "high standards of honest and honorable dealing and of methods used" for professions and businesses (Golen, Powers, and Titkemeyer 76). By following only the law, you can still act unethically because the law and ethics can give you significantly different viewpoints.

As a professional, consider these legal standards as you write and communicate:

- **Copyright laws protect the authors or owners of any document, whether published or unpublished, from unauthorized use of that document by individuals or corporations.** If an author sells or gives up his or her ownership of a document, such as to a publisher, copyright laws protect the corporation's ownership of the document. You must not use information from documents written by someone else without getting permission from the author—even if a corporation or other group owns the information. Be wary of using others' written information and making only cosmetic changes to it. You could be guilty of violating copyright laws, and you certainly would be guilty of violating the author's rights and your moral duty to be honest.

- **Liability laws protect the public from defective information from authors, editors, or publishers.** These groups are responsible for injury that occurs from defective information even if they gave out the information unknowingly.

- **Federal Trade Commission regulations protect the consumer from fraudulent and deceptive advertising.** For example, a manufacturer cannot claim that a side-impact airbag is completely safe when engineers report that 10 percent of the airbags did not fully inflate.

quickly to compete with other automobile manufacturers. However, she may not be acting in the company's best interest because the company could be hurt in the long run if one of the airbags fails, injures a consumer, and causes a lawsuit. Even if only one airbag fails to inflate, the consequences could be negative—negative publicity or a recall of all the cars with the new airbag design.

If Susan uses "90 percent of the airbags inflated fully, and 10 percent inflated only 60 percent," she is not unethically manipulating the language because the statement is truthful. She will be acting in the public's best interest because the company probably will not risk putting the airbag into the new automobiles before the designers eliminate its faults. The company could decide to install the airbags and issue a disclaimer. In any case, this statement offers Susan the only way to protect the public's interests.

However, the statement "90 percent of the airbags inflated fully, and 10 percent inflated only 60 percent" may not please the executives, who are anxious to get the new airbag design on the market. After all, the company hired Susan to work for them, not for the consumers; but she will safeguard the long-term interests of the company by protecting herself and the company from possible liability lawsuits and bad publicity—even if she angers the executives in the short term.

What If Everybody Acted in This Way?

When facing ethical dilemmas, ask yourself whether the action should become a general rule for all. In other words, if the action is right now, is it right for everyone else in the same situation (Golen, Power, and Titkemeyer 77)? If Susan uses the statements "all the airbags inflated" or "none of the airbags failed to inflate," she could endanger both consumers and the company. If everyone in the company reported information with such inaccuracy, the company could face lawsuits and lose the public's trust and business. If Susan uses the statement "90 percent of the airbags inflated fully, and 10 percent inflated only 60 percent," she will in the long run benefit the company. This statement does not withhold information from the company or the consumer. Although it may be unwelcome, it allows the executives and perhaps consumers to base their decisions on complete, accurate information. Presenting complete and accurate information is right for everyone in similar situations because it protects the company, the public, and the writer.

Are You Willing to Take Responsibility for the Action or Communication Publicly and Privately?

The "bottom line" for many people is to determine whether they are willing to take responsibility for an action or a piece of communication. Would you want your coworkers, employer, friends, family, or the public to know that you had written a particular document or taken a particular course of action? If you don't want these people to know what you have written or done, then perhaps you are acting or communicating unethically. When faced with an ethical dilemma, consider whether you are willing to take responsibility for your action or communication with your coworkers, employer, friends, family, or the public.

Susan would have trouble taking responsibility for the statements "all the airbags inflated" or "none of the airbags failed to inflate." These statements leave out important information. However, Susan could willingly take responsibility for the statement that "90 percent of the airbags inflated fully, and 10 percent inflated only 60 percent"; with this statement, she isn't withholding important information. Although Susan could willingly take responsibility for this statement, she has to recognize the potentially negative impact of her honesty: the company may have to spend thousands of dollars designing and testing a new side-impact airbag; and while testing this new design, the company could lose market share if its new cars aren't equipped with a side-impact airbag. Susan also has to consider that company executives may ignore the information in this statement and install the airbags without further testing. If they do so, Susan then may have to decide whether she wants to blow the whistle on them.

Does the Action or Communication Violate Anyone's Rights? Are You Treating Similar Situations Similarly?

When faced with ethical dilemmas in the workplace, you may also consider whether the action or communication violates the rights of your company, other employees, the public, or any others involved with the situation or communication (Wicclair and Farkas 16). These people have a right to be treated fairly and to receive "what is due or owed" and what they deserve or "can legitimately claim." What they deserve, however, may not always benefit them. Your company, your coworkers, and the public also have the right to expect similar situations to be treated similarly, so consider whether you would act or communicate in the same way in similar situations.

Susan knows that the statements "all the airbags inflated" and "none of the airbags failed to inflate" violate the rights of consumers and company executives. These statements violate consumers' rights because they don't include the negative test results. Consumers have the right to expect fully functioning equipment on their cars and to assume that the equipment has been adequately and appropriately proven to work. These statements violate the rights of the company executives because they withhold vital information that could affect the company and the consumer. The executives have the right to receive all the information available to make informed decisions. They especially have the right to know any information that could harm employees or consumers—even if Susan's disclosing the information is difficult or inconvenient.

The statement "90 percent of the airbags inflated fully, and 10 percent inflated only 60 percent" does not violate the rights of the consumer or the company executives. This statement provides *all* the information available—it does not withhold any important information.

PRINCIPLE 2: AVOID UNETHICAL MANIPULATING OF WORDS AND VISUALS

Through the words and the visuals that you select, you control how readers perceive you, your company, a product or service, and the subject. However, with this power, you also have an ethical responsibility to use words and visuals honestly and accurately. To meet this responsibility, avoid using misleading language and visuals and withholding information. Let's look at three scenarios.

Scenario 1[3]   Sulfuric acid (H_2SO_4) is a highly corrosive liquid that is compatible with stainless steel only in certain concentrations. Sulfuric acid is generally compatible with stainless steel in concentrations of 8 percent or less or in concentrations of 100 percent. Stainless steel piping is often used to transport sulfuric acid. Some piping manufacturers provide conflicting and misleading information about the concentrations of sulfuric acid compatible with stainless steel (see the three tables reproduced here as Figure 4.1). For example, in Table 1, the manufacturer recommends any concentration of sulfuric acid between zero and 77 percent and a concentration of 100 percent. This information misleads readers because concentrations over 8 percent will corrode stainless steel. Although Table 1 correctly recommends using concentrations of 100 percent sulfuric acid for stainless steel piping, the table doesn't explain that the cost of transporting sulfuric acid in concentrations of 100 percent is prohibitive. This table also has numerous abbreviations that compound the misleading information. The table contains abbreviations for the type of piping material as well as for the terms "recommended" and "not recommended." Readers must guess that "R" means "recommended" and "NR" means "not recommended." The writer should have spelled out these abbreviations or included a legend indicating what they mean.

In Table 2, another manufacturer rates a concentration of 100 percent sulfuric acid used with stainless steel as excellent and 77 percent or less as poor. Concentrations ranging from 9 to 77 percent are in fact poor because they will corrode stainless steel; but concentrations of 8 percent or less are not poor and should receive a rating of good, if not excellent. Table 2 could mislead readers to assume that concentrations between 77 and 100 percent, though not optimal, would be compatible with the stainless steel.

In Table 3, another manufacturer correctly recommends using a concentration of 8 percent sulfuric acid or less and no concentrations over 93 percent. However, this table could mislead readers because it does not indicate that concentrations between 8 and 93 percent will corrode stainless steel piping. For accuracy, the table should not include the information about 93 percent concentrations or indicate that concentrations from 9 to 99 percent will corrode stainless steel. As the table appears, some readers may assume that concentrations between 8 and 93 percent are somewhat compatible with stainless steel. The misleading information in this table is compounded by the abbreviations for the piping. These abbreviations may have little if any meaning for engineers who are not familiar with this manufacturer's notations.

---

3. I base this case on case study 2 in "Linking Ethics and Language in the Technical Communication Classroom" (Sims).

Table 1

	BRZ	CST	304	316*	PVC	CPVC	BUNA	VIT	TFE
Sulfur molton	N	N	R	R			N	R	R
Sulfur trioxide	R	R		R	R		N	R	R
Sulphur trioxide dry	R	R	R	R	R		N		R
Sulfuric acid 0 to 77%	N	N	N	R	R	R		R	R
Sulfuric acid 100%	N	N	R	R	N	N	N	R	R

*316 is a grade of stainless steel

Table 2

	Aluminum	Brass	Carbon Stl.	316	17- 4PH	Alloy 20	Montel
Sulfuric acid 0 to 77%	C	C	D	C		B	B
Sulfuric acid 100%	D	C	C	A	B	A	D
Sulfurous acid	C	D	D	B		B	D
Tall Oil	C	B	B	B		B	B
Tannic acid (tannin)	C	B	C	B	B	B	B

Ratings: A–Excellent   B–Good   C–Poor   D–Do not use   Blank–No information

Table 3

Service	Pressure*	Temp.**	CC1	CD1	CB1	CB2	SB1†
Fresh water	150 200 500	150 200 200	R NR NR	A R NR	A A NR	A A R	A NR R
Demineralized water	150 200 500	150 200 200	NR NR NR	NR NR NR	NR NR NR	NR NR NR	R R NR
Steam	100 150	350 550	NA NR	NA NR	R NR	A R	NR NR
Condensate	175 500	300 450	NA NR	A NR	R NR	A R	A NR
Air	150 200	150 200	R A	A R	A A	A A	A NR
H_2SO_4 93%	150	100	NR	NR	NR	NR	NR
H_2SO_4 0 to 8%	150	100	NR	NR	NR	NR	R

* psig   ** °F   †SB1 is stainless steel   R = Recommended   NR = Not Recommended   A = Acceptable

Source: Reprinted from Brenda R. Sims, "Linking Ethics and Language in the Technical Communication Classroom," *Technical Communication Quarterly* 2.3 (1993): 285–299. Courtesy of the Association of Teachers of Technical Writing.

◀ **Figure 4.1**

Tables from Three
Piping Manufacturers

All three tables give readers incorrect information that could cause damage to stainless steel piping. Unsuspecting readers could use the incorrect concentration of sulfuric acid and endanger not only the piping but possibly machinery and lives.

Scenario 2   A stereo radio headset comes with a booklet that opens with "Read this important information before using your headset." The booklet warns readers to "use extreme caution or temporarily discontinue use in potentially hazardous situations." However, the booklet never specifically describes any "potentially hazardous situations." For instance, it doesn't warn readers to retract the FM antenna and remove the headset during electrical storms. This imprecise language misleads and, more important, endangers readers. The writers may have used the ambiguous phrase deliberately (Shimberg 11) or carelessly. In either situation, their lack of precision could endanger the lives of customers who use the headset.

Scenario 3   A care booklet for an electric stove says that the burners have an "automatic temperature sensing control" that raises the heat level quickly and then monitors the temperature to keep food from burning. However, the booklet fails to tell readers that only certain models have this temperature sensing control. The booklet misleads readers because it doesn't indicate that only the highest-priced models have the sensing control. Readers who do have low-priced models may burn foods or even create fire hazards because they think that their stove has the sensing control.

As the three scenarios illustrate, language and visuals are powerful tools of communication. Through language and visuals, you control how your readers perceive you and the subject of your communication. As you write, think about the meanings underlying the words and visuals that you select. Make sure that the message that readers will receive is as close as possible to the message you intend and that you have not distorted the information. To avoid unethical manipulating of language, follow these suggestions.

Create Honest Impressions

Avoid creating false impressions that make readers think that conditions exist when they don't. For example, if the particular model of computer that you are including in your company's catalog comes without a compact-disc drive, don't show a computer with a compact-disc drive. If you are reporting test results, don't leave out information; by leaving out the information, you may give readers a distorted or inaccurate perception of the results.

Avoid Imprecise Language

Use precise language. Imprecise language can mislead or deceive readers. For example, if you are writing an instruction manual for a cordless vacuum cleaner, you might tell readers that the vacuum is "great for unexpected spills and messes and convenient for small, routine cleanup jobs around the house."

This information, however, is not precise unless you explain what you mean by "spills and messes." Many readers may consider spills of milk or juice as a job for the vacuum although it is designed to clean up only dry materials such as dirt or cracker crumbs, not liquids or wet items. Instead, the instruction manual could say that the vacuum is "great for picking up dry materials such as dust or cracker crumbs. Do not use the vacuum to clean up spills of liquids and other wet materials. These liquids and wet materials will damage the motor of the vacuum." You will learn more about using precise, specific language in Chapter 9, "Using Reader-Oriented Language."

Include All the Information That Readers Need or Have a Right to Know

Missing or omitted information can mislead readers. A memo about the O-rings involved in the *Challenger* disaster contains the following sentence: "The conclusion is that secondary sealing capability in the SRM field joint cannot be guaranteed." This sentence misleads readers because it doesn't give them enough information to correctly interpret it. A more accurate sentence might say: "The conclusion is that the secondary seal is not effective at temperatures below 50 degrees Fahrenheit, so the joint is highly vulnerable to catastrophic failure at such temperatures" (Winsor 15). The first sentence is technically accurate but doesn't give readers enough information to arrive at correct conclusions.

Make Sure That All the Information Is Correct and Accurate

You have a responsibility to give readers correct and accurate information. For example, a researcher may be tempted to tamper with his or her research data to make it look precise by smoothing out or omitting irregularities so that the data appears statistically significant. The researcher has a responsibility to give readers the actual, untampered data with its irregularities regardless of its statistical significance or insignificance.

Avoid Deemphasizing Important Information or Emphasizing Misleading Information

Writers can deemphasize information, especially negative information, or emphasize misleading or incorrect information through page layout, type size, or color. For example, the writer of an advertisement for a drug that controls heart rate emphasizes that the drug is safe. The word "safe" appears in a bright red band and in 36-point type; yet at the bottom of the page in 6-point, black type, the advertisement warns that a defibrillator and emergency equipment should be available for the drug user. Clearly, the drug is not completely safe; however, the reader may never see the warning because of the page layout, type size, and color.

Avoid "No Fault" Writing

When appropriate, include references to the writer. Your writing will be more effective when you include "I," "we," or an organization's name. Identifying

THE READER'S CORNER

Are Words Enough?

In a world dominated by spin and hype, it sometimes seems that a few choice words can sway any audience. So-called green marketing began with such assumptions. In the early 1990s, surveys showed that environmental responsibility was one of five top factors for consumers, and soon 10 to 15 percent of all new consumer products were being marketed as green. However, when the Federal Trade Commission determined that words like *recycled* and *biodegradable* had been used in misleading ways, the American consumer became skeptical of green advertising. Given recent events, such skepticism may be well founded.

In 1996, America was shocked to learn that television personality Kathie Lee Gifford's line of clothing was being produced abroad by child laborers working twenty-hour days. Gifford joined Labor Secretary Robert Reich and others at a Fashion Industry Forum to pledge to root out exploitative practices within the industry. A new apparel label, "No Sweat," would alert consumers to a company's fair labor practices, but are words enough? A "No Sweat" market exists: a 1995 study by the Center for Ethical Concerns at Marymount University showed that eight of ten Americans would avoid shopping in retail stores that sell sweatshop goods. Even so, some Americans have received the "No Sweat" pledge skeptically. Will the fashion industry allow outside groups to monitor labor practices? Will the industry allow such outside groups to award the labels? This time, words alone may not be enough.

the speaker or actor is a "necessary ingredient for ethical communication" (Rubens 335). Writing that omits references to a speaker or actor is easily manipulated. When a writer says, "Each of the participants was interviewed for 30 minutes," he or she is not taking responsibility for the data; and readers may not know who did the interviewing. Instead, the writer should say, "I interviewed each participant for 30 minutes." The revised sentence does not destroy the factual nature of the information; instead, it identifies the writer as the interviewer and places responsibility for data from the interviews on the writer.

PRINCIPLE 3: TAKE THE ETHICAL STANCE

Once you have considered the consequences of the proposed communication and the various language choices, you can choose the language that you will use in the communication. Ideally, the consequences of the proposed communication and language choices will all support the same ethical conclusion.

Such is Susan's case. All the questions and consequences tell her that the only ethical language choice is to report that "90 percent of the airbags inflated fully, and 10 percent inflated only 60 percent." However, with this choice, Susan faces the dilemma of giving her manager and the company executives information that they do not want to receive. This information could cause her company to lose profits and market share and could cause the company to incur the cost of further testing and redesigning the side-impact airbag. Susan could also face another, even harder, choice. If company executives put the new airbag into the new models and do not warn consumers of the danger, she will have to decide whether to become a whistle blower to protect consumers.

You may face similar ethical dilemmas as you communicate in the workplace. When faced with these dilemmas, consider the following suggestions for choosing ethical language:

- **Make sure that you have all the facts and that your facts are accurate.** You don't want to risk losing your job or your reputation if you don't have all the facts.

- **Think first and then communicate.** Once you are satisfied that you have all the facts and that they are accurate, consider all the possible communication choices and the ethical ramifications of those choices before you write. Don't just react to the situation.

- **Find out all you can about the people involved and about those who will read your communication, especially those who make the decisions.** Then you can determine the best way to approach these people if you want to argue for change or to suggest a course of action that they may not want to consider.

- **Talk to people whom you trust.** They may help you consider alternative yet ethical language choices. If you feel that you cannot trust anyone in the company, talk to someone whom you trust outside the company. Don't try to face the situation alone.

- **Aim to establish a reputation as a hard-working, loyal coworker with integrity.** Then, when you do take a stand on an ethical issue, your coworkers and superiors won't take your stand lightly.

- **Be willing to negotiate and to compromise when appropriate.** You may not get everything that you want changed. For example, if you eliminate the physical dangers to the company employees or prevent the misuse of public funds, you might want to compromise on smaller issues. By compromising, you may show that you are a team player, and you may even get the smaller issues changed later.

The answers to ethical dilemmas are never easy and clear-cut. The only clear-cut answer when dealing with them is that "the greater the moral wrong, the greater the obligation to take strong—and perhaps risky—action against it" (Wicclair and Farkas 19).

CONCLUSION

Communicating ethically is not only your responsibility but your right. Strive to communicate ethically in all your dealings with others. Sometimes the decision to communicate ethically may be difficult and confusing. The principles and suggestions in this chapter will help you as you face ethical dilemmas and as you try to use ethical language. The "Worksheet for Ethical Communication" summarizes these principles and suggestions. Refer to it when you have questions or concerns about using ethical language.

WORKSHEET for Ethical Communication

Principle 1: Determine What Course of Action the Ethical Viewpoints Suggest

- Is the communication honest and truthful?
- Are you acting in the best interests of the company, the public, and yourself?
- What if everybody acted in this way?
- Are you willing to take responsibility for the action or communication publicly and privately?
- Does the action or communication violate anyone's rights?
- Are you treating similar situations similarly?

Principle 2: Avoid Unethical Manipulating of Words and Visuals

- Have you created honest impressions?
- Have you avoided imprecise phrases that can mislead or deceive readers?
- Have you included all the information that readers need or have a right to know, even if that information is negative?
- Is all the information correct and accurate?
- Have you deemphasized or suppressed important information— information that you should emphasize or highlight?
- Have you highlighted or emphasized invalid, misleading, or incorrect information?
- Have you used "I," "we," or the organization's name in the document? *passive voice*
- Have you or has the company taken responsibility in the document for the actions and for the communication?

Principle 3: Take the Ethical Stance

- Have you considered all the possible communication choices and the ethical ramifications of those choices?
- Have you found out all that you can about the people involved and about readers of your communication, especially those readers who make the decisions?
- Have you talked to people whom you trust about the situation?
- Have you been willing to negotiate and to compromise when appropriate?

EXERCISES

1. This exercise is a team assignment. Your instructor will assign you to a team or allow you to select team members. You and your team will decide on the language to use in a report on the testing of a new battery-powered smoke detector. The situation is as follows:

   Testing revealed that the battery-powered smoke detectors do not always sound when the battery is low. Specifically, 75 percent of the smoke detectors emitted a sound to indicate a low battery, and the sound emitted by 20 percent of the detectors was so weak that a homeowner could not hear it beyond 20 feet. Your supervisor and her manager want to start mass production of the smoke detectors within two weeks. They are waiting for your test results. Because earlier reports from other employees have not indicated problems with the smoke detectors, your supervisor is assuming that the test results that you report will be insignificant. She and her manager will not be pleased if their division of the company can't begin manufacturing these smoke detectors since the division has not shown a profit in the last three quarters. If the division doesn't begin showing a profit, the company may downsize or eliminate the division.

   Your team should complete the following:

   a. Determine what language choices you have for reporting the test results.

   b. Apply Principle 1 from the "Worksheet for Ethical Communication" to analyze these language choices. Write a memo to your instructor listing each choice and explaining the consequences of each choice.

   c. Write a memo to your supervisor reporting the test results and recommending a course of action.

2. Interview a professional in your field who has faced ethical dilemmas when communicating in the workplace. Ask how he or she dealt with these dilemmas. Also ask the professional to give you some sample documents involved in one of these dilemmas or to give you examples of dilemmas that he or she faced. After the interview, write a memo to your classmates

   • Introducing the professional and describing his or her job
   • Describing how the professional deals with ethical dilemmas
   • If possible giving examples of dilemmas that the professional has faced and attaching sample documents involved in these dilemmas

3. Search newspapers, news magazines, the World Wide Web, professional journals, and trade magazines to find a recent public incident that involves ethics and language. Once you have found an incident, write a memo to your instructor

   • Describing the incident and explaining how it violated ethical standards
   • Describing how the individuals or organizations involved applied unethical standards in their public statements or actions during and after the incident

4. These two scenarios describe ethical dilemmas that professionals might face in the workplace. Be prepared to discuss them in class.

   a. You have to prepare a report of recent user testing of your company's new version of a popular desktop publishing program. Your company wants to get the software on the market in time for the Christmas shopping season. However, in the tests, the users encountered several problems with the software—problems that brought their workstations offline and crippled their networks. The tests revealed the following information:

      • 9 out of 10 users liked the newer version of the software better than the older version
      • 6 out of 10 users reported network problems because of the new software
      • When users used the software's on-line help feature, the computers of 5 out of 10 users locked up

When reporting these problems, you have to consider more than just the problems with the software; you also must consider that company executives and your supervisor plan to ship the new version to stores in time for Christmas shoppers—regardless of the test results. Use the "Worksheet for Ethical Communication" to consider the various language choices that you can use when reporting these results.

b. You write manuals for woodworking equipment such as power saws, electric sanders, and jigsaws.[4] You have just received the draft of a manual that you wrote last month for the company's new jigsaw. The legal department has added five pages of conditions under which the user should operate the saw; the legal department also has added many complex and confusing cautions and warnings throughout the manual. These changes make the manual much longer and harder to read. You believe that users will ignore such a lengthy and reader-unfriendly manual—possibly sustaining needless injuries as a result. You talk to your supervisor about your concerns. Your supervisor shares your concerns but explains that the company's legal consultant is trying to lessen the number of successful accident claims against the company. Your supervisor says that the company must protect itself against these expensive accident claims and instructs you to include the consultant's changes and to structure future manuals in the same way. Use the "Worksheet for Ethical Communication" to consider your language choices.

---

4. I have loosely based this scenario on a case by Wicclair and Farkas (18).

CASE STUDY   Understanding an Ethical Dilemma

Background

You are a programmer and software documentation specialist for Custom Programs, Inc., a company that writes software programs for technical applications in the medical field. For over a year, you have been writing software for Custom Programs customers. When you were hired, your manager understood that you knew little about the medical field and thus agreed that medical specialists would examine the software and the documentation to make sure that the information was accurate and complete. Your manager also assured you that a group of users would test the manuals. However, over the past six months, you have been concerned about the feedback that both the medical specialists and the users have been giving you. You have two concerns:

- You fear that the documentation and training materials that you write contain errors and inaccurate information because the medical specialists merely glance at the drafts that you send them. In question-and-answer sessions about the drafts, the specialists seem bothered and evasive about special problems with the drafts and about your questions. You believe that the medical specialists are not reading the drafts for accuracy and completeness but are merely "blindly" approving them.

- You believe that the documentation and training materials don't meet the needs of customers because the user testing is inadequate. The company is not appropriately compensating the individuals who test the drafts, so they don't spend adequate time testing them. In fact, they are annoyed by the tests and resent questions about the drafts. You have asked the company to allow you to increase the compensation to the testers, but the company says the current compensation is adequate. On the basis of this minimal user testing, the company claims that its documentation and training materials are user tested although no legitimate user testing occurs. Basically, whatever you write, the company prints and gives to its customers in medical clinics, hospitals, and emergency rooms, regardless of its accuracy, correctness, or usefulness to the readers.

Over the next six months you will be writing documentation for software used in the emergency center of a local hospital. The hospital staff may use this software and the accompanying documentation in life-threatening situations, and you are concerned about possible inaccuracies, errors, and usability.

Assignment

1. Decide what ethical dilemma you face.
2. Apply Principle 1 from the "Worksheet for Ethical Communication" to analyze the dilemma and to determine what language, if any, you might use to report this dilemma to your manager.
3. Write a brief memo to your instructor explaining this dilemma. If you were to report this dilemma to your manager, list the language choices available to you and the choice that you would select. Explain the consequences of this language and why you would use it.
4. Write the memo to your manager.

Chapter 5

Collaborating and
the Writing Process

As a professional in the workplace, you may work as part of a team to produce various types of documents. The team might collaborate to design a new product, to propose a project, to solve problems, or to write procedures. The type and level of the collaboration will depend on the project, its purpose, and the team's work style. Professionals collaborate because teams often can prepare solutions, products, designs, and written documents better and more efficiently than can individuals working alone. For many professionals, collaborating is frustrating and time-consuming because they don't know how to collaborate effectively and efficiently. Team members can minimize and frequently eliminate these frustrations and time problems by taking certain steps to get started, using current technology to simplify their tasks, and creating an environment favorable for collaborating.

This chapter presents three principles to help you effectively collaborate throughout the writing process. The first principle suggests steps that team members can take to ensure effective and organized collaboration from the start. The second principle suggests using electronic media to collaborate when team members are drafting, revising, and editing: you will learn how technology can simplify and enhance collaboration. The third principle presents guidelines to help you become an effective collaborator.

COLLABORATIVE WRITING IN THE WORKPLACE

You can write collaboratively in many ways in the workplace. You can collaborate as part of a team where members equally share writing responsibilities or as part of a team where primarily one member's task is writing. You do not have to be on a team, however, to work collaboratively. You also can collaborate by writing for others. Let's begin by discussing that type of collaboration.

Collaborating When Writing for Others

When you collaborate by writing for others, you write all or most of a document while other professionals supply the information you need to write, design, and perhaps publish. A good example of this type of collaboration is Paul's work on a proposal for a new telecommunications system for the Osteopathic Medical Center. Paul is a proposal writer for a telecommunications company. He has a strong background in the telecommunications industry. He understands the hardware used by his company and can communicate effectively with other technical experts and with his company's salespeople. To complete his proposal, Paul discusses the medical center's needs with the center's administrators and with the salespeople who are working with them. He also collaborates with several technical experts and with the salespeople who will present this proposal to the hospital administrators. Paul writes the proposal and then collaborates with graphic designers on the layout. The salespeople, however, will present the proposal to the Osteopathic Medical Center; Paul's name won't appear on the proposal.

You can also write collaboratively by preparing a document for someone else's signature. You might collaborate with that person to determine what he or she wants in the document; and then as you write, you and that person might collaborate to be sure that the document is meeting his or her expectations. In these situations, you will have the ultimate responsibility for gathering and analyzing the information needed for the document. You might collaborate with other professionals to obtain information, but you are responsible for using your expertise to write a document that will carry someone else's signature.

A good example of this type of collaborative effort occurs in Rhonda's job. Rhonda, an engineer for an architectural engineering company, is responsible for preparing construction specifications. She recently wrote specifications for protecting the underground pipes of a water-pumping station that the company is designing. She researched the protection required for the pipes and wrote the specifications, which the project manager ultimately signed.

Collaborating as a Team Member

When you collaborate as a team member, you work with one or more people to write a document. A good example of this collaboration is a team that prepares user manuals for computer hardware. Team members work together to determine the purpose of the manual and the types of information that users will need. Early in the project, the team leader determines each team member's strengths and expertise and uses this information to assign roles and delegate writing assignments. Before writing begins, the team sets a time schedule and creates an outline for the manual. The team creates style guidelines and prototype documents, so that each member knows how to lay out the pages. These early steps help each member to write drafts that the team can easily merge into one document. Individually, team members research and draft specific sections of the manual. They put their sections online in a shared directory where all members can review the sections. Together, team members revise the manual. One team member who serves as editor edits and proofreads the final draft for the team as a whole to approve.

In that collaboration, the team plans and writes the draft; team members are coauthors, equally sharing responsibility for the document. Team members also can collaborate by unequally sharing responsibility for a document: the team plans and outlines the document, but only one or two members write it.

For example, Neil collaborated with coworkers in engineering and management to prepare a proposal. They analyzed the writing situation together, brainstormed about what to include in the proposal, and outlined the proposal, but Neil wrote all sections of the proposal except the plan of action and the budget. The team members did not share the writing responsibility equally, yet each one contributed to the project. Neil wrote most of the proposal because he had worked most closely with the readers and understood their situation. His teammates worked on the plan of action and the budget because

THE READER'S CORNER

The Author Myth

Collaborative writing challenges a basic myth about authorship. Isn't writing ideally a moment of private inspiration, under a tree, as poets have claimed? Not according to historians. For most of recorded history, writing was the work of transmission, not creation, and most "authors" only reiterated the accumulated wisdom of the past. Writers in the Middle Ages, for example, copied their material straight out of huge manuals of writing models. Although the invention of printing from movable type (c. 1450) made writing a more profitable career for some, the writer was still usually no more important than the typesetter, printer, or bookbinder. In England, for example, the bookseller—not the writer—held the rights to published works as late as 1710, when Queen Anne's Act finally established the writer as the copyright holder. With copyright (and profits) thus in hand, the writer gained more respect, and by the late 1700s, some thought the author to be a minor deity. Romantic poets like Wordsworth and Goethe popularized the idea that their verse came to them in single flashes of brilliance. Later generations, adoring their verse, helped make the writer myth reality. In recent decades, however, literary historians have discovered in letters, drafts, and journals that these poets not only revised their work constantly but also relied extensively on other books, friends, and publishers for inspiration. These discoveries don't depreciate their work, but they do teach us that even the greatest poets revise and collaborate.

he didn't have the expertise to write either of them. In some team writing projects, you may have more or less responsibility because of your job position or expertise.

PRINCIPLE 1: COLLABORATE TO ANALYZE THE WRITING SITUATION AND PLAN THE DOCUMENT

To collaborate successfully, team members need to move through the stages of the writing process described in Chapter 2 (see Figure 2.1). Team members should start working together at the beginning of the writing process, not at the drafting stage. This section suggests ways of determining and organizing the team's tasks to analyze the writing situation and plan the document.

At the first team meeting, team members attend to some basic housekeeping tasks (see Figure 5.1). Take care of these tasks during the first meeting, to organize the project and to foster effective and efficient communication.

Figure 5.1
Tasks to Accomplish
at the First Team
Meeting

- **Introduce each team member** (if the team members don't know each other).
- **Trade phone numbers, e-mail addresses, and, if appropriate, fax numbers.** This information is especially important if the team members are geographically separated.
- **Select a project manager or managing editor** (if the team doesn't have one assigned).
- **Decide or assign roles for each team member** (if the roles aren't already assigned).
- **Decide how the team will communicate**—by means of e-mail, a listserv, a World Wide Web site, face-to-face meetings, video conferences, telephone conferences, or a combination of these media.
- **Decide what word-processing, desktop publishing, and/or graphics software** your team will use to prepare drafts of the document.
- **Decide whether team members will share computer files** of the drafting, revising, and editing by means of e-mail, a shared directory, a Web site, or diskettes.

As you and other team members discuss how you will communicate with each other, remember that effective communication need not be face to face. Many teams use electronic media to communicate. For example, a team can set up a listserv on a network. In the listserv, each team member can send messages to the entire team, and then individual team members can respond or ask questions. Each team member sees the responses and the questions. Team members can even "vote" on certain decisions by means of a listserv, or, alternatively, many teams choose to set up sites on the World Wide Web. Team members can post drafts and other needed information on the Web site. These electronic media allow teams to collaborate with relatively few face-to-face meetings or telephone conversations. With electronic media, you don't have to wait for a meeting or make a phone call to share an idea or ask a question. You can use electronic media at any time of the day or night—not just during traditional working hours.

Analyzing the Writing Situation as a Team

Before a team can begin determining and organizing the team's tasks, team members need to look at the writing situation together. But before the team can analyze the writing situation, all team members must understand the project. The team leader or a company representative needs to explain what the team is expected to accomplish. Once the members understand the team's assignment, they can begin analyzing the writing situation. Figure 5.2 suggests some questions that the team might ask. Be sure to allow ample time for analyzing the writing situation, as this step lays the foundation for the rest of the project.

Figure 5.2

Questions That Team
Members Might Ask
When Analyzing the
Writing Situation

- Who will read our document?
- Have our readers ever worked with individuals on our team or in our organization? If they have, what conflicts or problems, if any, occurred? How can we avoid such conflicts or problems?
- How will our readers use our document: to make a decision, to answer specific questions, to gather information, to complete a task?
- What do our readers know about the topic of our document?
- What are our readers' attitudes about the topic or our company?
- How will our readers react to the topic or to our company?

Gathering Information as a Team

Once the team has analyzed the writing situation, members can begin to decide what information to gather and how to structure that information. Team members might begin by brainstorming to gather ideas from each team member about the important information that the document should include. When setting up a brainstorming session, allow time for all team members to express their ideas. The team can also ask questions like those listed in Figure 5.3 to help determine what information to include.

Structuring the Document and Establishing Design and Style Guidelines

After developing ideas through brainstorming or asking questions, the team can set up clear guidelines for individual work. One method for setting up such guidelines is outlining. Outlining can guide team members as they work individually. In a team situation, members cannot assume that each member will keep the same outline in his or her head. Even in the best of teams, oral agreement about what a document will include can create conflicts and misunderstandings. A written outline will help the team to avoid such conflicts and misunderstandings. A written outline also can record what the team intends to include in the document and how the team wants that information arranged.

Figure 5.3

Questions That Team
Members Might Ask
When Deciding What
Information to Include

- What is the primary purpose of our document?
- What are the objectives?
- What important information should we include?
- What additional information can we include?
- What information can we exclude?
- What types of information will we gather?
- Where can we gather the information, and how will we gather it?

This record can help team members to prepare their individual sections as the team intends.

The team can also establish design and style guidelines. By deciding on design and style guidelines before writing begins, the team simplifies later editing and proofreading, because from the outset all team members use the same style and format when writing individual sections. One way to set up these guidelines is to prepare a start draft, as discussed in Chapter 2. A more formal version of the start draft is the specifications document often used by programmers and documentation writers. Specifications documents describe the readers, outline the document, provide sample layouts, and establish style guidelines. When setting up these guidelines, consider the design and style questions listed in Figure 5.4. (For more detailed information about design guidelines, see Chapter 10, "Designing Documents for Your Readers.")

Setting a Schedule and Deciding How the Team Will Communicate

Once the team has analyzed the writing situation and gathered and structured the information, the team can establish a schedule for drafting, revising, and editing. A schedule will clarify

- Each member's responsibility
- How each member's work relates to the work of the whole team
- When each member should complete his or her work

Figure 5.4

Design and Style Questions That Team Members Might Consider

Possible Design Questions

- What page layout will be most effective for the readers?
- What typeface and type size will we use for the text and the headings?
- Where will the headings appear on the page? Will they be indented? If so, how far will they be indented?
- What page margins will we use?
- What bullet style will we use for bulleted lists? Will we indent the bullets? If so, how far?
- What file format will each team member use to submit drafts? What word-processing or desktop publishing format will the team use?

Possible Style Questions

- Will we use any specific abbreviations, terminology, or language?
- Will we use words or numerals for chapter numbers, section numbers, and other enumerations? Will we use Arabic or Roman numerals?
- What terminology will we use when referring to the readers, to the company, or to the team? Will we use second-person pronouns when referring to the readers?
- What conventions, if any, will we use when writing? (For example, if your team is writing software documentation, how will you refer to specific function keys or to the arrow keys on the keyboard? Will you use any icons?)
- How will you refer to figures and tables?

The schedule should list specific and reasonable dates for completing individual work and allow for team meetings or other communication to discuss the individual work—especially the drafts written by team members. The schedule also should encourage team members to communicate frequently. Team members need to know how each member's work is progressing, so the team and the project manager can track the project. These meetings and the communication will also help the team to identify and resolve any problems.

If possible, the schedule should allow for the unexpected, such as team members being transferred to other projects or not being available because of illness or other personal situations. At any stage of the writing process, the team may face unexpected problems. For example, the information team members have gathered may turn out to be insufficient, or a draft may fail to meet the needs of readers. Unexpected problems will frustrate even the most organized team; however, a schedule with room for flexibility will alleviate some of the frustration.

PRINCIPLE 2: USE ELECTRONIC MEDIA TO COLLABORATE WHEN DRAFTING, REVISING, AND EDITING

A team can use any of the following electronic media to make collaborating easier and more efficient:

- Word-processing software to write, revise, and edit drafts
- E-mail, shared directories, or the World Wide Web to exchange drafts and to communicate
- Desktop publishing software to create the final draft

Using Word-Processing Software

When a team uses word-processing software, team members can exchange drafts by means of diskettes, e-mail, or the Web and can comment on or revise drafts directly on the electronic copies. When you receive a revised draft, you will have a record of those comments and revisions on the diskette. Team members also can put their drafts on diskette and then give the diskette to one team member who will combine the drafts of various parts of the document. Putting your drafts on diskette rather than just on paper not only makes revising much easier, but also creates an efficient way of combining the various drafts into one document or file for revising and editing.

Some word-processing packages have a document-compare function that allows the writer to compare an original draft with revised versions. When team members revise and comment on each other's drafts, they can use the document-compare function to see how a revised version differs from the original. You can use this function to mark passages in the revised draft that differ from the original; this function allows you to mark added phrases (redline), deleted phrases (strikeout), and moved phrases. Added or redline phrases may appear red on color monitors; on monochrome monitors, the appearance of the redline phrase varies. When printed, the redline phrase usually has a shaded background when printed with a black and white printer or is marked with a vertical bar in the margin. Strikeout or deleted phrases usually print with a horizontal line through the middle of the text. A moved phrase generally has "THE FOLLOWING TEXT WAS MOVED" inserted before it and "THE PRECEDING TEXT WAS MOVED" inserted after it. Figure 5.5 shows a revised paragraph with a team member's revisions marked on it. If your word-processing package does not have functions such as redline and strikeout, you can use asterisks, bullets, or brackets to indicate the revised text.

Using Electronic Media to Exchange Drafts

Team members can use various types of electronic media to exchange drafts and share information. Depending on the computer facilities and software available at your company or campus, you can use e-mail, listservs, shared directories, and the World Wide Web. These electronic media allow team members to share drafts created with word-processing and other types of software. For example, the team might set up on your local area network (LAN) a shared directory where members can exchange or share files. Team members then send their drafts to the assigned directory for other team members to read, comment on, revise, and possibly approve. Everyone on the team can view all documents posted to that directory.

The team also can use e-mail to exchange drafts in two ways: traditional e-mail or a listserv. Using traditional e-mail, team members send their drafts to other members by attaching the file to an e-mail message or by embedding the draft into the message. The most efficient method is to attach the draft to an e-mail message, so the formatting remains in the draft and team members can use their word-processing package to edit. With this method, only team members who receive the message see the draft and the comments.

With a listserv, all team members receive the draft and see the comments. When using a listserv, a team member can simultaneously send a copy of a draft to everyone on the listserv; so everyone receives the draft and can comment on it. Every member of the listserv receives all the comments made by other members over the listserv, so a team can simulate a discussion of a draft over the listserv. Many teams send a draft by means of traditional e-mail, fax, or diskette and then discuss the draft on the listserv. Sending drafts by way of e-mail saves time, especially if team members work in different geographic locations. It also can make the revising stage of the team's work easier.

The team also can create a site on the World Wide Web. Team members then post drafts and other information to the site, where all team members can view the drafts. To use the World Wide Web in the workplace, your team must work at a company where employees have access to the Web. To use the Web as a student, check with officials at your university to find out how to set up a Web site.

At times, some team members may not have access to e-mail, or the computer systems of some may not be compatible with those of the other team

Figure 5.5
A Marked Paragraph

I missed them p

~~Some e-mail programs are more sophisticated than others.~~ With some e-mail programs, you can send and receive not only short messages, but also whole files that have been created using other software programs such as *WordPerfect* or Microsoft *Word*. For example, you might write a draft using ~~a word processing program~~ *WordPerfect* and then want to send it to another team member who also has *WordPerfect*. You and your team members could send drafts of your work to everyone on the team, THE FOLLOWING TEXT WAS MOVED so they could read and possibly revise each member's draft before the next meeting. THE PRECEDING TEXT WAS MOVED ~~in this way, the team members would perhaps have time to read and revise others' drafts before the next team meeting. This process~~ Sending these drafts by way of e-mail could save time, especially if the team members work in different geographic locations. It will also make ~~and could enhance~~ the revising stage of the team's ~~your~~ writing much easier and more efficient.

members. When that is the case, the team might consider using a fax machine to exchange information and drafts. Many computers now have a fax/modem installed, allowing members to send a fax from their computer terminals. Fax machines are generally slower and more expensive than e-mail, listservs, or the Web.

Using Desktop Publishing Software

If your team uses word processing to create a draft, you can use desktop publishing software to give your document a professional appearance. If you don't have access to desktop publishing software, your word-processing program may have some desktop publishing capabilities. Desktop publishing allows you to produce professional, high-quality printing from a personal computer. Using desktop publishing, the team can integrate graphics, manipulate text, and use different typefaces without the traditional cutting and pasting associated with photographic production.

PRINCIPLE 3: COLLABORATE EFFECTIVELY

As you collaborate on a writing project, the relationships that develop among team members can affect the project. The collaboration is more likely to go smoothly if team members like, respect, and understand each other. For example, if one member of a writing team likes to correspond by way of e-mail, team members might agree to use e-mail when they want to give information to each other. By encouraging the team to use e-mail team members show respect for and understanding of one of the team members. If you have never worked with some or all of the members of the team, you and they might spend some time getting to know each other and each team member's expertise. As team members begin to work together, they can frequently share information relevant to the project. Such contact will help all team members to feel that they are important and valued members of the team. This section of the chapter presents five guidelines to help team members to collaborate successfully.

Encouraging Team Members to Share Their Ideas

You and the other team members bring unique creativity and expertise to the project. Together, you and the other team members represent a wealth of knowledge and ideas. To best use this knowledge, all members must share their knowledge and ideas. Even when ideas clash, team members can learn and the document may benefit because the exchange of ideas may generate an ingenious solution to a problem or an especially effective way to organize the document. All team members should feel free to express their ideas—even when those ideas differ from the prevailing views expressed by the majority. To encourage this sharing of ideas, team members can

- Listen intently and respectfully to all team members
- Share ideas even when they differ from the views of other team members
- Disagree and criticize respectfully and politely
- Be open to criticism of their ideas and writing

Listening Intently and Respectfully

Have you ever tried to express your ideas about something that you are truly interested in, but some of your listeners talked to others while you were speaking? Have you ever spoken to a group of people who weren't really listening—who didn't give you their undivided attention? Have you ever talked to listeners who appeared to hear what you were saying, but when you ask for their comments, you discovered that they hadn't really heard you? They

looked as though they were listening, but their minds were elsewhere. Such situations are always frustrating, and in a collaborative setting they can discourage members from sharing their ideas. Each team member needs to know that the team will listen and will consider his or her ideas. Team members shouldn't expect the team to accept any or every idea that they present, but they can expect the team to listen and consider each idea.

To encourage other team members to share their ideas, listen intently and respectfully to everyone's ideas. Use both nonverbal and verbal signals to let speakers know that you are paying attention. Such signals help you to be an active listener—a listener who shows that he or she is paying attention. Simple nonverbal signals include

- Maintaining eye contact with the speaker
- Avoiding physical gestures that may distract the speaker
- Letting the speaker finish his or her statement before asking questions

You let speakers know that you are actively listening if you maintain eye contact with them. Speakers who receive little eye contact feel that their listeners aren't paying attention. To signal that you are listening intently, look at the speaker and avoid gestures that may be distracting.

You also can encourage all members of a team to speak by letting speakers finish their statements before you ask questions or comment. If you continually interrupt, speakers may become distracted or assume that you aren't listening. Such interruptions may discourage team members from sharing their ideas—especially team members who may be shy or timid.

Verbal signals that let speakers know that you are listening include

- Using phrases that show that you are listening intently
- Asking questions when you want something clarified or when you want more information
- Occasionally paraphrasing or summarizing what the speaker has said

Use expressions such as "I agree," "good idea," or "I like that" to let the speaker know that you agree. If you disagree with a speaker, try to paraphrase what the speaker said or ask relevant questions to clarify. By paraphrasing or asking questions, you can make sure that you and the speaker are on the same wavelength, and you give the speaker the opportunity to correct any misunderstanding (you may discover that you actually agree with what the speaker said). You also can ask questions or paraphrase to get more information to determine whether you agree or disagree with the speaker. Asking questions will encourage other team members to share their ideas and to ask questions.

Sharing Information Willingly and Asking Others to Share Their Ideas

You can encourage others to share their ideas if you are willing to share information. If you discover information that may help another team member or that may affect what another team member is doing, share that information with the team in a timely manner. If you share such information, your team

ISSUES IN CONTEXT

Collaborating Over the Internet

Long-distance collaboration is becoming a "corporate standard," especially for large projects that take several months or years (Wambeam and Kramer 349). When professionals collaborate over long distances, they often encounter complications that don't usually occur in other projects. Often the most frustrating complication is exchanging documents over the Internet. You can lessen these frustrations by following these guidelines:

- **Find out the hardware and software that each team member will use** (Tumminello and Carlshamre 418). Before you begin writing, identify the hardware and software that the team members will use. This information will help the team to eliminate potential difficulties before exchanging files.
- **Determine the format of all the documents that you will exchange electronically** (Tumminello and Carlshamre 417). Identify all the documents that you will exchange electronically and discuss the most appropriate file format for each document (for example, ASCII or word-processed files).
- **Decide which files will not be appropriate for the Internet.** For example, if the files contain classified information or information protected by privacy laws, use regular mail. Currently, "data sent over the Internet is not secure" without encryption or other means to protect its security (Tumminello and Carlshamre 418).
- **Attach simple files as e-mail messages.** You can attach ASCII files or small word-processed documents to e-mail. You can also paste simple documents directly into the e-mail.
- **Use regular mail for files over 100K.** Files over 100K don't transfer well over the Internet as e-mail attachments (Tumminello and Carlshamre 418).

members will be more likely to share with you information that may affect your work on the project, and you will develop good working relationships.

Some team members may be shy or quiet and may not feel comfortable expressing their ideas during team meetings. If you see that some team members aren't participating in the team discussions, ask those members to share their ideas. You might ask, "Rob, what do you think of that approach?" or "What are your ideas about the project, Susie?" You might direct the discussion toward the shy or quiet members by saying, "Let's hear what John has to say about this topic" or "We've heard some good ideas from Linda and Patrick. Let's hear what Juan has to say." Ask shy or quiet members to participate, and help the team to include them in the discussions. These members can contribute valuable ideas.

Disagreeing and Criticizing Respectfully

One of the benefits of collaboration is the diversity of ideas and the conflicts that naturally occur. Conflicts are a healthy part of working with others. Conflicts can help a team to discover the best way to handle a project or the best way to organize a report. To encourage healthy conflict, team members can respectfully disagree and criticize by

- Criticizing ideas or writing, not the person
- Criticizing objectively rather than subjectively
- Including positive comments when you criticize or disagree

When you disagree with team members or criticize their writing or ideas, remember that they have feelings. Respect each member's feelings by criticizing his or her ideas or writing—not the person directly. When you want to criticize, avoid comments such as "Jenny, you didn't organize this section correctly." Instead, comment directly about the writing without referring to the writer: "Let's try organizing this section in another way."

Similarly, you might criticize a specific part of the writing or disagree with a specific part of an idea or draft instead of making broad, subjective comments that you can't back up. For example, when criticizing a team member's writing, comment on specific aspects such as the style, the content, or the organization. You might say, "The draft is free of passive voice, but the style would be friendlier if we included more second-person pronouns," instead of saying, "I don't like the writing in your draft." The first statement objectively comments on the style; the second gives only the speaker's subjective opinion about the style.

You can help team members accept your criticisms or arguments by including positive comments. When you criticize a draft written by another team member, at the same time also comment on the strengths of his or her writing. For example, you might explain that you are suggesting ways to improve a basically good draft. Focus on the positive qualities of a draft or an idea, and tell the member about those qualities when you suggest changes or when you disagree.

Being Open to Criticism of Your Ideas and Writing

Just as you will criticize and disagree with your team members, they too will criticize and disagree with you. Be prepared to listen and be open to this criticism. Think of your writing and your ideas as belonging to the team and not to you. Then, when team members criticize your writing or your ideas, you won't automatically take the criticism personally. In this way, you will be able to discuss the best way to write the *team's* document or the best ideas for the *team's* project rather than trying to protect and defend *your* document and *your* ideas. When the team begins to evaluate your draft or your ideas, participate in the discussion and be willing to look at your draft or your ideas objectively—even offering suggestions for improving your own work. However, do not hesitate to try to persuade team members to use your idea or a part of your writing if you feel they are overlooking or dismissing it too quickly.

CONCLUSION

Working as part of a team to create a document can be a rewarding and enjoyable experience. When you and other team members listen to and respect each other's ideas, you can exchange ideas and improve your documents. Use the "Worksheet for Successful Collaboration" to help your team work effectively.

WORKSHEET for Successful Collaboration

Principle 1: Collaborate to Analyze the Writing Situation and Plan the Document

- At the first team meeting, did your team take care of basic housekeeping tasks (see Figure 5.1)?
- Did your team analyze the writing situation?
- Did your team gather information for the document?
- Did your team decide how to structure the document?
- Did your team establish design and style guidelines?
- Did your team set a schedule?
- Did your team decide how the team will communicate?

Principle 2: Use Electronic Media to Collaborate When Drafting, Revising, and Editing

- Can your team use word-processing software to prepare your drafts? If it can, have you used the commenting functions to edit and revise each other's drafts?
- Can you use electronic media to exchange drafts? If you can, will you use e-mail, a listserv, a shared directory, or the World Wide Web? Who will set up the listserv, shared directory, or World Wide Web site?
- Will you use desktop publishing software to publish your document? If you will, which team members will be responsible for the desktop publishing?

Principle 3: Collaborate Effectively

- Have you encouraged team members to share their ideas?
- Have you listened intently and respectfully?
- Have you shared information willingly?
- Have you asked others to share their ideas?
- Have you respectfully disagreed and criticized?
- Have you been open to others' criticism of your writing and ideas?

EXERCISES

1. The city council is trying to get more people to visit your city. The council has hired you and your classmates to write a brochure and prepare a World Wide Web site promoting the city. The council wants information about the city's history, attractions, entertainment, shopping, restaurants, and hotels and motels. Your instructor will divide your class into six teams and will select one editor-in-chief for the brochure and another for the Web site. Each editor-in-chief will determine style and design guidelines and will assign each team a section of the brochure or Web site. Once your team has an assignment, team members should

   - Select a managing editor or team leader
   - Analyze the writing situation (remember to determine what information readers will expect)
   - Determine who will research and gather the information that readers will expect (make sure that all team members are responsible for some part of the research)
   - Set a schedule for the research and future meetings

   After team members have completed their research, the team should

   - Organize the information into an outline
   - Determine who will write each section of the outline (your managing editor or team leader may assign sections, or team members may select the sections that they want to write)
   - Set a schedule for completing the drafts of the sections and for revising (remember to use computer software—such as word processing and e-mail—to draft, revise, and exchange information)

   After your team has completed its assigned sections, your managing editor or team leader will give your sections to the editor-in-chief, who will suggest revisions and then put the entire brochure and Web site together.

2. Keep a record of your work on the brochure or Web site in Exercise 1. You can keep your record on paper or on diskette. Each time that you work on the brochure, do the following:

   - Note the date and the amount of time that you spend working.
   - Note whether you worked alone or with another person.
   - Describe the work that you expected to get done.
   - Describe the work that you accomplished and any problems, if any, that you encountered.

   Record not only the facts but also your experiences collaborating. After you and your team have completed the brochure or Web site, write a memo to your instructor describing how collaboration affected your work and your team's section of the brochure or Web site. Use specific information from your record to support and illustrate the information that you include in the memo.

3. Interview a professional in your chosen field of study to gather information about the kinds of collaboration that you might expect as a professional. For example, if you are majoring in biology, interview a biologist. Before the interview, remember to

   - Call the professional for an appointment
   - Gather some background information on the professional's job
   - Prepare and write down questions about collaboration based on the information in this chapter

   After the interview, write a memo to your instructor summarizing the information that you gathered about collaboration.

4. If your campus has computer facilities, visit these facilities and find out what software programs and electronic media a team could use to collaborate. Write a memo to your classmates telling them about these software programs and electronic media.

A Public Relations Problem at Big Lake

Background

This assignment is based on an actual situation that occurred at a power plant owned by a utility company based in Dallas, Texas.[1]

Big Lake Steam Electric Station, a power plant near a small south Texas town, uses steam to produce electricity. The main steam piping system at the plant carries steam to a turbine which drives a generator that produces electricity. In March of 1986, the manager at Big Lake Steam Electric Station (Big Lake) observed that areas of this main steam piping system were sagging. The main steam system uses constant support hangers (a spring-type hanger) to carry the weight of its pipes and to reduce the effect of the piping system on the plant equipment it serves. Since the late 1960s when the plant was built, engineers have learned that constant support hangers alone cannot support the weight of the pipes over a long period of time. Instead, engineers recommend using a combination of constant support hangers and rigid supports (hangers without springs; see Figure 5.6). Without rigid supports, the sagging worsens, and the weight of the pipes transfers to the plant equipment. This equipment is not designed to carry the weight and will be permanently damaged if the sagging continues.

Knowing the damage that continued sagging could cause, the Big Lake manager asked the Power Engineering Division from the home office of his utility company to study the pipe support problem at his plant. Power Engineering's survey of the plant revealed that the main steam piping system was sagging over

1. This case, written by Brenda R. Sims, is adapted from Richard Louth and Ann Martin Scott, eds., *Collaborative Technical Writing: Theory and Practice* (St. Paul, Minn.: ATTW, 1989). Courtesy of the Association of Teachers of Technical Writing.

six and a half inches. Their survey also indicated that this sagging would become more pronounced in the future and would severely damage plant equipment.

Power Engineering's Solutions for Repairing the Plant

On July 17, 1987, the Power Engineering Division suggested two solutions: the first solution would only stabilize the pipes while the second would stabilize the pipes while correcting the existing sagging in the main steam piping system:

Solution 1: Replace two of the constant support hangers with rigid supports in the area where the main steam piping system was sagging (at a cost of $132,100).

Solution 2: Shorten the piping system by cutting out and removing a short section of the main steam piping system and then adding the rigid supports, thus pulling up the lower portion of the system and eliminating the sag (at a cost of $403,600).

Solution One: Replacing the Constant Support Hangers with Rigid Supports

The first solution would stabilize the pipes but would not eliminate the existing sagging. First, the Power Engineering Division would have to run a computer stress analysis on the pipes to verify that the existing sagging did not result in stresses that would exceed allowable limits. This analysis would require about forty hours; however, the plant would not have to be shut down during that period.

Once the stress analysis was completed and Power Engineering certified that the stress levels were acceptable, the plant personnel could schedule repair for the regular spring maintenance shutdown, so the plant personnel would not lose any work time. The Power Engineering Division estimated that a maintenance crew

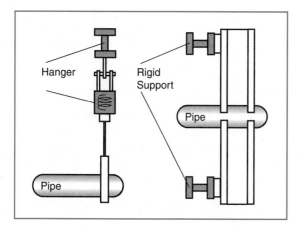

Figure 5.6 Constant Support Hangers Versus Rigid Supports

could complete the work in approximately eighty hours.

Although this solution is relatively inexpensive and could occur without an additional, unscheduled plant shutdown, the Power Engineering Division would not recommend it as the best solution because without correcting the existing sag, a permanent low point would be created in the piping system. Low points can trap water and can lead to a serious problem called *water hammer*. Therefore, the plant would have to install a manual drain in the low point; and the plant personnel would have to periodically drain the low point manually. The Power Engineering Division was not convinced that the Big Lake personnel would consistently drain the low point throughout the year.

Solution Two: Shortening the Main Piping System and Adding Rigid Supports

The second solution would stabilize the pipes and eliminate the sagging in the main steam piping system. Unlike the first solution, shortening the main piping system would eliminate the possibility of a low point occurring after the rigid supports were added. Therefore, even though the second solution costs $271,500 more than the first, it is a long-term solution to the sagging

problem. The Power Engineering Division stressed that the plant probably would save money and time in the long run by shortening the piping system along with adding rigid supports because the plant would avoid any possible water hammer damage and additional repairs.

Shortening the piping system would take an additional two weeks beyond the scheduled spring maintenance shutdown. Since this would be an unscheduled shutdown, some of the plant personnel would have to take vacation time or time off without pay.

Discussions About the Solutions

After reviewing these two solutions, the Big Lake manager met with representatives from the Power Engineering Division on July 23 to discuss the feasibility of the solutions and to express his concerns over the cost in time and money posed by both solutions. The Big Lake manager believed that shortening the piping system would cost the plant and the consumer too much money. Since the Big Lake manager was also concerned about the time involved with both solutions, the Power Engineering Division sent a memo to him after the meeting outlining in detail the work needed to shorten and reweld a section of the main steam piping system and to replace the constant support hangers with rigid supports.

An Emergency Plant Shutdown and the Chosen Repair Solution

On August 30, before the plant manager decided how to repair the sagging piping system, the Big Lake plant experienced a boiler tube leak unrelated to the sagging pipes. The plant personnel had to perform an unscheduled plant shutdown to repair the leak. While they were cooling the plant down so that the repair work could begin, one of the constant supports broke, causing the main steam pipe to sag approximately two additional feet. The damaged hanger was temporarily repaired, so that the plant could resume operation and the plant manager could have more time to decide how to deal with the sagging pipe.

Ten days after the unscheduled shutdown, the Big Lake manager rejected the second solution (shortening the main piping system and adding rigid supports) primarily because of its high cost and chose the first solution (replacing the constant support hangers with rigid supports). With this solution, the repair work could occur during the regularly scheduled spring maintenance shutdown; and the plant would avoid an additional unscheduled shutdown and the expense of the second solution.

Citizens' Concern About the Plant Shutdowns and the Sagging Pipes

The August 30 shutdown at the plant greatly concerned the citizens of the surrounding town since the plant employs a large portion of the town's population. When the plant manager first discovered the pipe sagging problem in the main steam piping system, the citizens feared that

- The pipe sagging problem could close the plant permanently
- The steam carried by the sagging pipes could kill plant personnel if the sagging caused the pipes to rupture

Since these fears were unwarranted, the Big Lake manager had bought airtime on the local radio and television stations to explain that Big Lake would remain open and that the plant personnel were safe.

However, the shutdown on August 30 unnecessarily renewed the citizens' fears. They again feared that the plant would possibly close permanently, leaving the plant personnel without jobs. They also feared that if the plant did not close, the personnel would be in danger from the sagging pipes and would be laid off without pay when the pipes were eventually repaired. Now, the Big Lake manager had to convince the citizens that the plant needed only minor repairs that could be handled without an unscheduled shutdown and that the plant personnel were not in any danger.

Team Assignment

Your team ultimately will write a letter—from the plant manager to the citizens of the small town near Big Lake—to be published in the local newspaper. The purpose of the letter is to

- Convince the citizens that the plant will not close permanently
- Convince the citizens that the sagging of the pipes could not cause a piping rupture that would endanger plant personnel
- Explain the type of repairs the plant manager has planned for the plant

You will interact with the team to

1. Decide what to include in the letter
2. Comment on the individual letters that each team member will write
3. Merge the individual letters into one final draft to turn in to your instructor

Your team will meet during three sessions. The instructions for each session follow below.

Session 1: Deciding What to Include in the Letter

After reading the assignment, your team should discuss the Big Lake situation and complete steps 1 and 2 below.

1. List the characteristics of the audience of the letter, the citizens of the small Texas town near Big Lake. The team can answer the following questions to determine the audience's characteristics:

   - Are the town's citizens interested in the Big Lake situation?
   - What is their current attitude toward the plant?
   - How would a permanent plant shutdown affect the town's citizens?
   - What will the citizens want to know about how sagging pipes will be repaired?
   - What rumors have many of the citizens heard about the sagging pipes and how

these pipes will affect the plant and its personnel? Are these rumors accurate?

2. Decide specifically what information your team will include in the letter to the citizens of the small town near Big Lake. Put this information in list form and give a copy to your instructor at the end of Session 1.

Before Session 2, each student should write an individual version of the letter and provide copies for each member of the group and for the instructor.

Sessions 2 and 3: Commenting on the Individual Letters

During Sessions 2 and 3, your team will read and respond to each other's letters by completing the form "Responses to Group Members' Writing" (Figure 5.7) and identify sections from the different letters that the team could include or revise for the final draft of the letter. After reading the letters, each team member will

1. Write the name of the author under "Member 1" at the top of the second column

Figure 5.7 Responses to Group Members' Writing

Questions	Member 1	Member 2	Member 3	Member 4
Does the letter convince the citizens that the plant will not close permanently?				
Does the letter convince the citizens that the plant personnel are not in danger?				
Does the letter explain how the plant will be repaired?				
Does the tone of the letter establish empathy between the citizens and the plant personnel?				
Does the opening of the letter get the reader's attention?				
What is the letter's greatest strength?				

2. Answer each of the response questions about Member 1's letter in the appropriate place in the second column of the form

3. Follow steps 1 and 2 for each team member's letter (except your own)

After each team member has completed the response form, your team will

1. Discuss their responses to the different letters

2. Make a list of specific sections from the letters that you could include or revise for the final version of the letter

3. Give a copy of the above list to the instructor at the end of Session 3

Sessions 4 and 5: Merging the Individual Letters into One Final Draft

At the end of Session 5, your team will give one final draft of the letter to your instructor. To produce this draft, your team has several options:

- Write the draft using only sections from the individual letters written by the team members

- Revise sections of the individual letters to create the final draft

- Combine unrevised sections with revised sections of the individual letters to create the final draft

- Write the final draft using only the ideas gained from the individual letters

Regardless of the option chosen, your team should complete the final draft and turn it in to your instructor by the end of Session 5.

PART II

KNOWING THE
TOOLS OF THE WRITER

Chapter 6

Gathering Information for Your Documents

B ill Simmons, a staff engineer for a utility company, must determine why some water pipes in the condensate system of a steam-power plant are vibrating and then write a report recommending a solution. Before making an appointment to go to the plant, Bill thinks about the information he will need to recommend a solution and to write an effective report. He doesn't know how to gather or determine the kinds of information his readers will expect. He is especially interested in using the Internet and the World Wide Web.

Bill's dilemma is not unusual. Many writers, especially beginners, don't know how to plan the research necessary for a document or what techniques to use for gathering information. This chapter presents four principles to help you research, gather, and document information.

PRINCIPLE 1: PLAN YOUR RESEARCH TO SUIT YOUR PURPOSE

Bill thinks about the purpose of his document. He decides that he is writing primarily to recommend a viable solution to the problem of the vibrating pipes. His solution must be not only cost-effective and feasible but also well supported with research and testing. Bill also recognizes a long-term goal—to establish a reputation as a problem solver and to establish positive relationships with his supervisor and the plant manager. Bill therefore decides to gather information about the pipes from the plant manager and the operations personnel, information about similar vibration problems at other plants, and information about types of pipes from the pipe manufacturer. In addition, he decides to talk with his supervisor about the expected cost of a potential solution and with the plant manager about what solutions would be acceptable and feasible.

As a professional, you too may conduct research to complete documents or projects. For some documents, you may need only a single fact or figure while for others you'll extensively research using several information-gathering techniques. How can you decide which techniques to use? Base your research on your purpose for writing.

After determining the purpose for the document, develop a detailed plan for your research. Some writers like to draw up an informal flow chart listing the steps in the process. Others prefer to list the questions they must answer first and then the steps to answering those questions. Let's consider Bill's situation again. After determining the type of information he needs, he decides to interview the plant manager and operations personnel, observe the vibrating pipes, examine company files and archives for instances of similar problems, investigate technical literature on similar problems and their solutions, and test the pipes. Before calling the plant manager, Bill writes these steps down in an informal flow chart (see Figure 6.1). Having planned his research to suit his purpose, Bill is now ready to select the techniques he will use to gather information.

Figure 6.1
Bill's Research Plan

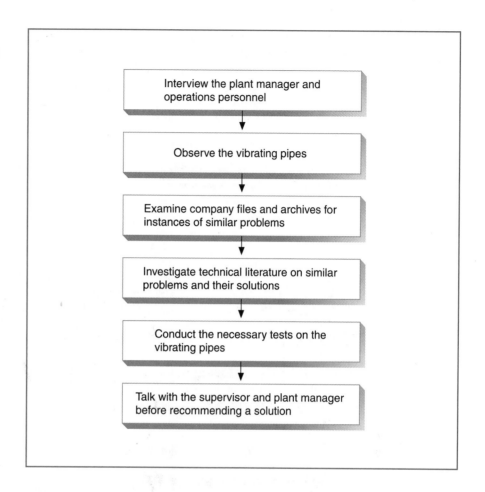

PRINCIPLE 2: SELECT APPROPRIATE PRIMARY RESEARCH TECHNIQUES

As you plan your research, select research techniques that will give you the information needed to answer your readers' questions. Frequently you will select more than one technique, as did Bill. In this section, you will learn some of the more common primary research techniques used in technical writing: interviews, questionnaires, and other firsthand techniques. Primary research (sometimes called original or firsthand research) is gathering information for the first time—not relying on research previously conducted by others. For example, the data collected by the Mars *Pathfinder* is primary research—firsthand information about Mars' composition and climate.

Interview to Gather Information

You can gather valuable firsthand information from informal and formal interviews. Interviews give you the opportunity to get factual information from an expert, to hear firsthand observations of a situation, and to discover the feelings and experiences of the interviewee. Bill plans to interview the plant manager and the operations personnel who have observed the vibrating pipes. From these interviews, he hopes to determine the characteristics of the problem, such as how frequently the pipes vibrate or whether the vibration is associated with any particular plant operation.

Informally Interview Coworkers and Colleagues

Interviews may be informal conversations in the office, by telephone, or by electronic media such as e-mail. Informal interviews are a valuable method for gathering information. For many writing situations, informal interviews are the primary means of gathering information. Bill will informally interview plant managers and other engineers to determine what they know about vibrating pipes and how to stop the vibration. The following tips will help you to conduct successful informal interviews:

- **As you plan your research, write down questions that you might ask.**
- **Make a list of all the people who could answer your questions.** From this list, select people whom you work with or know well to interview informally. (Set up formal interviews with people whom you don't work with or know well.)
- **Try to interview these people when they are least busy.** They will more freely share information with you and answer your questions more accurately.
- **Be willing to return the favor.** If you are open to answering your coworkers' and colleagues' questions, they, in turn, will be more willing to answer yours.

Formally Interview People Whom You Don't Work With or Know Well

Formal interviews are the best choice for gathering accurate and thorough information from some people. Bill will probably set up formal interviews with the plant manager and the operations manager since he doesn't work regularly with them. They will want to gather statistics and data about the vibrating pipes before talking to Bill, and a formally scheduled interview will give them the lead-time they need. Use the following tips for formal interviews:

- **Identify the purpose of the interview.** Before setting up an interview, identify its purpose and the specific information you want to gather. Let's consider Bill's interview with Richard Hampton, operations manager at the power plant. Bill might identify the purpose of this interview as follows:

  The purpose of my interview with Richard Hampton is to identify the frequency of the vibration, the effect of the vibration on the plant operation, and the operations that seem to trigger the vibration. I also want to know what he believes is causing the vibration.

  By identifying the purpose of the interview, Bill can better gather the information he needs and to identify other possible interviewees.

ISSUES IN CONTEXT

The Library of the Future

As the Internet and the World Wide Web increasingly dominate how we disseminate information, will it replace the public and university libraries as we know them today? Instead of driving our cars or walking across campus to the library, will we visit a virtual library while sitting at our computer? Will that library visually simulate the libraries we know today? From our desktops, we can already access the online catalogs of major university libraries across the globe—libraries of institutions such as the Massachusetts Institute of Technology or Oxford University in England.

At a traditional public or university library, you can find all the holdings of that library through their online catalog. Through the Internet and the World Wide Web, you can't access one catalog or database that lists all the sources or "holdings." Instead, you must access many catalogs and databases and hope that they are complete and reliable. One day, will we be able to find all the information on the Internet or the Web through one virtual catalog? We can only hope. Until then, use the online catalogs and databases listed in this chapter. However, since the information available over the Internet and the Web changes weekly, check with the reference libraries at your library and use these two sources, which have proven to be reliable and up-to-date:

- The Library of Congress *LC Marvel* (Machine-Assisted Realization of the Virtual Electronic Library)
- *Sci Ed: Science and Mathematics Education Resources*

- **Call the interviewee to set up the interview.** Once you identify the purpose of your interview, call the interviewee to set up an appointment. When you call, state the purpose of your interview, so that the interviewee can tell you whether he or she can give you the needed information.
- **Prepare for the interview.** After you set up the interview appointment, plan the questions you will ask.

Once you have gathered the background information, write down your questions. Too frequently, beginners go to an interview with only a notepad and pencil—expecting to ad-lib the questions. Although this strategy (or lack of it) may work for experienced interviewers, beginners who arrive without a written list of questions often leave without much of the information they intended to gather.

As you prepare your questions, remember to ask specific, generally open-ended questions. When Bill interviews the plant operations manager, he might ask, "Have the vibrations been occurring for a long time?" Such a closed-ended question would yield a short "yes" or "no." A more effective question would be "When did the vibrations begin?" This open-ended question will yield specific information. For the same reason, "Do you know what is causing the vibrations?" would be less effective than "What do you think is causing the vibrations?"

Send Questionnaires

Questionnaires are excellent research techniques for quickly and often inexpensively gathering information from a large group. To determine whether the pipes have a history of vibration problems, Bill might survey the managers of other plants that use the type of pipes he is studying. In this section, you will learn how to administer and prepare questionnaires.

Administering a Questionnaire

To survey people, you can use

- A written questionnaire sent by way of traditional mail, e-mail, or the Internet
- A written questionnaire delivered and picked up by hand
- An oral questionnaire administered over the telephone

Written questionnaires sent through the mail or electronic media are useful in surveying a large group of respondents from a wide geographic area. However, these questionnaires have two disadvantages: First, sent by traditional mail, they are more expensive than the other two options because of the postage. Second, the response rate for traditionally mailed questionnaires is poor, usually 15 to 20 percent. If you decide to use electronic media to administer the questionnaire, the response rate may be higher. For best results with traditionally mailed questionnaires, follow these guidelines:

- **Ask only the questions you need.** Respondents often ignore questionnaires that are long or that seem to waste their time.
- **Attach a cover letter.** Clearly and concisely explain the purpose and significance of the questionnaire.
- **Include a self-addressed, postage-paid envelope for returning the questionnaire.** Your respondents will be more likely to complete the survey and return it to you in a timely manner if they can simply drop it in the nearest mailbox.
- **In the cover letter, thank the respondents for their time.**

If you hand-deliver a written questionnaire, the response rate will be higher, but the geographic area you can survey is greatly reduced. To guarantee the higher response rate, personally pick up the questionnaires. Follow these tips to improve your response rate to hand-delivered questionnaires:

- **Ask only the questions you need.** Respondents often ignore questionnaires that are long or that seem to waste their time.
- **Attach a cover letter or a brief introduction explaining the purpose and significance of the questionnaire.**
- **In the cover letter or in the introduction to the questionnaire, thank the respondents for their time.**
- **Tell the respondents when you will pick up the questionnaire.** Also, include this information in the cover letter or written introduction.

You can also administer a questionnaire by telephone or in person. When you use either method, follow these tips:

- **Introduce yourself and the questionnaire.** Clearly and briefly state the purpose and the significance of your survey. (As you develop the questionnaire, write an introduction about yourself and the purpose of the questionnaire.)
- **Keep the questionnaire as short as possible.**
- **Thank the respondents for their time.**

Preparing Questions

Both closed-ended and open-ended questions are appropriate. Closed-ended questions will elicit answers that you can count or quantify. A survey that uses closed-ended questions might include

- Multiple-choice questions
- Yes/no questions
- Ranking questions that ask respondents to arrange items in order of preference
- Ranking questions that ask respondents to rate items on a scale, such as "completely satisfied," "somewhat satisfied," "somewhat dissatisfied," and "completely dissatisfied"

Because closed-ended or quantitative questions yield totals and percentages, computer software can read and tabulate the answers that they generate. Such surveys are particularly valuable when you have a large number of respondents.

Open-ended questions will yield answers that you cannot easily tabulate, but they may give you valuable information that you can't gain through closed-ended questions. Open-ended questions tend to elicit more accurate information because they don't limit the respondents to the writer's suggested answers (Anderson). For example, with the question "Why didn't you choose to use the Fleet Assistance Program when you bought your 1998 car?" respondents can list whatever reason may come to mind, whether or not the writer of the survey has considered it as a possibility.

Whether you choose closed-ended questions, open-ended questions, or a combination of both, design your questions carefully:

- **Write unambiguous questions.** If respondents can interpret a question in more than one way, then your results will be meaningless. (For more information on ambiguity, see Chapter 9, "Using Reader-Oriented Language.")
- **Avoid questions that influence your respondents' answers or that indicate your opinions.** For example, the following questions unnecessarily influence or "lead" readers: "Do you think that curbside recycling is an environmentally sound idea?" and "Do you think that curbside recycling is a waste of the city's valuable tax dollars?"
- **Test your questions on a small group of respondents to make sure the questions are clear and unambiguous.**

Figure 6.2 is a questionnaire that a computer systems analyst might use to gather information about an e-mail system from the employees who use it. It includes both closed- and open-ended questions.

Use Other Primary Techniques

Along with interviews and questionnaires, you can gather primary (first-hand) information from other sources. You might examine company records and publications, or you might observe people and situations. These are not the only techniques for gathering primary information, but they are some of the most commonly used ones.

Examine Corporate Records and Publications

Company records can be an excellent source of information. These records might include reports, correspondence, maps, blueprints, and test results. Along with these records, many companies publish annual reports, pamphlets, and brochures for employees, customers, investors, or the government. These publications may provide valuable information for your research. Let's consider Bill again. To solve the pipe vibration problem, Bill might look in the company records for information on vibrating pipes at similar power plants; he also might look for information on the testing of the pipes, the results of the tests, and the selected solutions.

Observe People and Situations

Once you have gathered adequate background information, you may decide to look firsthand at the problem or situation. Bill might personally observe the vibrating pipes and then conduct appropriate tests. These direct observations and tests will help Bill to pinpoint solutions. If you directly observe people and situations as part of your research, remember these guidelines:

Figure 6.2 Questionnaire with Open-Ended and Closed-Ended Questions

I am studying our current e-mail software to determine whether we should upgrade this software or purchase a new office suite. This questionnaire will help to determine whether the current software is meeting your needs. Please take a few minutes to respond. Thank you for taking time to complete this questionnaire. Please e-mail your response to cas/burger by Friday, March 26. The results will appear on our home page by April 30.

1. What is your job title?

2. What division do you work in? (Please delete all but your division.)

    Administration   Communication   Software Design   Personnel
    Manufacturing   Engineering   Documentation

3. How long have you worked for this company?

4. What types of information do you send by way of e-mail?

5. How many times during the day do you send information by way of e-mail? (Please delete all but the correct answer.)

    0–10 10–20 20–30 30–40 40–50 50–60 other (Please specify.)

6. How many times during the day do you receive information by way of e-mail? (Please delete all but the correct answer.)

    0–10 10–20 20–30 30–40 40–50 50–60 other (Please specify.)

7. Please rate the following characteristics of the e-mail system as good, fair, or poor.

    Speed
    Editing
    Options
    Appearance of Incoming Mail
    Compatibility with Word-Processing Software

8. What, if any, characteristics of the current e-mail system increase its effectiveness?

9. What, if any, characteristics of the current e-mail system lessen its effectiveness?

10. How satisfied are you with the current electronic mail system? (Please delete all but the correct answer.)

    Completely satisfied   Somewhat satisfied
    Neither satisfied nor dissatisfied   Somewhat dissatisfied
    Completely dissatisfied

11. Comments:

- **Gather background information.** Before you observe, gather as much background information as possible. Without this information, you may not know what to look for and, therefore, waste your time.
- **Know what to look for.** Do your homework. Find out what you are looking for and where to find it.
- **Take notes as you observe.** Record your observations immediately. Don't rely on your memory. You might forget an important detail.

PRINCIPLE 3: SELECT APPROPRIATE SECONDARY RESEARCH TECHNIQUES

Secondary research is gathering information from previously documented research or studies. For example, if you wanted to research the climate of Mars, you might look at reports written by scientists who analyzed data from the Mars *Pathfinder*. You can find valuable secondary information by conducting library, online, and Internet research. Libraries contain several types of resources: books, periodicals, trade publications, newspapers, indexes, abstracts, and government documents. You will find many of these resources in traditional card catalogs and book-type indexes and reference works. However, you will also find many catalogs, indexes, and reference works online or on CD-ROM. To use the library and Internet resources effectively, follow these guidelines:

- **Talk to reference librarians.** Reference librarians are your most valuable library resource. They can help you locate the appropriate resources and teach you how to use them. Reference librarians can save you time and frustration.
- **Take detailed notes.** Don't rely on your memory or on haphazard notes. Write down all needed information in a detailed, systematic manner. As you take these notes, include accurate, complete bibliographic information—enough information for your readers to locate the same information.
- **If you are using the Internet and the World Wide Web, write down the complete addresses of the sites you wish to visit.**

The following sections discuss library and Internet tools you can use to gather secondary information in a variety of fields.

Using Library Tools

You may find library information in a variety of media—books, journals, magazines, microfiche, videos, compact discs, newspapers. You can find most information through a book search, a periodical search, a computerized database search, or a government documents search. Focus primarily on tools available in college, university, and public libraries. Your company, however, may have a library containing some or all of these reference tools.

Searching for Books

You can find books by searching either the traditional card catalog or the online catalog. In either catalog, you can search for books by author, title, or subject. If you know the author's name or the book title, you can easily locate the book. If you have a topic such as "electronic literacy," you can locate one or more books related to that topic. Figure 6.3 shows three cards—an author, a title, and a subject card—from a card catalog. The cards are for the same book.

Although a subject search is the most commonly used approach, you may find this approach challenging and time-consuming, especially if your topic is broad—such as "machinery vibration." You can lessen the challenge and save time by narrowing the topic through brainstorming or primary research. Each subject card will direct you toward narrower topics such as "the causes of machinery vibration," "vibration analysis," or "diagnosing vibration analysis." If you haven't narrowed your topic before searching the subject catalog, you may spend time looking for information that you don't need. When you have narrowed your topic, you will have several keywords to help you conduct a meaningful and productive subject search. For example, if you are looking for information on analyzing and measuring vibration, you will have several keywords to narrow your search—words such as "measurement instruments," "measurement transducers," and "vibration analysis."

Searching for books in an online card catalog is much less time-consuming and frustrating than using traditional card catalogs. Most libraries—even small public libraries—have online card catalogs. The software used to access these catalogs differs, but the process you follow is basically the same. You can search online catalogs by author, title, or subject. To find a book on vibration analysis in most online catalogs, you would type "s=vibration analysis." You also can find books by consulting reference books such as

- *Library of Congress: Subject Catalog* (1950 to present): a cumulative listing—organized by subject—of all books represented by the Library of Congress cards since 1945. For books published after 1983, use the microfiche.
- *Books in Print* and *Subject Guide to Books in Print*: annual listing of books available in print from 3,600 U.S. publishers.
- *Cumulative Book Index*: listing of all books published in English since 1928.

Searching for Periodicals

You usually can find current and up-to-date information in periodicals. The following types of periodicals are useful:

- **Research journals** contain up-to-date, often cutting-edge research and data in various technical and scientific fields. They report on studies conducted by university and industry researchers.

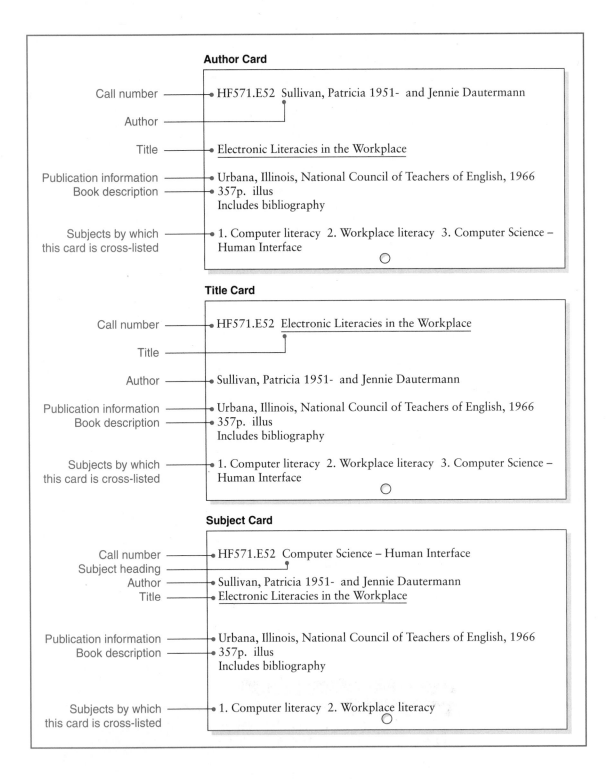

◀ **Figure 6.3**
Author, Title, and
Subject Cards

- **Trade journals** help practitioners interpret and apply information and recommendations reported in research journals.
- **Popular magazines and newsletters** inform and entertain general readers. You might use these periodicals to get an overview of your topic.
- **Newspapers** contain all types of information but don't cover most subjects in depth. Newspapers may summarize some topics—especially local issues—and present statistics, trends, and demographic information.
- **Reports** often contain some of the most up-to-date information on a topic. Reports are published by university, industry, and government agencies.

You can search for periodicals primarily in two types of reference guides:

- Indexes, which list citations by author, title, and subject
- Abstracts, which include not only the bibliographic information presented in an index but also a summary of each article

You can search through many indexes and abstracts both manually and electronically. Using the electronic version is easier and takes less time. Check with your reference librarians to see what indexes and abstracts are available online. Also find out whether your library's periodical holdings are cataloged online, so you can access them on the library's computer or your own. Figure 6.4 lists some indexes and abstracts that you might refer to as you search. The list contains only indexes and abstracts still being updated. You may also find useful information in indexes and abstracts no longer being updated annually. This list also identifies indexes and abstracts that were available electronically at the time of publication of this book; however, others on the list may now be available electronically.

Searching Computerized Databases

You also can search computerized databases to find citations on various topics. To access many of these databases, you go through commercial or government services that offer a variety of databases. Although these databases can provide a wealth of information, accessing them can be costly. An average search can cost from $5 to $60, depending on the database and your planning. A customized search may cost more than $100. Generally you will spend less if you have carefully narrowed your topic to several specific keywords.

You can search some databases on CD-ROM at university and public libraries. CD-ROM databases allow free access and printing. Figure 6.5 lists some online databases that you can access through university libraries.

Searching Government Publications

Every year the U.S. government publishes more than 25 million documents for specialized and general offices. You can find documents published by federal agencies and departments such as the Department of Labor, the Department of Housing and Urban Development, the Environmental Protection Agency, and

Figure 6.4

Examples of
Periodical Indexes
and Abstracts

Indexes
- *Aerospace Database*
- *Applied Science and Technology Index*
- *Art Index*
- *Arts and Humanities Citation Index* (electronic)
- *Biological and Agricultural Index* (electronic)
  [Continued from *Agricultural Index, Subject Index to a Selected List of Agricultural Periodicals and Bulletins, 1916–1946*]
- *Business Periodicals Index*
- *Computer Data Base* (electronic)
- *Computer Literature Index*
- *Current Technology Index*
  [Continued from *British Technology Index, 1962–1980*]
- *Engineering Index*
- *Food Service and Technology Index* (electronic)
- *General Science Index*
- *Government Reports Announcements and Index*
  [Previously titled *Government Reports Announcements, 1971–1975*; *U.S. Government Research and Development Reports, 1965–1971*; and *U.S. Government Research Reports, 1954–1964*]
- *Index to U.S. Government Periodicals*
- *National Newspaper Index* (electronic)
- *New York Times Index*
- *Public Affairs Information Service Bulletin (PAIS)*
- *Social Sciences Index*
- *The Wall Street Journal Index*

Abstracts
- *Abstracts and Indexes in Science and Technology: A Descriptive Guide*
- *Biological Abstracts*
- *Chemical Abstracts*
- *Computerized Periodical Indexes and Abstracts* (electronic)
- *Ecology Abstracts*
- *Electrical and Electronics Abstracts*
- *Energy Research Abstracts*
  [Continued from *Nuclear Science Abstracts, 1947–1976*]
- *Environmental Abstracts*
- *Information Science Abstracts*
- *International Aerospace Abstracts*
- *Mathematical Reviews*
- *Metals Abstracts*
  [Originally in two guides: *Metallurgical Abstracts* and *ASM Review of Metal Literature*]
- *Meteorological and Geoastrophysical Abstracts*
- *Microbiology Abstracts*
- *Mineralogical Abstracts*
- *Oceanic Abstracts*
- *Pollution Abstracts*
- *Psychological Abstracts*
- *Science Abstracts. Section A—Physics Abstracts; Section B—Electrical and Electronic Abstracts; Section C—Computer and Control Abstracts*
- *Scientific and Technical Aerospace Reports*
- *Selected Water Resources Abstracts*
- *Sociological Abstracts* (electronic)

Figure 6.5

Selected Online
Databases

- AGRICOLA (agriculture)
- BRS, BRS Information Technologies (multiple topics)
- CA Search (chemistry)
- COMPENDEX (engineering)
- DIALOG, Dialog Information Services (multiple topics)
- ENVIROLINE (environment)
- EPIC Service, OCLC Online Computer Library Center (multiple topics)
- GEO-REF (geosciences)
- INSPEC (science)
- ISMEC (mechanical engineering)
- MATHSCI (mathematics)
- METADEX (metallurgy)
- NTIS (multiple topics from reports prepared by the Department of Commerce)
- PSYCFIRST (psychology)
- SCISEARCH (science and technology)
- SPIN (physics)

the Internal Revenue Service. You can find these documents through libraries that are registered repositories for U.S. government documents. Many university and some large public libraries are repositories. They usually have a separate reference librarian and staff for the government documents because these documents are cataloged separately. You won't find government documents cataloged within the library's Library of Congress system. Instead, government documents constitute a library within the main library. Some libraries also house publications published by state agencies. These publications can provide valuable information on topics such as food, nutrition, agriculture, animal science, natural resources, and state demographics. To find state and federal government documents, look in specialized indexes and catalogs of government publications, or ask a reference librarian. Figure 6.6 lists some of these indexes and catalogs.

Figure 6.6

Selected Indexes and
Catalogs of
Government
Documents

- *American Statistics Index and Abstracts, Annual and Retrospective Edition. A Comprehensive Guide to the Statistical Publications of the U.S. Government*
- *Bureau of the Census Catalog of Publications, 1790–1972* [brought up-to-date with supplements]
- *CIS/Index to Congressional Publications*
- *County and City Data Book*
- *Cumulative Subject Index to the Monthly Catalog of United States Government Publications, 1900–1971*
- *Federal Register*
- *Government Reports Announcements and Index*
- *GPO Publications Reference File*
- *Monthly Catalog of United States Government Publications*
- *Monthly Checklist of State Publications*
- *National Economic, Social, and Environmental Data Book*
- *Subject Bibliographies*

Using Internet Tools

The Internet links computer networks around the world. The Internet links local area networks (LANs)—computers within a company or university— metropolitan area networks (MANs)—computers throughout a city—and even larger wide area networks (WANs)—computers all over the globe. The Internet provides several types of information and ways for you to access that information. You can access hundreds of university card catalogs through the Internet. You also can access information from various government and non-profit agencies. From your desktop, you can access information across the United States and the globe. You can access "thousands of independent data-bases, archives, and online services . . . making" the Internet "one huge virtual library" (LaQuey 85). Although this virtual library is not as well organized as your university or public library, you can use several tools to help you locate information on the Internet. Before you can use these tools, however, learn how to access and use the Internet. If you don't know how, ask your instructor or the computing personnel at your college or university for help. Once you know how to access the Internet, you can use Gopher, Archie, Veronica, Jughead, WAIS, and the World Wide Web to search for information.

Gopher

Gopher is a tool for accessing Internet information through a system of menus. These menus allow you to browse through archives and databases at any Gopher site. Without Gopher, you would have to electronically link to each database separately. Using Gopher, you can search databases at different loca-tions without having to contact and connect to each location. You can explore information located in different countries or different universities. For exam-ple, if you want to find information on the environmental impact of illegal landfills, you can use Gopher to search all its databases and archives. During this search, you might explore a variety of university libraries and the archives of state and federal government agencies such as the Environmental Protection Agency—without leaving your desktop. As you search with Gopher, you may want to use the bookmark feature to mark places of interest and assemble them into one menu. To learn how to use bookmarks, visit with your instruc-tor, explore your computer desktop, or ask the computing personnel at your college or university.

Archie, Veronica, and Jughead

Archie, Veronica, and Jughead are tools to help you search the Gopher menus. With Archie, you can search through a master list of files housed at any Gopher public site—sites where you can copy and transfer files free of charge. Veronica lists every menu item from every Gopher site. With Veronica (an acronym that stands for Very Easy Rodent-Oriented Net-Wide Index to Computerized Archives), you can search all Gopher menus. You supply Veronica with a keyword (or keywords), and it will compile one Gopher menu of the items containing the keyword(s). When Veronica is busy, try using

THE READER'S CORNER

Internet Research

The abundance of information available on the Internet doesn't always benefit researchers. First, the Internet offers great breadth but rarely offers depth. The contents of many catalogs are accessible, but the contents of very few books are; similarly, periodicals often provide their tables of contents but only rarely offer the actual contents. Second, the Internet doesn't yet logically tell users what information is or is not available. For example, the U.S. government has made the latest breast cancer research available but currently provides little information on nutritional supplements. Third, Internet search engines pass no judgment on their findings. One of the Internet's great strengths is that everyone has a voice. For researchers, this leveling of sources has a dark side. Traditionally, publishers have acted as gatekeepers, limiting the amount of material to enter the marketplace of ideas. The Internet, however, has no such gatekeepers—the home page of the U.S. Department of Defense is on essentially equal footing with that of suicide cult Heaven's Gate. Serious researchers will make distinctions among such sources, of course, but that is a credit to the researchers, not to the Internet itself. If you plan to use the Internet, your most important research skills may be skepticism and willingness to check sources offline.

Jughead. Jughead searches local parts of Gopher rather than all of it. For example, if you are interested in searching a local library such as the library at the University of California at Berkeley, you look for the following menu item: "Jughead: Search menus in University of California at Berkeley gopherspace <?>." You use Jughead in the same way you use Veronica.

Wide Area Information Servers

To find out what's in a file, you can use a wide area information server (WAIS). This tool lets you search a variety of Internet databases by looking for keywords in files rather than simply looking at file titles. When WAIS finds the types of files you need, you can ask it to find more files with the same characteristics. For example, if you are looking for information on the environmental impact of illegal landfills on metropolitan areas, WAIS might find newspaper articles on the public's reaction to these landfills in Detroit and Seattle and files from the Environmental Protection Agency (EPA). If you are more concerned about the environmental impact, you ask WAIS to find files with characteristics similar to those of the EPA files. WAIS is quite powerful and covers more than six hundred databases (LaQuey 124). You can access WAIS through a Gopher or a World Wide Web interface.

The World Wide Web

The World Wide Web makes searching the Internet more efficient. The Web uses hypertext (or nonlinear) links to search Internet databases. The Web is a hypertext system that allows you to use keywords to move or jump quickly from one database (or Web site) to another. To move through the Web, you need a browser—a program for navigating the Internet. You can use a graphic browser such as Mosaic, Netscape, or Microsoft Explorer or a text-only browser such as Lynx. To find out more about browsers, search the Web for information, or look at some books about the Web.

Locating Specific Internet and Web Sites

Before learning how to search for information on the Internet and World Wide Web, let's look at an address, or URL (uniform resource locator), for one of these sites:

protocol   domain   directory path
http://www.hmco.com/college

The letters *http* indicate the protocol or kind of link: *http* stands for "hypertext transfer protocol." All Web sites begin with *http*. The protocols for other Internet sites differ. For example, the URL for a Gopher site begins with *gopher://*. A colon and two forward slashes (://) separate the protocol from the next part of the site address—the domain, or host computer. The domain identifies the owner of the site. The owner of the site whose address appears above is Houghton Mifflin Company (abbreviated "hmco"). The owner's name is followed by a period and "com." "Com" indicates that the owner is a commercial entity. When the owner is a government or an educational entity, "gov" or "edu" follows the owner's name. A forward slash (/) separates the owner's domain from the directory path. The directory path is the address of the part of the site to which the URL refers. Thus, the URL displayed above tells you that at Houghton Mifflin's World Wide Web site, you will find a particular site for the College Division.

To search for information on the Internet and the Web, use the following methods:

- **Use search directories (sometimes called catalogs) and topical indexes.** These directories and indexes arrange information by category, subdividing information into menus of topics and subtopics. Figure 6.7 lists some directories and topical indexes that you might use to begin an Internet search.

- **Use a search engine to search specific indexed Internet and Web sites.** Search engines allow you to search these sites by keyword(s). These engines search the entire Internet for information on your topic or for "hits" containing the keywords. Figure 6.8 lists some search engines.

- **Search subject-specific Web sites with search engines.** These engines don't search the entire Internet. Instead, they search specific Web sites or a specific set of resources. Figure 6.9 lists some subject-specific search engines.

Figure 6.7
Directories and Indexes with URLs for Searching the Internet and World Wide Web

SITE	URL[1]
The Argus Clearinghouse (formerly The Clearinghouse for Subject-Oriented Internet Resource Guides)	<http://www.clearinghouse.net/searching/find.html>
EINet Galaxy	<http://www.einet.net/galaxy.html>
InfoSeek Guide	<http://www.infoseek.com/>
Inter-Links	<http://www.alabanza.com/kabacoff/Inter-Links>
The Internet Public Library	<http://www.ipl.org>
The Internet Services List	<http://www.spectracom.com/islist>
Library of Congress	<http://lcweb.loc.gov/global>
Netscape's Net Directory	<http://home.netscape.com/home/internet-directory.html> (Or you can click on Directory, Internet Directory)
WWW Virtual Library	<http://www.w3.org/pub/DataSources/bySubject/Overview.html>
Yahoo	<http://www.yahoo.com/>

Figure 6.8
Search Engines with URLs to Search Specific Indexed Internet and Web Sites

SEARCH ENGINE	URL
All-In-One Search Page	<http://www.albany.net/allinone>
Alta Vista	<http://www.altavista.digital.com>
Excite	<http://www.excite.com>
HotBot	<http://www.hotbot.com>
InfoSeek	<http://www2.infoseek.com/Query>
Isleuth	<http://www.isleuth.com>
Lycos	<http://www.lycos.com>
Magellan	<http://www.mckinley.com>
Netscape's Net Search	<http://home.netscape.com/home/internet-search.html> (Or click on Directory, Internet Search)
Open Text	<http://www.opentext.com>
SavvySearch	<http://www.cs.colostate.edu/~dreiling/smartform.html>
Search.com	<http://www.search.com>
WebCrawler	<http://webcrawler.com>

---

1. The URLs for the Internet and World Wide Web sites and search engines were accurate at the time of publication.

- **Use online library catalogs and databases for libraries across the United States and the world.** The Internet and the Web allow you to connect to many libraries' online catalogs. You can use directories of worldwide or U.S. libraries. Using these directories, you can easily link to a library's online catalogs. Figure 6.10 lists some library interfaces that may help you.

As you use the Internet and the Web to research a topic, remember these tips:

- **The Internet and the Web may not contain all the information available about your topic.** Even in this digital age, not all printed records have been transferred to digital storage; so you may find important information about

Figure 6.9 Sample Subject-Specific Web Sites with URLs

SITE	URL	SUBJECT
Biologists Resources	<http://www.bio.cam.ac.uk>	Biology
CERN Particle Physics Laboratory	<http://www.cern.ch>	Physics research
Chemical Engineering Catalog	<http://www.che.ufl.edu/WWW-CHE/Index.html>	Chemical engineering
EINet Galaxy Engineering and Technology	<http://www.galaxy.einet.net/galaxy/ Engineering-and-Technology.html>	Engineering
EINet Galaxy Math Guide	<http://www.galaxy.einet.net/galaxy/ Science/Mathematics.html>	Mathematics
Industrial Engineering Index	<http://homer.isye.gatech.edu/www-ie>	Industrial engineering
Legal Information Institute	<http://www.law.cornell.edu/tcopical.html>	Law
Smithsonian Natural History Museum	<http://nmnhwww.si.edu/nmnhweb.html>	Research resources at the museum
Social Sciences (within the WWW Virtual Library)	<http://coombs.anu.edu.au>	Social sciences
Telesource	<http://www.telesource.com/library.html>	Telecommunications companies and information
U.S. government legislation	<http://thomas.loc.gov>	Legislation passed by the U.S. Congress
Voice of the Shuttle Humanities Server	<http://humanitas.ucsb.edu>	Art, history, literature, and philosophy

Figure 6.10
Online Library
Catalogs and
Databases with URLs

SITE	URL
Daedalus's Guides to the Web: Libraries	<http://www.georgetown.edu/labyrinth/ library/library_catalogues.html>
Eric Morgan's Directory of Libraries with Web Interfaces	<http://www.lib.ncsu.edu/staff/morgan/ index-morganagus.html>
Libcat	<http://www.metronet.lib.mn.us/ lc/lc1.html>
Libweb: Library Servers Via the Web	<http://sunsite.berkeley.edu/Libweb>

your topic in traditional print sources such as journals, books, and trade publications. Until all these traditional sources are transferred to digital records, be sure to include traditional library research as part of your search strategy.

- **A search by means of Internet and Web directories and search engines is only as good as the directories and engines.** Generally, the bigger a directory or index is, the better or more comprehensive it will be. If you want to find everything available about your topic on the Web, use a combination of directories and search engines.

- **Some Internet and Web sources are not reliable or up-to-date.** Few if any standards regulate publications that appear on the Internet or Web. No editorial board oversees most Internet publications. Currently, no market forces are driving incompetent or unreliable publications off the Web, so carefully research and evaluate any Internet or Web sources that you use in your work.

- **You need to accurately document Internet and Web sources that you use in your work.** Give your readers enough bibliographic information, so they can find the source on the Internet or the Web. To document any Internet or Web source, you will need the author's name, the title, the URL (electronic site address), the publication date, and (for MLA-style citations, discussed below) the date you retrieved the source.

PRINCIPLE 4: DOCUMENT YOUR SOURCES

When you use any source for your work, you must document that source. The documentation recommended by the American Psychological Association (APA) is frequently used in the sciences and social sciences. The documentation style recommended by the Modern Language Association (MLA) is frequently used in the humanities. Your company may have a preferred style that differs from those two. In the sections that follow, you will find some examples of APA-style and MLA-style documentation of traditional and electronic sources. To answer your questions as you document your sources, consult the following style guides:

- American Psychological Association. *Publication Manual of the American Psychological Association.* 4th ed. Washington, D.C.: APA, 1994.
- Council of Biology Editors. *Scientific Style and Format: The CBE Manual for Authors, Editors, and Publishers.* 6th ed. New York: Cambridge UP, 1994.
- *The Chicago Manual of Style.* 14th ed. Chicago: U of Chicago P, 1993.
- Gibaldi, Joseph. *MLA Handbook for Writers of Research Papers.* 4th ed. New York: MLA, 1995.
- Li, Xia, and Nancy B. Crane. *Electronic Style: A Guide to Citing Electronic Information.* Westport, CT: Merlermedia, 1996.

APA-Style Documentation

Book

LaQuey, T. (1994). *The Internet companion: A beginner's guide to global networking.* Reading, MA: Addison-Wesley.

Edited Book

Sullivan, P., and Dautermann, J. (Eds.). (1996). *Electronic literacies in the workplace: Technologies of writing.* Urbana, IL: National Council of Teachers of English.

E-Mail

Raign, K. <raign@casafac.unt.edu> (1997, May). Kairos project [Office communication].

FTP (file available for downloading via file transfer protocol)

McKinney, T. (1995, February 6). Developing customer-centered Web sites. Available FTP: ism.swb.com Library/Article/Web/dev.txt

Government Publication

U.S. Department of Education. (1994). *The condition of education 1994.* Washington, DC: U.S. Government Printing Office.

Internet Source

Include only the date the Internet source was published. You can omit the date you found the source.

Berners-Lee, T. (1995). *Style guide for online hypertext* [Online]. Available: http://www.w3.org/hyptertext/WWW/Provider/Style/Overview.html

Journal Article

December, J. (1996). An information development methodology for the World Wide Web. *Technical Communication, 43*(4), 369–375.

MOOs, MUDs, and IRCs (synchronous communication)

GlenRoseMoo. (1997, April 7). Seminar discussion on writing government specifications for the nuclear industry. Available: telnet://glenrose.unt.edu: 6790

Plummer, M. (1997, May 12). Regulations. Group discussion. Available: telnet://moo.tu.org/port=7890

Newspaper Article

Blow, S. (1997, April 2). Raising kids in the electronic age. *Phoenix Sun Times,* p. C1.

MLA-Style Documentation

Book

LaQuey, Tracy. *The Internet Companion: A Beginner's Guide to Global Networking.* Reading, MA: Addison, 1994.

Edited Book

Sullivan, Patricia, and Jennie Dautermann, eds. *Electronic Literacies in the Workplace: Technologies of Writing.* Urbana: National Council of Teachers of English, 1996.

E-Mail

Include the author's name, a description, the e-mail's recipient, the e-mail's date, the date that you found the source, and the location of the source if you weren't the recipient.

Raign, Kathryn. E-mail about kairos project to Brenda Sims. 2 May 1997.

Smith, Susan. E-mail to Interscripta discussion list. 4 June 1997. Online posting. Internet. 10 Oct. 1997. Available: http://www.mun.ca/lists/interscripta/ interscripta.log9310d.

FTP (file available for downloading via file transfer protocol)

McKinney, Tonya. "Developing Customer-Centered Web Sites." 6 Feb. 1995. Available FTP: ism.swb.com Library/Article/Web/dev.txt (21 Oct. 1996).

Government Publication

United States. Dept. of Education. *The Condition of Education 1994.* Washington: GPO, 1994.

Internet Source

Include the date the source was published on the Internet and the date you found that source.

Berners-Lee, Teresa. *Style Guide for Online Hypertext*. World Wide Web Consortium, 1995. Online. Internet. 2 Apr. 1997. Available: http://www.w3.org/hyptertext/WWW/Provider/Style/Overview.html.

Journal Article

December, John. "An Information Development Methodology for the World Wide Web." *Technical Communication* 43.4 (1996): 369–75.

MOOs, MUDs, and IRCs (synchronous communication)

GlenRoseMOO. "Seminar Discussion on Writing Government Specifications for the Nuclear Industry." 7 Apr. 1997. Available: telnet://glenrose.unt.edu: 6790 (10 June 1997).

Plummer, Martha. "Regulations." 12 May 1997. Group discussion. Available: telnet://moo.tu.org/port=7890 (9 Aug. 1997).

Newspaper Article

Blow, S. "Raising Kids in the Electronic Age." *Phoenix Sun Times* 2 Apr. 1997: C1.

CONCLUSION

The manner in which you plan and gather information for your documents can make a difference in the success of that document. Allow ample time to gather information, so you can effectively anticipate and answer your readers' questions. You might begin your search for information in traditional library resources; however, be sure to take advantage of the many electronic databases and Internet resources now available. After you have gathered your information, be sure to accurately cite and document it.

WORKSHEET for Gathering Information for Your Documents

Principle 1: Plan Your Research to Suit Your Purpose

- Have you narrowed your topic? Is your topic specific?
- What is the purpose of your research?
- What types of information will you need?

- Have you developed a research strategy using primary and secondary techniques?

Principle 2: Select Appropriate Primary Research Techniques

Interviews

- Will the interview be formal or informal?
- What is the purpose of the interview?
- What questions will you ask?
- What background information do you need for the interview?

Questionnaires

- How will you administer your questionnaire?
- What types of question will you ask?
- Are your questions clear and unambiguous?

Observation

- Will observing people or situations help you to answer your questions?
- Do you have the necessary background information to be an informed observer?

Principle 3: Select Appropriate Secondary Research Techniques

- Have you searched for books and periodicals in the library?
- Have you searched through government documents?
- Have you searched online and CD-ROM databases?
- Have you searched for information electronically: on the Internet and the World Wide Web?

Principle 4: Document Your Sources

- Have you accurately and correctly documented all sources, including Internet and World Wide Web sources?

EXERCISES

1. For this exercise, your instructor will assign you to a team or ask you to select a team. You and your team are engineering consultants for a city landfill. Managers of the landfill are concerned about the environmental impact of raising the landfill. The city has approved raising it by 10 feet. As the engineering consultants, your team will explain how the raising will affect the local environment and suggest ways to minimize that impact. Your assignment is to list the steps that your team might take to research the environmental impact and then suggest appropriate research techniques that your team might use to gather information.

2. Conduct a formal interview with a professional in your field of study. For example, if you are majoring in chemical engineering, you might interview a chemical engineer who works for an oil company. Before the interview, call the interviewee for an appointment, gather background information on the interviewee, and write down questions that you want to ask. After the interview, write a memo to your instructor summarizing the interview.

3. Search the Internet and the World Wide Web for sites and reference tools related to your major field of study. Write a memo to your classmates listing these sites and tools. Be sure to include complete URLs and a brief description of each site or tool.

4. Select a topic on which you will write a report for this class. The topic can relate to your major field of study or to your job. Make sure that you have appropriately narrowed the topic. After you have selected a topic, complete these exercises:

   a. Plan a research strategy for your report using the following questions:

   (1) Along with the card catalog, which periodical indexes and abstracts will contain citations related to your topic? Which of these tools are available online in your library?

   (2) Which computerized and CD-ROM databases will contain citations related to your topic? Can you access these at your library? What, if any, will be the cost to you?

   (3) Will government publications contain information related to your topic? If they will, what indexes and catalogs will you use? Which of these tools are available online in your library?

   (4) Which directories and indexes will you use to search the Internet and the World Wide Web?

   (5) What search engines will you use to search the Internet and the World Wide Web? What keyword(s) will you use for these searches?

   (6) Are there any subject-specific Web sites that relate to your topic? If there are, what are the URLs for these sites?

   b. Prepare a preliminary bibliography of the sources that you might use for your report. Include traditional library, Internet, and World Wide Web sources. Be sure to use the appropriate citation style for each source.

   c. For the Internet or World Wide Web sources, attach a brief note evaluating each source. Why is it reliable? How do you know it is reliable?

CASE STUDY   Discovering Job Prospects in Your Field

Background

Ann Goodgame is trying to decide whether to continue in her particular field of study. She read that job prospects in her field are not good. However, she won't graduate from college for two years, so she has decided to find out more about the job prospects. In particular, Ann wants to answer these questions:

- What are the job prospects in her field, nationally and locally?

- What areas of her field seem to have the best prospects for employment?

- What can she do to best prepare for finding a job? What types of skills and knowledge will she need?

- What annual salary should she expect to receive for an entry-level job in her field?

- What local and regional companies hire in her field?

Ann decides to go to the library and to access the Internet and the World Wide Web to answer these questions.

Assignment

Assume that Ann's field is the same as your major field of study. Then complete the following steps:

1. Develop a research plan to answer the questions listed above about employment in your field.

2. Find bibliographic citations giving you employment and salary information. Include two citations from each of the following sources:

   a. Government or state publications

   b. Periodical publications, such as trade journals, research journals, or newspapers

   c. Internet or World Wide Web sources

3. Using the Internet, the World Wide Web, or your instructors, find the names of three professionals in your field who can give you information about employment, needed skills, and salaries.

4. Write a memo to your instructor explaining your research plan. Be sure to include the citations you found for Assignment 2 and the names in Assignment 3.

Chapter 7

Structuring Information for Your Readers

CHAPTER OUTLINE

P aul Das sits at his desk looking at the pages of data he has collected for a manual to minimize pollution from waste disposal sites. Paul works in a research laboratory where he and his coworkers develop technology for cities to use in treating and managing wastewater and solid and hazardous waste. They have a contract with the Environmental Protection Agency (EPA) to prepare this manual. After eighteen months, they have completed their research on ways to minimize pollution, and Paul is ready to begin writing the manual. He considers the ways he can structure the information and realizes that structuring it is more than just preparing an outline. It is a process that goes beyond the data he has collected; it involves understanding the readers and the social and cultural forces at work in his company.

In this chapter, you will learn four principles for structuring information. Before thinking about these principles, let's consider how the structure can help readers read and use your documents.

READERS AND YOUR DOCUMENTS

Have you ever tried to read a document where the sentences and paragraphs aren't structured logically? Did you have trouble gathering the information you needed? Documents with an illogical structure make readers' tasks difficult—whether that task is to follow a procedure, to make a decision, or to gather information (Felker et al. 9). As an example, let's consider a section that one of Paul's coworkers prepared for the manual on minimizing pollution (see Figure 7.1).

Let's look at the information in each paragraph of Figure 7.1:

Paragraph 1   Introduction to using chemicals to stabilize or destroy waste
Paragraph 2   More information about using chemicals to stabilize or destroy waste
Paragraph 3   The process of chemical fixation
Paragraph 4   An alternative to applying chemicals to in situ landfills
Paragraph 5   Firms that provide the chemicals to stabilize the waste
Paragraph 6   Problems with chemical fixation in the landfills
Paragraph 7   Problem landfills and chemical fixation

The structure of the document has several problems:

- Information about in situ landfills appears in paragraphs 4 and 6. The writer should have pulled this information together, combining it in one paragraph or presenting it in two successive paragraphs.
- The paragraphs do not follow a logical order.
- The document lacks informative headings that identify major topics for readers.
- The document lacks a brief overview describing its structure.

Figure 7.1

An Example of
Information
Structured Illogically

Chemical Fixation

[1] The application of chemicals to destroy or stabilize hazardous materials and potential pollutants has been a common practice for many years, particularly for industrial wastes. Generally, chemical treatment is quite waste-specific. Thus, an effective system in one case may be ineffective or totally inapplicable in another.

[2] Since the 1970's, several processes involving chemicals have been developed which may be effective on a broader range of wastes. Some of these newer processes are more effective on liquids and thin sludges while others function best with heavier sludges and solids. These processes rely on the reactions of such materials as Portland cement, lime, and common silicates to encapsulate, solidify, or cement waste material.

[3] Each of these processes involves the mixing of a chemical agent such as cement, lime, or silicates with the waste material. With liquid water, the agent absorbs the waste. With solids, the agent coats the surface of the solids to cement them together. With sludges, the agent absorbs and cements the waste. Some of these processes rely mainly on the ability of the chemical system to insulate each particle of pollutant from adjacent leaching fluids; others rely on the formation of a relatively impermeable mass to exclude leaching fluids from passing through the waste.

[4] An alternative to the application of chemical fixation agents to the in situ landfill is to use these agents for stabilizing waste materials. These waste materials can then serve as cover for a problem landfill. After proper processing, these waste materials can be spread, graded, and thereafter cemented into a stable, relatively impermeable cover.

[5] The earliest commercially prominent stabilization system was a process offered by Chemfix for applying to hazardous liquids and sludges. Now, stabilization processes are offered by other firms such as the Environmental Technology Corporation, IU Conversion Systems, Inc., and the Dravo Corporation. The latter two firms primarily offer systems for stabilizing sulfur dioxide scrubber sludge.

[6] We have included information on stabilizing waste materials with chemical agents because, in particular instances, the process is a viable means for controlling potential pollutants. However, this process is not feasible for in situ landfill problems because the success of the system depends on the intimate mixing of the chemical agents and the material to be stabilized; without this mixing, the municipal refuse cannot be coated and encapsulated, and the normal landfill processes of degradation and leaching cannot occur. To ensure the mixing of the chemicals with the refuse would require excavating the entire landfill, which provides little advantage over excavating and relocating the landfill to an environmentally sound site.

[7] An ideal situation would be a problem landfill located near a source of chemically stabilized waste material. The material would be readily available for applying to the landfill as a cap. The chemically stabilized material would then be applied at an approximate compacted thickness of 0.6 m, with appropriate drainage swales to remove surface water.

Source: Adapted from Andrews L. Tolman, Antonio P. Ballestero Jr., William W. Beck Jr., and Grover H. Emrich, *Guidance Manual for Minimizing Pollution from Waste Disposal Sites*, EPA-600/2-78-142 (Washington: GPO, Aug. 1978) 52.

Because the information in Figure 7.1 doesn't have a logical structure, readers can't easily remember it. A more logical structure will help them to remember, understand, and perhaps follow the document (Duin 186).

The information would be easier to follow in a general-to-specific structure as in Figure 7.2:

Paragraph 1   Introduction to using chemicals to stabilize or destroy waste

Paragraph 2   The process of chemical fixation

Paragraph 3   Problems with chemical fixation in the landfills

Paragraph 4   An alternative to applying chemicals to existing (in situ) landfills

Paragraph 5   Use of stabilized waste materials as cover for existing landfills

In this version, the writer has pulled together closely related information into five instead of seven paragraphs. The information on existing landfills now appears in successive paragraphs. The document begins by briefly introducing chemical fixation, moves to more specific information about how chemicals stabilize or destroy hazardous waste, and ends with even more specific information about when chemical fixation is ineffective. The document gives readers a brief overview in paragraph 1 and includes informative headings that allow readers to read only those paragraphs that interest them.

You may be faced with several possible structures for the documents that you write. The principles that follow will help you to choose appropriately.

PRINCIPLE 1: DECIDE HOW TO STRUCTURE YOUR DOCUMENT[1]

Often, you may have two or more options for structuring information. By recognizing these options, you can select the one that will work best for your readers. Ask yourself the following question to determine the most effective structure: Can I group similar information? Pulling together closely related information is "one of the most important organizational principles" in writing (Podis 199). It helps readers to gather the information they need and to receive the intended message of your document. The writer of the document shown in Figure 7.3 presents all the information about scientific studies of electric and magnetic fields (EMF) in one section titled "What About Scientific Studies?"

To determine how to group similar information in your documents,

- Use the standard patterns of organization
- Consider your readers
- Consider the organizational context—the social and cultural conventions—of your workplace

---

1. Based on a suggested approach to arranging business documents created by Jack Selzer in "Arranging Business Prose."

Figure 7.2

A Document with a
Logical, Reader-
Oriented Structure

Chemical Fixation

[1] The application of chemicals to destroy or stabilize hazardous materials and potential pollutants has been a common practice for many years, particularly for industrial wastes. Generally, chemical treatment is quite waste-specific. Thus, an effective system in one case may be ineffective or totally inapplicable in another. For example, applying chlorine to destroy cyanide and applying lime to precipitate and insolubilize fluorides are standard but waste-specific processes. Since the 1970's, several firms have developed chemical fixation processes that may be effective on a broader range of wastes.[1] In this section, we will discuss how chemical agents destroy or stabilize waste and when chemical agents are ineffective.

How Chemical Agents Destroy or Stabilize Waste

[2] To destroy or stabilize waste, each of these chemical fixation processes mixes a chemical agent such as Portland cement, lime, or silicates with the waste material. With liquids, the chemical agent absorbs the waste. With solids, the agent coats the surface of the solids to cement them together. With sludges, the agent absorbs and cements the waste. Some of these processes rely mainly on the ability of the chemical system to insulate each particle of pollutant from adjacent leaching fluids; others rely on the formation of a relatively impermeable mass to exclude leaching fluids from passing through the waste.

When Chemical Agents Are Ineffective

[3] Although chemical fixation is a viable means for controlling potential pollutants, this process is not feasible for existing landfill problems because the success of the process depends on the intimate mixing of the chemical agents and the material to be stabilized. Without this mixing, the municipal refuse cannot be coated and encapsulated, and the normal landfill processes of degradation and leaching cannot occur. To ensure the mixing of the chemicals with the refuse would require excavating the entire landfill, providing little advantage over excavating and relocating the landfill to an environmentally sound site.

[4] An alternative to applying chemical fixation agents to an existing landfill is to use these agents for stabilizing waste materials not currently in a landfill. These waste materials can then serve as cover for a problem landfill. After proper processing, these waste materials can be spread, graded, and thereafter cemented into a stable, relatively impermeable cover.

[5] When such waste material serves as cover, the problem landfill must be near a source of chemically stabilized waste material. The material would be readily available for applying to the landfill as a cap. The chemically stabilized material could then be applied at an approximate compacted thickness of 0.6 m, with appropriate drainage swales to remove surface water.

1. Chemfix offered the earliest commercially prominent stabilization system for hazardous liquids and sludges. Now, other firms such as the Environmental Technology Corporation, IU Conversion Systems, Inc., and the Dravo Corporation offer stabilization processes. The latter two firms offer systems for stabilizing sulfur dioxide scrubber sludge.

Source: Adapted from Andrews L. Tolman, Antonio P. Ballestero Jr., William W. Beck Jr., and Grover H. Emrich, *Guidance Manual for Minimizing Pollution from Waste Disposal Sites,* EPA-600/2-78-142 (Washington: GPO, Aug. 1978) 52.

Figure 7.3
A Document That
Groups Similar
Information

What About Scientific Studies?

Scientists have been studying a possible link between electric and magnetic fields (EMF) and health effects since the 1960s. Despite a large number of high quality studies, no one knows whether EMF causes health problems. Some studies have not found a link between EMF and health problems, but other studies do provide at least some support for the position that exposure to EMF may be harmful.

Scientists have conducted two types of studies of electric and magnetic fields: laboratory studies of cells, organs, animals and people; and epidemiological studies of people.

Laboratory studies have indicated that EMF can have biological effects. Reported effects include changes in levels of hormones, in cell functions and in heart rate. These changes may or may not cause health problems. For example, a single cup of coffee can produce biological changes such as increased heart rate, yet a cup of coffee is generally believed to be harmless.

Epidemiological studies compare two groups of people: those with an illness such as leukemia, and a similar but healthy group, to try to identify one or more factors often associated with the illness. All epidemiological studies involve uncertainties such as the possibility that scientists may have overlooked an important cause of an illness or have been unable to accurately identify environmental exposures years after the actual exposures.

While some epidemiological studies have not found a link between EMF and health problems, some studies have found that children who live near powerlines assumed by the researcher to carry high currents, have a greater risk than other children of developing leukemia. Interestingly, most of the studies have not found links between the actual measured fields and increased leukemia risk. All of the studies either assumed or indicated that electric fields are not a problem but that magnetic fields may be.

Other studies have focused on people who are exposed on their jobs to potentially high EMF levels. These studies have indicated that EMF may cause increased health problems. For example, several studies have indicated a link between increased cancer risk and occupations such as electrician, telephone worker, electric utility worker, and electrical engineer. Most of these studies, however, have not accounted for other possible causes and have not measured the EMF.

The studies conducted so far do not prove or disprove the theory that EMF exposure is harmful. They do indicate areas which deserve additional research. Further studies are underway and planned which will focus on possible occupational risks of EMF, childhood leukemia and the effects of EMF on cell functions. These studies should provide information in the next three to five years.

Source: Adapted from Texas Utilities Electric Company, *Electric and Magnetic Fields* (Dallas: Texas Utilities Electric Company, n.d.). Courtesy of Texas Utilities.

Use the Standard Patterns of Organization

Standard patterns for organizing information include spatial order, chronological order, general-to-specific order, classification and division, partition, comparison/contrast, problem and solution, cause and effect, and order of importance. The first two patterns are sequential: the items that you arrange follow each other in physical location (spatial order) or in time (chronological order). The other seven patterns require you to choose the main point and then group the subpoints in a specific way. You can use more than one pattern. For instance, you can use partition to break a whole into parts and then use spatial order to describe the parts. The information you will include in your document determines which pattern(s) to use. Occasionally you may encounter a writing situation where none of the standard patterns is appropriate. In such a situation, try grouping closely related information together.

Spatial Order

When you describe parts by their location—for instance, from left to right—you are using spatial order. Figure 7.4 describes the pull-down menu items on the online menu bar for an Internet service. Notice that the writer begins with "Help"—the first item on the left of the screen—and then moves from left to right discussing each item on the menu bar in turn.

Chronological Order

You encounter information arranged chronologically almost daily—in recipes, in instructions, in the newspaper. Chronological order occurs most fre-

Figure 7.4
A Passage Illustrating
Spatial Order

With the menu bar, you can access many of the program's functions.

| help | file | edit | go to | mail | users | window |

The pull-down menu items on the online menu bar are

- **Help**–to access the help system.
- **File**–to create a new file, open an existing file, save or print a file, cancel an action, or exit.
- **Edit**–to cut, copy, or paste text.
- **Go To**–to see what's new on the service, use key words, or scan the directory of services.
- **Mail**–to write, check, and read mail; or send a fax or paper mail.
- **Users**–to send an instant message, get member information, locate a member online, or access the member directory.
- **Window**–to hide or close windows.

quently in instructions, process descriptions, and descriptions of events or developments. When you read information arranged in order of occurrence or sequence, you are reading information arranged chronologically. Figure 7.5 shows some instructions. The writer has listed the steps for installing the software in the order that the reader must complete them—in chronological order.

General to Specific Order

For most documents, "write about the 'big picture' before you describe the parts and pieces that make up the whole" (Felker et al. 10). Write first about the general topic and then about the specifics. Most readers also need the conclusion or recommendations first, so they can interpret and understand the specific information in the context of the conclusions or recommendations (Samuels 308). When you solve a problem or make a recommendation, you come to that solution, recommendation, or conclusion last; however, for your readers to understand your work, they need the solution, recommendation, or conclusion first.

Figure 7.6 is an excerpt from an Environmental Protection Agency (EPA) document that uses a general-to-specific arrangement in the sequencing of paragraphs as well as in individual paragraphs. The writer begins by briefly introducing plume management methods in the first paragraph and then moves to specific categories of plume management in the second and third paragraphs. In the final paragraph, the writer moves to the specific topic of plume management and leachate. Within the third paragraph, the writer uses a general-to-specific arrangement. The paragraph begins with a definition of injection and then moves to specific ways to apply injection.

Classification and Division

At first, the information for your document may seem to be a list of miscellaneous facts, ideas, and comments. If you can find items that share common characteristics, you may be able to classify and divide the information into meaningful categories or groups. To classify information, identify the broad group to which that information belongs. To divide information, identify categories within that broad group. For example, let's look again at

Figure 7.5
A Passage Arranged in Chronological Order

To install the software on your fixed disk drive (also commonly referred to as a hard disk drive):

1. Turn on your computer.
2. Insert the software diskette in drive a:
3. Click on YOUR SOFTWARE from the main menu.
4. Click on a:
5. Select INSTALL from the program folder.

Figure 7.6

A Document That Uses a General-to-Specific Pattern

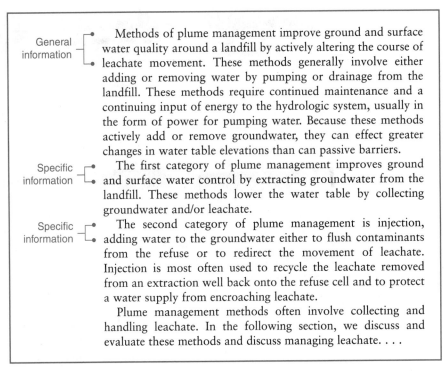

General information

Methods of plume management improve ground and surface water quality around a landfill by actively altering the course of leachate movement. These methods generally involve either adding or removing water by pumping or drainage from the landfill. These methods require continued maintenance and a continuing input of energy to the hydrologic system, usually in the form of power for pumping water. Because these methods actively add or remove groundwater, they can effect greater changes in water table elevations than can passive barriers.

Specific information

The first category of plume management improves ground and surface water control by extracting groundwater from the landfill. These methods lower the water table by collecting groundwater and/or leachate.

Specific information

The second category of plume management is injection, adding water to the groundwater either to flush contaminants from the refuse or to redirect the movement of leachate. Injection is most often used to recycle the leachate removed from an extraction well back onto the refuse cell and to protect a water supply from encroaching leachate.

Plume management methods often involve collecting and handling leachate. In the following section, we discuss and evaluate these methods and discuss managing leachate. . . .

Source: Adapted from Section 4, "Plume Management," in Andrews L. Tolman, Antonio P. Ballestero Jr., William W. Beck Jr., and Grover H. Emrich, *Guidance Manual for Minimizing Pollution from Waste Disposal Sites,* EPA-600/2-78-142 (Washington: GPO, Aug. 1978) 68–70.

the document about exposure to electric and magnetic fields shown in Figure 7.3. The writer divides scientific studies of electric and magnetic fields (EMF) into two categories: laboratory studies of cells, organs, animals, and people; and epidemiological studies of people. The writer further divides epidemiological studies into two subcategories: studies of children who live near power lines and studies of people exposed to EMF at work. Figure 7.7 shows the categories and subcategories.

When you classify and divide information, follow these guidelines:

- **Make sure each item will fit in only one category.** Categories should not overlap. The classification shown in Figure 7.7 works because the categories are mutually exclusive.

- **Classify and divide the items in ways suited to your readers and your purpose.** The writer of the document presented in Figure 7.3 could have divided scientific studies of electric and magnetic fields into two other categories: studies indicating that EMF causes health problems and studies indicating no connection between EMF and health problems. However, such a division would not have fulfilled one of the important purposes of the document: to assure readers that Texas Utilities is providing safe electric

THE READER'S CORNER

Structuring Web Sites

When arranging information on paper, one can draw on centuries of tradition. Similar in some ways to the printed page, Web sites nevertheless pose significant new design challenges. Consider how differently we read the printed page and the Internet. Reading traditional text is naturally understood as a two-dimensional experience; but people—so far at least—seem to read the Internet in three dimensions. Consider how we talk about the Internet: "cyberspace" is something through which we "navigate," perhaps hoping to "enter" a specific home page. We seem to have an extra dimension when presenting ourselves or our organization on the Internet.

An advertising copywriter for an organization, for example, seeks to establish that organization's presence in a brochure, using language, design, typography, graphics, and colors. A Web site designer has to consider all of these elements and master new skills. As a three-dimensional experience, a site cannot be the final, palpable product like the brochure. Instead, sites act as gateways to more sites, to provide links that allow readers to continue their journey through cyberspace. Unlike traditional print, effective Web sites must be dynamic environments, presenting readers with familiar yet fresh new structures of information with each visit. Web site structure is maturing rapidly, but we should remember that it took centuries for printers to master their craft. (For more information on structuring Web sites, see Appendix B.)

Figure 7.7

Classification and Division of Scientific Studies of Electric and Magnetic Fields and Health Effects

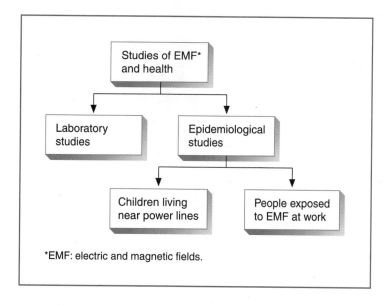

service to customers at home and a safe working environment for employees on the job.

Partition

Partition is the division of an item into its individual parts. To identify the parts of a personal computer for a beginning user, you might identify the lights, buttons, and switches that the user can use (see Figure 7.8). In contrast, for the technician who repairs personal computers, you might identify the interior parts of the central processing unit (CPU)—parts that most beginning users don't need to know about to use their computers effectively.

When you use partition, remember the following guidelines:

- **Choose a principle for partitioning that will meet your readers' needs and your purpose.** For example, you might group the external parts of the personal computer by structure as in Figure 7.9: parts of the monitor (contrast, brightness, and volume controls; on-off switch; screen; keyboard and CPU cables); parts of the keyboard (function keys, number keys, character keys, CPU cable); parts of the CPU (hard drive, disk drive, in-use lights for drives, and so on). You might also group the parts by function: parts the computer uses to process and store information (CPU, disk drive, hard drive) and parts the user uses to input information (monitor, mouse, keyboard).

Figure 7.8
The Parts of a Computer Identified for a New User

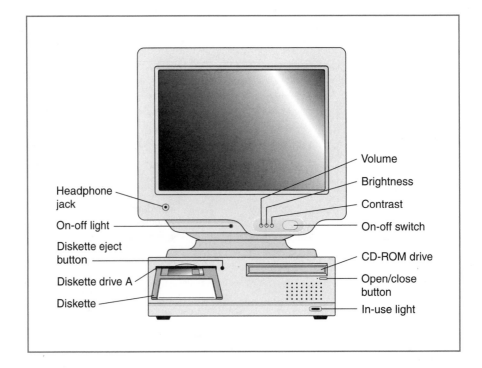

Figure 7.9
The Parts of a
Personal Computer
Grouped by Structure

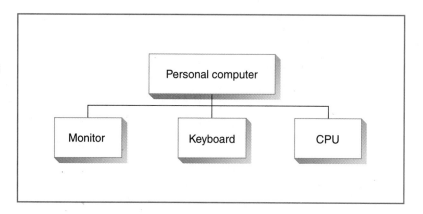

- **Organize the parts in a way that your readers will find helpful.** You can help readers to use and understand your document if you discuss each group of parts in a logical, orderly fashion. For example, if you are discussing the parts of the keyboard, you might number those parts on a drawing and then discuss them in numerical order. You might also use spatial order, beginning with the parts on the left and moving to the parts on the right.

Comparison/Contrast

You may need to compare or contrast two or more alternatives. When you examine these alternatives, you'll need standards or criteria for comparing. For example, if you were deciding which apartment to rent, you might compare the apartments based on size, cost, amenities, and location. You might even rank these criteria in order of importance to help you select the best apartment for you and your situation.

Likewise, in the workplace you'll compare alternatives. As you report your comparisons, you can organize by the alternatives or the criteria used to compare the alternatives. Figures 7.10 and 7.11 illustrate how you might organize a document comparing Mars and Earth. Figure 7.10 is organized according to the alternatives. Notice that all the information about Mars appears in one

Figure 7.10
Comparing by
Alternatives

Mars
- Climate
- Atmosphere
- Composition of the Planet's Surface

Earth
- Climate
- Atmosphere
- Composition of the Planet's Surface

Figure 7.11

Comparing by Criteria

Climate
- Mars
- Earth

Atmosphere
- Mars
- Earth

Composition of the Planet's Surface
- Mars
- Earth

section and all the information about Earth appears in another section. This organization has the advantage of presenting the whole picture for each alternative in one section. This organization emphasizes the alternatives.

In Figure 7.11, the writer has organized according to the criteria used to compare Mars and Earth. In this figure, the writer groups the information about the climate of Mars and Earth into the same section, the information about the atmosphere of both planets in another section, and the information about the surface of both planets in another section. This organization emphasizes the criteria and helps the readers to more easily compare alternatives based on individual criteria. The advantage of this organization is the point-by-point comparison using the criteria.

Figure 7.12 is a document in which the writer organizes by alternatives to compare three methods for recycling leachate in a landfill. The writer uses the criteria of cost and odor to compare and contrast these methods. When you compare or contrast information, follow these guidelines:

- **Choose criteria for comparing and contrasting.** For example, if you are going to compare various personal computers, you might use the criteria of cost, reliability, and speed.

- **Arrange your comparison or contrast in a way that will help your readers and meet your purpose.** In comparing personal computers, you could arrange the document so readers can easily gather the information to decide which computer to purchase. You might organize by criteria to group all the information about the cost (base price, software costs, printer costs) in one section of the document and all the information about reliability (warranty, customer service, previous service records) in another section. You could also organize by alternatives and group the information about one personal computer in one section, the information about the other computer in another section, and so on.

Problem and Solution

You can use a problem-and-solution pattern to explain both actual and proposed solutions. The problem-and-solution pattern is frequently used in persuasive documents such as proposals and progress reports. To use this pattern effectively, follow these guidelines:

- **Identify the problem early in the document before you begin discussing the solution.** Before your readers can understand and appreciate your solution, they must first know the problem. Emphasize the parts of the problem that your solution addresses and the significance of the problem to your readers.

Figure 7.12
A Document That Uses Comparison/ Contrast

To eliminate contaminants in landfills, leachate can be collected and then recycled through the landfill. Recycling accelerates the stabilizing of the landfill. The three most widely used recycling methods are

- spray irrigation
- overland or at-grade irrigation
- subgrade irrigation.

Spray irrigation uses spray nozzles to spray effluent onto the landfill surface. Spray irrigation has one advantage over the other two methods: it effects some leachate treatment during the spraying event through both aeration and infiltration through the surface soil layer. However, it does not eliminate odor problems and is expensive. Spray irrigation has a total cost of $68,900 the first year and $28,000 each subsequent year.

Overland irrigation spreads effluent with trenches, spreading basins, or gaged pipe. During the irrigation, leachate is pumped into the distribution system once or twice a week and allowed to infiltrate into the ground. Overland irrigation does not eliminate odor problems but costs less than spray irrigation. Overland irrigation costs $7,100 the first year and $2,500 each subsequent year.

Subgrade irrigation uses a tile field or well. In the tile field construction, perforated pipe is buried in gravel-lined trenches to spread the leachate. The wells use an injection system. Unlike spray or overland irrigation, subgrade irrigation avoids local odor problems. It also is less expensive than the other two methods. Subgrade irrigation costs $12,350 the first year and $1,550 each subsequent year. Table 1 compares the costs of the three methods.

Table 1. Costs of Leachate Recycling Methods*

Method	Capital Costs	Annual Operation and Maintenance Costs	Annual Power Costs	Total Cost First Year
Spray Irrigation	$30,900	$3,500	$24,500	$68,900
Overland Irrigation	$ 4,600	$2,500	-0-	$ 7,100
Subgrade Irrigation	$10,800	$1,550	-0-	$12,350

*Source: Pound, C. E., R. W. Crites, and D. A. Griffes, *Costs of Wastewater Treatment by Land Application.* EPA- 430/9-75-003.

Source: Adapted from Section 4, "Plume Management," in Andrews L. Tolman, Antonio P. Ballestero Jr., William W. Beck Jr., and Grover H. Emrich, *Guidance Manual for Minimizing Pollution from Waste Disposal Sites*, EPA-600/2-78-142 (Washington: GPO, Aug. 1978) 48–51. Reprinted by permission of the Texas Agricultural Experiment Station and Bruce Lawhorn.

- **Show how your solution will solve the problem.** Your readers will see the value of your solution only if they understand how it relates to the problem. Give specific details revealing how your solution will eliminate the problem.
- **Group the various stages of your solution into meaningful categories.** If your solution has several stages, you can help your readers by grouping the stages into mutually exclusive, nonoverlapping categories.
- **Give readers ample reasoning and evidence for your solution after you state the problem.** If you are trying to persuade readers to use a solution that you are recommending, give them the evidence and reasoning they need to accept it. Even if the solution is already in place, you may want to persuade readers that it is worthwhile and effective.

Let's again consider the document on electric and magnetic fields (a portion of which appears in Figure 7.3). In the first paragraph, the writers identify the problem: "Scientists have been studying a possible link between electric and magnetic fields (EMF) and health effects since the 1960s." In the final section, "What Are We Doing?," the writers briefly identify the solutions (as shown in color in Figure 7.13).

Cause and Effect

You can use the cause-and-effect pattern to help readers understand the consequences or the cause of a particular action or series of actions. Depending on

Figure 7.13
An Example of a
Solution Section

What Are We Doing?

TU Electric is committed to devoting the resources necessary to address the EMF issue in a responsible manner. TU Electric formed a task force in January 1987 to keep abreast of any developments regarding EMF, to conduct research, and to coordinate responses to customer EMF inquiries. Through this task force, TU Electric has become a leader in the industry in addressing the EMF issue.

TU Electric helps fund the Electric Power Research Institute's EMF research. This institute has spent over $40 million on EMF research in the last 18 years. TU Electric has also testified before Congress on behalf of the Edison Electric Institute to support increased federal research.

TU Electric is also conducting its own research into EMF levels produced around its facilities and in customers' homes, and TU Electric considers the potential for reducing magnetic fields when designing new facilities.

Company employees have participated in two studies monitoring home and work exposure. The company will also participate in a third study, monitoring magnetic fields in the homes of approximately 36 residential customers who volunteer for the project.

TU Electric shares information with concerned customers and employees. We send printed materials upon request, measure at no charge, and present information to any interested group.

Source: Adapted from Texas Utilities, *Electric and Magnetic Fields* (Dallas: Texas Utilities Electric Company, n.d.). Courtesy of Texas Utilities.

your purpose, you can move from the cause to the effect or from the effect to the cause. For example, you can talk about a leak (effect) in a steam-generated electric plant and then explain the cause, sagging pipes. You can also discuss the sagging pipes (cause) and predict the effect, a leak. To write effective cause-and-effect arrangements, follow these guidelines:

- **Identify either the cause or the effect near the beginning of the document.** Near the beginning of the document, tell your readers what you are trying to do in the document—to explain the causes of a specific effect or the effects of a specific cause. If your readers know how you have arranged the information, they can better understand it.

- **Show how the cause directly relates to the effect or how the effect directly relates to the cause.** Make sure that your readers understand the links between the cause and the effect or between the effect and the cause. Don't expect readers to infer the connections; explain them.

- **Group the various causes or effects into logical categories.** Grouping helps readers to understand the relationships among causes and effects.

Figure 7.14 presents a document with a cause-and-effect arrangement. The document explains the effects of babesiosis, a tick-transmitted disease of dogs. The writer identifies and explains the disease and its cause at the beginning of

Figure 7.14
An Example of the Cause-and-Effect Pattern

Babesiosis: Its Cause, Effects, and Treatment

Babesiosis, also known as Malignant Jaundice, is a tick-transmitted disease of dogs. Babesiosis is caused by a protozoan organism, *Babesia canis,* that enters and destroys the red blood cells. The principal carrier of babesiosis from infected to non-infected dogs is the brown dog tick. The disease can also spread through blood transfusions or in rare cases from an infected female dog to her pups before birth.

When a dog becomes infected with the *Babesia* organism, it may become critically sick and die in a few days; or it may become a carrier without showing any signs of the disease. The most specific signs for babesiosis are

- bloody urine
- jaundiced mucous membranes and skin

Other signs include poor appetite, listlessness, fever, weight loss, and pale mucous membranes from anemia; however, these signs also occur with other diseases.

A veterinarian can diagnose babesiosis by finding the microscopic organisms in the red blood cells. If a diagnosis is not possible with this method, the veterinarian must test the blood serum for *Babesia* antibodies. Even if a dog tests positive for babesiosis, the veterinarians cannot treat it because the most effective drugs for treating babesiosis are unavailable in the United States.

Source: Adapted from W. Elmo Crenshaw and Bruce Lawhorn, "Tick-borne Diseases of the Dog," L-22667, rpt. 10M-7-88 (College Station: Texas Agricultural Extension Service, n.d.).

the document and relates the disease to its specific effects with the sentence beginning "When a dog becomes infected with the *Babesia* organism."

Order of Importance

You can organize information according to its importance. You can use either a descending or an ascending order. You can begin with the most important and move to the least important (descending), or you can begin with the least important and move to the most important (ascending). With the descending organization, you get the reader's attention with the most important point. You may want to use ascending order when you are trying to persuade a reader who may be hostile or who may not welcome your document. Whether you use descending or ascending order, remember to give your readers a context for the information by stating the main point or topic at the beginning.

The document shown in Figure 7.15 moves from the most important to the least important question for the readers. The readers of this document are employees of a utility company. If the readers had been customers, the writers probably would have begun with the final question about how customers' bills would change.

Consider Your Readers

Even though your information seems to suggest a particular organizational pattern, that pattern may not work for your readers. Because the readers matter "more than anything" when a good writer structures a document (Selzer 44), ask yourself the following questions before you decide how to organize the information in your document:

- **Can I put important information at the beginning of the document?** Readers like to have the important information—or a summary of that information—at the beginning of the document. For instance, readers of proposals like to know at the beginning of the document what you are proposing. They don't want to wait until the middle or the end of the document for the basic proposal. Therefore, whenever possible, place the most important information or a summary of it at the beginning of the document.

- **Can I order the information from the simplest to the most complex, the easiest to the most difficult, or the most familiar to the least familiar to clarify it for readers?** If you structure the information so that readers begin with what they already know or understand and move to what they don't know or don't understand, you will help them to read and remember.

- **Will readers scan the document or read it selectively?** Readers rarely read documents from beginning to end. Therefore, choose a structure that allows readers to find the information they need without reading the whole document. Make your structure visible to these readers by using headings.

- **Can I begin with the least controversial or surprising information and move to the most controversial or surprising?** Generally, you will want to begin

Figure 7.15
A Document Organized by Order of Importance (Most to Least)

On June 12, 1991, nearly 17 months after we filed the company's rate request, the Public Utility Commission examiners issued their joint recommendations to reduce our rates from 10.2% to 8.2%. Beginning on July 15, the Public Utility Commission will hear our final arguments about the rate request. To help all of you understand the examiner's recommendations and their potential effects on you and the company, the Chairperson of the company answered the following questions.

What is the effect of the commission's recommendation to reduce the company's 10.2% requested increase to 8.2%?

We requested the absolute minimum increase necessary to begin restoring our financial integrity. Our rates have been low for many years—25% below the national average. We have not increased rates since early 1984. Since then, our rates have declined 10%; therefore, the requested 10.2% increase returns our rates to about where they were in 1984.

Under normal circumstances, the company might be able to get by with an order that grants only 80% of the amount requested. However, our financial condition has declined so that we simply do not have any cushion. Since 1984, our credit has dropped from the highest rating, AAA, to minimum investment grade, BBB.

Other companies in the state got less rate relief than they requested. Why can't we get by as they have?

The key financial indicator in determining a company's ability to borrow is its coverage ratio, the number of times interest can be paid with earnings. The minimum coverage is generally two times. With the rate increases recently granted two other utility companies, their projected coverage ratios are 2.2 times and 2.9 times. Based on the examiners' report in our rate case, our coverage ratio would be negative this year and would recover to 1.6 times by the end of next year. We would be unable to sell preferred stock or finance with bonds or unsecured debt. This inability to finance would significantly impair current construction and would jeopardize a necessary level of operations.

How have our customers reacted to the proposed 10.2% increase?

With the exception of some orchestrated opposition created by paid solicitors and a few longtime opponents, the customers have had little reaction. Most customers recognize the company's long record of good service at low rates. Our opinion surveys reflect a high level of customer satisfaction at or above that prior to the rate filing.

How will customers' bills differ between the 10.2% increase and the 8.2%?

The difference between the 10.2% and the 8.2% increases is a small amount. With the 10.2% increase, about one-third of our customers' monthly bills are less than $50. The difference on a $50 bill would be about $1.20 per month—again, returning rates to about 1984 levels. We believe that we have a remarkable record in maintaining comparatively low rates, particularly since inflation has increased about 30% since 1984.

Source: Adapted from Texas Utilities Electric Company, *Spotlight: Special Rate Case Report* (Dallas: Texas Utilities Electric Company, 1991). Courtesy of Texas Utilities.

ISSUES IN CONTEXT

Structure Makes a Difference

Researchers have found a positive correlation between outlining or other writing plans and the quality of the subsequent text (Perl; Taylor and Beach; Kellogg; Spivey and King). According to this research, effective writers tend to prepare outlines and to "spend more time on macrowriting issues" such as structure (Baker 457). Less effective writers "spend less time on outlining and more time on microwriting issues (sentence structure, grammar, spelling)" (Baker 457; Hayes and Flower). Researchers have also discovered that readers process information on two levels: microprocessing (focusing on the meaning of individual words and sentences) and macroprocessing (focusing on the relationship of paragraphs and sections) (Lorch and Lorch). Through macroprocessing, readers create a mental road map of a document (Baker).

Readers can more easily remember and process information from documents with an effective macrostructure (or structure) than from documents with an ineffective structure (Lorch and Lorch). An effective structure allows readers to more easily process word- and sentence-level information and to relate this information to the document as a whole. Without an effective structure, readers relate individual sentences and words—local information—only "to the immediately preceding ones"; the readers don't have a clear structure in which to integrate the local information (Baker 457; Kintsch).

What does this research mean for your writing? If you want readers to understand your documents and better recall the information, use a logical, clear structure that gives readers a mental road map (Baker).

with the information that will least surprise or upset readers—especially if you are trying to persuade them to take some action or to adopt your viewpoint. Try to establish common ground with your readers by beginning with information that is not controversial or surprising.

Consider the Organizational Context

The organizational context is the social and cultural conventions of your workplace. Your manager, your company's policies, and your peers may influence how you structure information in documents. You may not be the sole decision maker in determining how you will structure your documents. Before you decide on a structure, consider the social and cultural conventions at work in your workplace. The following questions may help you:

- **How will my manager want me to structure the information?** Frequently, your manager will expect you to structure a document in a particular way. If you are in doubt about what he or she expects, discuss your planned structure with your manager or with the person who assigned you to write the document.

- **Does my company have a predetermined structure for similar documents?** For some documents, your company will determine the structure before you even begin writing, "perhaps because you are responding to another document or because you have been given a strict format from which to work" (Felker et al. 11). In these situations, you may not have much control over the structure of sections or paragraphs in the document. However, within paragraphs, you can arrange sentences logically (Felker et al. 11). You can find out whether your company has a predetermined structure by looking at similar company documents, asking your manager, or reading the company style manual.

PRINCIPLE 2: PREPARE AN OUTLINE

After you have considered your readers' needs and the context for your document, prepare an outline. An outline helps you to see the structure of your document, so you can spot sections that are structured illogically or lack information. An outline also gives you a plan to follow as you begin writing.

Don't feel bound to write the various sections of the outline in sequence. Instead, begin with the section that you know the most about or for which you have gathered all the necessary information. Feel free to change the outline as you are writing. An outline is only a plan, not a permanent document. You can use informal or formal outlines.

An Informal Outline

An informal outline may simply be a list of what you plan to include in a document, or it may be a preliminary draft of a more formal outline. Informal outlines don't have to include sentences or parallel structure. Instead, they may be lists of initial thoughts and pieces of information that you write down but don't organize. Informal outlines may be sufficient for short reports, instructions, and correspondence.

Let's look at how a writer expands the discussion of babesiosis (see Figure 7.14) into a document on tick-borne diseases of the dog. The writer begins with an informal outline (see Figure 7.16). You can use informal outlines to create drafts for a formal outline. These drafts help you learn where the information is incomplete or where the structure is illogical.

A Formal Outline

A formal outline differs from an informal outline in two ways: it shows a more detailed structure for the information, and it uses numbers and letters. Because

Figure 7.16

An Informal Outline for a Document on Tick-borne Diseases of Dogs

Ehrlichiosis
- ehrlichiosis is a frequently diagnosed tick-borne disease
- the symptoms of ehrlichiosis are depression, poor appetite, weight loss, fever, enlarged lymph nodes, pale mucous membranes, and bleeding tendencies
- ehrlichiosis has either an acute form or a chronic form. Acute form may cause death within a few days of infestation or may last for 3 to 6 weeks. If dog survives acute, the disease may become chronic
- diagnosis ehrlichiosis through finding the rickettsial organism in blood cells or testing of blood serum for ehrlichia antibodies

Babesiosis
- babesiosis is caused by Babesia Canis transmitted by the brown dog tick
- babesiosis is treated with drugs not currently available in US
- babesiosis symptoms: poor appetite, listlessness, fever, weight loss, and pale mucous membranes from anemia, bloody urine, and jaundiced mucous membranes and skin
- diagnose babesiosis by finding Babesia Canis in the blood cells or its antibodies in the blood serum

Borreliosis
- borreliosis or lyme disease first diagnosed in 1975
- borreliosis signs include intermittent lameness in one or more legs from swelling and pain in the joints of the legs and feet, fever
- borreliosis usually occurs in dogs less than 4 years old
- treat borreliosis with antibiotics

Prevention
- most effective prevention is treatment such as dipping, spraying, or using powders to kill ticks before they can cause the anemia or spread disease
- the lawn where the dog lives should also be sprayed to eliminate ticks
- the pet owner should carefully follow the label instructions for any dip, spray, or powder or have a professional treat the dog

a formal outline establishes a hierarchy among pieces of information, you can easily convert topics and subtopics into headings for a document or into a table of contents for a formal report (see Chapter 12, "Preparing Front and End Matter"). As you prepare your outline, determine what format you will use for it, and then use parallel structure for the topics and subtopics.

Selecting a Format

If you are writing an outline that you will not show to others, use any format that you can read, understand, and follow. However, if you are going to use your outline when collaborating or if your document requires a table of contents, select one of the traditional outline formats:

- Topic outline
- Sentence outline

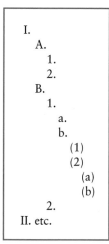

Figure 7.17
Outline Style with
Numbers and Letters

```
1.0
   1.1
      1.1.1
      1.1.2
   1.2
      1.2.1
      1.2.2
2.0 etc.
```

Figure 7.18
Outline Style with
Decimals

Topic outlines use phrases for the topics and subtopics. For example, a topic outline might use the phrase "signs of ehrlichiosis." Sentence outlines use sentences for the topics and subtopics: "A dog with ehrlichiosis may exhibit any one of seven signs."

Once you have determined which format to use, decide how to number the outline—with a combination of numbers and letters (see Figure 7.17) or with decimals (see Figure 7.18).

Using Parallel Structure

The statements of topics and subtopics in a formal outline should be parallel in structure. In other words, they should be the same grammatically. The items in the following numbered list are not grammatically parallel:

> A. Logging on to a computer network
> 　1. Find the login prompt
> 　2. Typing your login phrase
> 　3. Passwords
> 　4. What you will see if you login correctly

Items 1, 2, 3, and 4 have different grammatical structures. Item 1 begins with a verb; item 2 begins with a different verb form; item 3 begins with a noun; and item 4 begins with a pronoun. These differences obscure the writer's reason for listing the items in this sequence. The list makes much better sense when the items are parallel in structure:

> A. Logging on to a computer network
> 　1. Find the login prompt
> 　2. Type your login phrase
> 　3. Type your password
> 　4. Look for the message "Welcome to the network"

Now items 1, 2, 3, and 4 have the same grammatical structure—they begin with verbs.

Using an Outline Draft

You can use a draft of a formal outline to analyze the information you have gathered and the structure you plan to use for a document. Let's consider the information for the document on tick-borne diseases of dogs (see Figure 7.16) and put it in a draft for a formal outline (see Figure 7.19). The draft reveals several problems:

- **The information is incomplete and inconsistent.** The sections on the three diseases contain different kinds and amounts of information. The sections on ehrlichiosis and babesiosis each have three subsections, but the subsections are different. The section on borreliosis has only two subsections: signs and treatment. If possible, all three sections should have the same subsections, to create consistent and complete information.

Figure 7.19

A Draft of a Formal Outline

Topic: Tick-Borne Diseases of Dogs

I. The most frequently diagnosed tick-borne diseases in dogs
  A. Ehrlichiosis
    1. Signs that a dog may have ehrlichiosis
      a. Depression
      b. Poor appetite
      c. Weight loss
      d. Fever
      e. Enlarged lymph nodes
      f. Pale mucous membranes
      g. Unusual bleeding
    2. Stages of ehrlichiosis
      a. Acute stage
      b. Chronic stage
    3. Diagnosing ehrlichiosis
      a. Blood test for ehrlichiosis canis
      b. Blood serum test for ehrlichia antibodies
  B. Babesiosis
    1. How to know if a dog has babesiosis
      a. Poor appetite
      b. Listlessness
      c. Fever
      d. Losing weight
      e. Pale mucous membranes
      f. Bloody urine
      g. Mucous membranes and skin that are jaundiced
    2. Methods for diagnosing babesiosis
      a. Blood tests for babesia canis
      b. Blood serum tests for babesia antibodies
    3. Treatment of babesiosis
  C. Borreliosis
    1. Signs of borreliosis
      a. Intermittent lameness in one or more legs
      b. Swelling and pain in the joints of the legs and feet
      c. Fever
    2. Treatment of borreliosis
II. How to prevent tick-borne diseases of dogs
  A. Treatment is the most effective way to prevent tick-borne diseases
    1. Dipping
    2. Spraying
    3. Use a powder
    4. Spray the yard where the dogs live

Annotations (left margin):

Subheadings 1, 2, and 3 are not parallel.

Subsections A, B, and C are not consistent in content.

Subheadings d and g are not parallel to a–c and e–f.

Heading II is not parallel to I.

Subheadings 1–4 are not parallel. II has only one subsection.

- **The structure of section II is not logical because it has only one subsection.** Each section of an outline should have at least two subsections.
- **The draft lacks parallelism in several places.** (See the parallelism errors marked on Figure 7.19).

A revised version of the draft eliminates some of the problems in the first draft (see Figure 7.20; improvements are shown in color):

- **The information is complete and consistent.** The sections on the three diseases contain consistent information on signs, diagnosis, and treatment. Ehrlichiosis is the only one of the three diseases that has a chronic stage; thus, the section on ehrlichiosis contains a subsection on the stages of the disease.
- **Section II has two subsections instead of one.**
- **The wording is now parallel.**

PRINCIPLE 3: TELL READERS WHAT YOU ARE WRITING ABOUT

Have you ever had difficulty understanding what a document was about? Like you, your readers want to know what they are reading about. At the beginning of a document and at the beginning of each section and paragraph, they want to know what is coming. You can help them by using summarizing statements. Specifically, you can use overviews and topic sentences to introduce the document as a whole, individual sections, and individual paragraphs.

Use Overviews to Introduce Readers to Your Document

Overviews are introductory statements that describe what a document is about, what it may be used for, or how it is structured (Felker et al. 13). Overviews preview the topic and the overall structure of information in your document. They help readers in the following ways (Felker et al. 15–16):

- If readers must read the document, overviews help them to understand its contents.
- If readers are merely curious about the document, overviews may stimulate them to read the document or at least sections of it.
- If readers aren't sure whether the document is what they need, overviews help them to decide.

Place overviews immediately before the text that they describe or summarize. That text might be a short document, a specific section of a document, or an individual chapter. For some short documents, such as interoffice memos and letters, overviews may not be necessary. Instead, a topic sentence at the beginning can function as an overview. You can use overviews in three different ways (Felker et al. 13–15): to point out the type of information presented in the text, to identify the specific sections included in the text, or to give instructions about how to use the text.

Figure 7.20
The Revised Formal
Outline

Topic: Types and Treatment of Tick-Borne Diseases of Dogs

I. The most frequently diagnosed tick-borne diseases in dogs

A. Ehrlichiosis

> Subheadings 1, 2, 3, and 4 are parallel.

1. Signs of ehrlichiosis
   a. Depression
   b. Poor appetite
   c. Weight loss
   d. Fever
   e. Enlarged lymph nodes
   f. Pale mucous membranes
   g. Unusual bleeding
2. Stages of ehrlichiosis
   a. Acute stage
   b. Chronic stage
3. Diagnosis of ehrlichiosis
   a. Blood test for ehrlichiosis canis
   b. Blood serum test for ehrlichia antibodies
4. Treatment of ehrlichiosis

> Subsections A, B, and C are consistent in content.

B. Babesiosis
1. Signs of babesiosis

> Subheadings a–g are parallel.

   a. Poor appetite
   b. Listlessness
   c. Fever
   d. Weight loss
   e. Pale mucous membranes
   f. Bloody urine
   g. Jaundiced mucous membranes
2. Diagnosis of babesiosis
   a. Blood tests for babesia canis
   b. Blood serum tests for babesia antibodies
3. Treatment of babesiosis

C. Borreliosis
1. Signs of borreliosis
   a. Intermittent lameness in one or more legs
   b. Swelling and pain in the joints of the legs and feet
   c. Fever
2. Diagnosis of borreliosis
   a. Blood tests for borrelia burgdorferi
   b. Blood serum tests for borrelia antibodies
3. Treatment of borreliosis

> Heading II is parallel to I.

II. Prevention of tick-borne diseases of dogs

A. Eliminate ticks on the dog

> Subheadings 1–3 are parallel. II has two subsections.

1. Dips
2. Sprays
3. Powders

B. Eliminate ticks in the yard

Overviews That Point Out the Types of Information in the Text

Let's consider the overview in the TU Electric document titled "Electric and Magnetic Fields." The writer tells readers about the three major sections in the document, listing them in the order in which they appear:

> Reports about possible health effects from exposure to electric and magnetic fields (EMF) continue to cause concern among some employees and TU Electric customers. The following information will help you to understand this issue. This information describes electric and magnetic fields, existing and planned scientific studies, and TU Electric and industry efforts to address the EMF issue.[2]

With this overview, readers can quickly decide whether the document contains the information they need.

Overviews That Identify the Specific Sections of the Text

You also can write overviews that identify the sections of the text and describe the information that they contain. These overviews are particularly helpful because they lay out the structure of the text that follows and provide signposts to that structure (Felker et al. 14). With the addition of such signposts, the overview in "Electric and Magnetic Fields" reads as follows:

> Reports about possible health effects from exposure to electric and magnetic fields (EMF) continue to cause concern among some employees and TU Electric customers. The following sections will help you to understand this issue. The first section, "What Is EMF?," defines and describes electric and magnetic fields. The second section, "What About Scientific Studies?," describes existing and planned scientific studies of EMF. The third section, "What Are We Doing?," describes what TU Electric and the industry are doing to address the EMF issue.

Such overviews are especially useful in long documents, in documents divided into sections, and in documents written for more than one type of reader (Felker et al. 14).

Overviews That Tell Readers How to Use the Text

In some overviews, you may want to tell readers how to use the text. This type of overview combines signposts with instructions for using the text. Figure 7.21 shows an overview with instructions for a software manual. In the first paragraph, the writer lists the manual's three major sections and then tells readers how to use each section. This type of overview clearly tells readers "what the document is about, who should use the different parts of it, and when they should use it" (Felker et al. 14).

---

2. Adapted from Texas Utilities, *Electric and Magnetic Fields* (Dallas: Texas Utilities Electric Company, n.d.).

Figure 7.21
An Overview with
Instructions

Which Sections Should I Use? This manual has three major sections: *Getting Started, Learning the Basics,* and *Using the Advanced Features.*

Getting Started
Getting Started will help you install and start the spreadsheet. Complete this section before moving to the other sections of the manual.

Learning the Basics
If you are new to spreadsheets, try working through the lessons in *Learning the Basics* to learn spreadsheet fundamentals.

Using the Advanced Features
After you are familiar and comfortable with the fundamentals, you can move to *Using the Advanced Features.* This section is for the more experienced users.

Use Topic Sentences to Tell Readers Your Topic

To understand the sentences in a paragraph, readers must have a frame of reference for those sentences. Consider the following paragraph. What is its topic?

> When you compare the heating bills with those of traditional gas furnaces, you can cut your bills by as much as 60%. You can reduce your air conditioning costs from 25% to 50%. What's more, since no outside unit is necessary, you can avoid the noise and visibility concerns that you have with regular air conditioners.

The paragraph is about some type of air conditioner or heater, but if you are like most readers, you can't determine the exact topic. Consider the same paragraph with a topic sentence at the beginning:

> **The geothermal heat pump will save you money on your heating and air conditioning bills.** When you compare the heating bills with those of traditional gas furnaces, you can cut your bills by as much as 60%. You can reduce your air conditioning costs from 25% to 50%. What's more, since no outside unit is necessary, you can avoid the noise and visibility concerns that you have with regular air conditioners.

A **topic sentence** announces what a paragraph is about; it provides the frame of reference that readers need to easily establish meaning in a paragraph. The topic sentence gives readers a key to unlock the meaning of the sentences that follow; without that key, readers might not be able to unlock the meaning.

PRINCIPLE 4: USE HEADINGS TO SHOW THE STRUCTURE OF YOUR DOCUMENT

Headings are subtitles within a document. If you have prepared a formal outline, you can use the entries in the outline as headings and subheadings in your document. Headings help readers in several ways (Felker et al. 17). They

- Indicate the structure and scope of a document—a service that is especially helpful to readers who want to determine whether a document contains information they need
- Help readers locate specific information
- Give readers cues to the information contained in specific sections

Figures 7.22 and 7.23 show how adding headings can help to reveal content.

Effective headings are informative, grammatically parallel, and visible. The following sections will help you to create such headings. In Chapter 10, "Designing Documents for Your Readers," you will learn how to design and lay out headings that are easy for readers to find.

Figure 7.22
A Section of a
Document Without
Headings

> Soybeans plants are photoperiodic. They grow most of their vegetation during long days and begin flowering as day lengths decrease. Soybean varieties are classified into 11 groups according to their response to different day lengths. For example, Group 00 soybean varieties grow in the northern part of the United States while Group VIII varieties grow in the South. Group IX varieties grow close to the equator. The varieties adapted to the southern parts of the United States have flowering initiated by shorter days than those varieties adapted to the northern parts of the United States. The following sections suggest optimum planting times and insect and disease problems for the southern varieties.
>
> Soybeans are most productive if planted during periods of increasing day lengths when the days are too long to stimulate flowering. Planting at this time will allow the soybean plants to grow taller before they produce flowers and pods. The plants should grow tall enough for mechanical harvest.
>
> Insect damage and disease can commonly reduce soybean yield. In the southern latitudes, stinkbugs and foliar-feeding lepidoptera can damage soybean plants and thus reduce soybean production. Stinkbugs feed upon the developing soybean seed; they may infect the seed with a yeast fungus. The fungus results in poor bean quality, lower yields, and poor flavor. Stinkbugs can be controlled with methyl parathion; however, methyl parathion should not be used near livestock or housing because it is highly toxic.
>
> Soybeans are susceptible to phytopathogens such as virus diseases. One such disease is bud blight. Bud blight can infest whole fields, causing the soybean plants not to produce seeds. If this disease becomes severe, it can seriously damage a developing soybean industry.

Source: Adapted from R. A. Creelman and S. A. Reeves, Jr., *Soybean Variety Performance Trials in the Rio Grande Valley of Texas, 1967–75* (College Station: Texas Agricultural Experiment Station, MP-1287, 1976). Reprinted by permission of the Texas Agricultural Experiment Station.

Figure 7.23

A Section of a
Document with
Headings

Growing Soybean Plants in the South

Soybean plants are photoperiodic. They grow most of their vegetation during long days and begin flowering as day lengths decrease. Soybean varieties are classified into 11 groups according to their response to different day lengths. For example, Group 00 soybean varieties grow in the northern part of the United States while Group VIII varieties grow in the South. Group IX varieties grow close to the equator. The varieties adapted to the southern parts of the United States have flowering initiated by shorter days than those varieties adapted to the northern parts of the United States. The following sections suggest optimum planting times and insect and disease problems for the southern varieties.

Optimum Planting Times for Soybean Plants

Soybeans are most productive if planted during periods of increasing day lengths when the days are too long to stimulate flowering. Planting at this time will allow the soybean plants to grow taller before they produce flowers and pods. The plants should grow tall enough for mechanical harvest.

Insect and Disease Problems in Soybean Crops

Insect damage and disease can commonly reduce soybean yield. In the southern latitudes, stinkbugs and foliar-feeding lepidoptera can damage soybean plants and thus reduce soybean production. Stinkbugs feed upon the developing soybean seed, they may infect the seed with a yeast fungus. The fungus results in poor bean quality, lower yields, and poor flavor. Stinkbugs can be controlled with methyl parathion; however, methyl parathion should not be used near livestock or housing because it is highly toxic.

Soybeans are susceptible to phytopathogens such as virus diseases. One such disease is bud blight. Bud blight can infest whole fields, causing the soybean plants not to produce seeds. If this disease becomes severe, it can seriously damage a developing soybean industry.

Source: Adapted from R. A. Creelman and S. A. Reeves, Jr., *Soybean Variety Performance Trials in the Rio Grande Valley of Texas, 1967–75* (College Station: Texas Agricultural Experiment Station, MP-1287, 1976).

Write Informative Headings

Effective headings inform readers, giving them enough information to decide whether a section contains the information that they need or want. Compare the headings in column A and column B:

Column A	Column B
Introduction	How to Use This Manual
Body	Description of the Rheumatoid Arthritis Rehabilitation Clinic
Part 2	What Is the Taxpayer's Role?
Donation Limitations	How Frequently Can Donors Give Blood?

The headings in column A don't give any clues about the information in the sections that they introduce. "Body" doesn't give readers any idea about the information they will find if they turn to that section of the document. "Body" could refer to a human body, a body of people, or the body (main part) of the document. Because the headings in column A don't give any clues about the information contained in a section, they can't help readers locate specific information. In contrast, the headings in column B give readers a good idea of the information they will find in each section.

You can create informative headings in three ways:

- **Identify the primary topic of the section.** Many headings simply state the primary topic or the main point of the section that they introduce. For example, in Figure 7.23, "Optimum Planting Times for Soybean Plants" describes specifically the information that follows.

- **Use questions to tell readers the topic of a section and to create a friendly tone** (Felker et al. 18). You can draw the reader into your document and add a friendly tone by using question-style headings. For example, in a document on property taxes, you might use headings like these: "Does My Home Qualify for Tax Exemptions?" or "How Is My Property Valued?" The personal pronoun "my" adds a personal, informal tone to the headings, yet the headings are still clear and informative. You can use "you" in your headings to create a similar effect.

- **Use keywords carefully to tell readers the topic of a section.** Often writers use keywords such as "Budget" or "Valuing Property" as headings. In many instances, these short headings adequately inform readers and are appropriate. Instead of "Budget," the writer of a proposal might have written "The Proposed Budget for the Waste Disposal Project." Although the latter heading is more informative, readers would more quickly gather all the information they need from the single word "Budget." However, be careful when using single-word headings to avoid vagueness.

Write Grammatically Parallel Headings

Use the principles to write parallel headings that you use to write a formal outline. All the main headings in a document have equal rank, so they all should have the same grammatical structure. All the subheads at the same level under a main heading also have equal rank and should have the same grammatical structure.

Figure 7.24 shows the various levels that you might have in a document and sample headings that correspond with those levels (the headings are from the revised formal outline presented in Figure 7.20). Notice that both main headings have the same grammatical structure, a noun or noun phrase followed by a prepositional phrase. The three subheadings under the main heading 1, "The most frequently diagnosed tick-borne diseases in dogs," are parallel in grammatical structure with each other but not with the subheadings under the main heading 2, "Prevention of tick-borne diseases of dogs." Subheadings or sub-

Figure 7.24

Levels of Headings

Title	*Types and Treatment of Tick-Borne Diseases of Dogs*
Main Heading 1	*The most frequently diagnosed tick-borne diseases in dogs*
Subheading 1	*Ehrlichiosis*
Sub-subheading 1	*Signs of ehrlichiosis*
Sub-subheading 2	*Stages of ehrlichiosis*
Sub-subheading 3	*Diagnosis of ehrlichiosis*
Sub-subheading 4	*Treatment of ehrlichiosis*
Subheading 2	*Babesiosis*
Sub-subheading 1	*Signs of babesiosis*
Sub-subheading 2	*Diagnosis of babesiosis*
Sub-subheading 3	*Treatment of babesiosis*
Subheading 3	*Borreliosis*
Sub-subheading 1	*Signs of borreliosis*
Sub-subheading 2	*Diagnosis of borreliosis*
Sub-subheading 3	*Treatment of borreliosis*
Main Heading 2	*Prevention of tick-borne diseases of dogs*
Subheading 1	*Eliminate ticks on the dog*
Sub-subheading 1	*Dips*
Sub-subheading 2	*Sprays*
Sub-subheading 3	*Powders*
Subheading 2	*Eliminate ticks in the yard*

subheadings in any section of a document have to be parallel, or grammatically equal, only with each other, not with all other subheadings or sub-subheadings in the document. Subheadings under main heading 1 need not be parallel with subheadings under main heading 2 and so on. The multiple-word sub-subheadings at the beginning of a document need not prevent you from using single-word sub-subheadings at the end.

CONCLUSION

As you consider the information that you have gathered for your documents, select a structure that will help readers to find and use that information. Readers of technical documents have specific goals—to obtain information, to complete a task, to answer a question. Select a structure that will help them to accomplish their goals efficiently and easily. After selecting an appropriate structure, preview the document—tell readers what you are writing about. Then use headings to show your approach to the topic. Use the "Worksheet for Structuring Your Documents" to guide you.

WORKSHEET for Structuring Your Documents

Principle 1: Decide How to Structure Your Document

- Can you group similar information?
- Can you use one or more of the standard patterns for organizing information?

Consider Your Readers

- Can you put important information at the beginning of the document?
- Can you order the information from the simplest to the most complex, the easiest to the most difficult, or the most familiar to the least familiar?
- Will readers scan the document or read it selectively?
- Can you begin with the least controversial or surprising information and move to the most controversial or surprising?

Consider the Organizational Context

- How will your manager want you to structure the information?
- Does your company have a predetermined structure for similar documents?
- How has your company structured similar documents in the past?

Principle 2: Prepare an Outline

- Can you create an informal outline to list what you will include in a short, relatively simple document or to serve as a draft of a formal outline?
- For complex or lengthy documents, which type of formal outline will you select: topic outline or sentence outline?
- Have you used parallel structure in your formal outline?

Principle 3: Tell Readers What You are Writing About

- Have you used overviews to introduce readers to your document?
- Do the overviews point out the types of information in the document?
- Do the overviews identify the specific sections of the document?
- Do the overviews tell readers how to use the document?
- Have you used topic sentences?

Principle 4: Use Headings to Show the Arrangement of Your Document

- Have you written informative headings?
- Can you name the primary topic of a section in a heading?

- Can you use questions to tell readers the topic of a section and to create a friendly tone?
- Can you use keywords to tell readers the topic of a section?
- Are your headings grammatically parallel?

EXERCISES

1. Select an appropriate criterion that you can use to compare or contrast two or more items or groups of items. Some suggested items appear below. Depending on your instructor's instructions, prepare a formal outline or write a brief document in which you compare or contrast the items.

   - Apartment complexes in your town
   - Dormitories on your campus
   - Grocery stores in your town
   - Computers
   - State parks in your home state
   - Internet service providers
   - Planets

2. Partition a single object into its parts. Use one of the items listed below, or choose one of your own. Specify the specific brand or model of the object. In other words, don't partition a generic lawnmower; instead, partition Snapper mulching/recycling mower model 5961. Partition the object into at least two levels of parts—main parts and subparts. For example, you might partition the handle of the mower into the braking controls and the speed controls. Then, depending on your instructor's instructions, diagram your partitioning as in Figure 7.9, or create an informal outline of your partitioning.

   - Lawnmower
   - Electric mixer
   - Refrigerator
   - Printer
   - Auditorium
   - Tools, equipment, or instruments that you use in your major field of study

3. Using the outline or diagram that you created in exercise 2, write a brief description of the parts of the item you outlined or diagrammed. Use spatial order to describe the parts.

4. Determine the most effective principle of classification or division for a topic and specific readers. Select one of the topic and reader combinations listed below or a combination of your own choosing. Then, depending on your instructor's instructions, prepare a formal outline, a diagram (as in Figure 7.7), or a brief description of your classification or division. Remember that the categories of the classification or division must not overlap.

   - Types of financial aid available to students at your campus
     Readers: students or parents
   - Restaurants
     Readers: visitors to your town or potential restaurant owners in your town
   - Colleges or universities in your state
     Readers: potential students or parents of potential students
   - Types of employment available in your field after graduation
     Readers: graduating seniors or first-year students

5. Prepare a document that explains the cause of some situation, event, or occurrence for a specific reader such as a friend, family member, or classmate. Select one of the topics listed below or one of your own choosing.

   - Acid rain
   - Thinning of the ozone layer
   - Hurricanes
   - Eclipse of the sun
   - Tornadoes
   - Comets

6. Prepare a document that explains the effects of some situation, event, or occurrence for a specific reader such as a friend, family member, or classmate. Select one of the topics listed below or one of your own choosing.

   - Unemployment in your town or state
   - Recycling
   - Budget deficit of the U.S. government
   - Air pollution

7. Select a problem in your community, on your campus, or at your workplace; and determine an appropriate solution. Then formally outline the problem and your proposed solution. Your formal outline should have at least two levels. Using the outline, write a letter detailing the problem and solution to the appropriate community leader, to your local or campus newspaper, or to the appropriate person on campus or at your workplace.

8. Assume that a friend has asked you to describe a process or procedure. Using chronological order, write a description of the process or procedure for your friend. You can use one of the processes or procedures listed below or select one of your own choosing.

   • How to set the security alarm in your apartment
   • How fax machines work
   • How to use the Internet and the World Wide Web
   • How to use a tool, machine, or equipment that professionals in your field regularly use

9. The following excerpt, titled "What Is the Taxpayer's Role?," lacks an overview and headings.[3] Provide an overview and headings for the document. Then identify the topic sentence of each paragraph.

   As a tax payer, you have certain rights concerning the appraisal of your property: you have the right to

   • equal and uniform tax appraisals. Your property value should be the same as similar properties.
   • have your property taxed on its market value or its agricultural value if it qualifies for agricultural appraisal.
   • receive all tax exemptions or other tax relief that you are entitled to.
   • receive notices of changes in your property value or in your exemptions. Taxing units must tell the public of proposed tax rate increases and give taxpayers time to comment on them.

   As a taxpayer, you also have the right to understand what actions you may take if you disagree with the appraisal of your property or with the tax rates. If you believe that your property value is too high or if you were denied an exemption or agricultural appraisal, you can protest to the appraisal review board. If you don't agree with the review board, you can take your case to court. You can speak at public hearings when your elected officials are deciding how to spend your taxes and are setting the tax

rate. If you and your fellow taxpayers disagree with the tax rate, you may limit the tax increases by petitioning for an election to roll back or limit the tax rate.

   To claim your rights as a property owner, you must fulfill the following responsibilities:
   • Make sure that your property appears correctly on the tax records with your correct name and address
   • Pay your taxes on time

10. Decide whether each of the headings listed below is uninformative or informative and explain why. Rewrite the uninformative headings so that they are informative. As you rewrite the headings, you may have to add information.

   • Visual Impairment
   • What If My Property Value Rises?
   • Foreword
   • Disabled Employees' Review Committee Findings
   • Guidelines
   • Description
   • The Cost of Extracting Water from Landfills

11. Interview a professional in your field to find out how his or her workplace and manager influence the way he or she structures documents. You might ask the following questions:

   • Does your company have a predetermined structure for some of the documents that you write? If it does, what types of documents are affected, and how does that structure compare with the guidelines you learned in school?
   • How frequently does your manager tell you or expect you to structure a document in a particular way? How flexible is your manager in agreeing to alter that structure? What do you do when you disagree with the structure that your manager expects?
   • Do you ever consider how your company or your peers have structured certain documents in the past—documents such as proposals, letters, memos, or progress reports? Where do you find out about the structure of these documents: from a company library, company files, secretaries, coworkers?

Write a memo to your instructor reporting the information that you gained from this exercise.

3. Adapted from John Sharp, "Taxpayers' Rights, Remedies and Responsibilities," Publication #96-295 (Austin, TX: Comptroller of Public Accounts, Tax Division, 1991).

Chapter 8

Writing Reader-Oriented Sentences and Paragraphs

CHAPTER OUTLINE

You read every day—the mail, newspapers, textbooks, reports, Internet sites, magazines. Some of the writing that you read is effective, but much is ineffective. Because you read so much ineffective writing, you may be used to verbose, indirect sentences that contain unnecessary words, ineffective verb phrases, and buried action and actors. Many writers think this type of convoluted writing impresses readers. However, readers prefer a simple, direct style that doesn't require them to search for information and meaning.

The following paragraph contains several examples of convoluted writing. Can you spot them?

Convoluted

Let it be known that VISA will send each cardholder a statement at the beginning of the month. Please be aware that VISA will place a charge of $10 on a cardholder's account as a late payment charge each time the "Total Payment Due" is not received before VISA bills the cardholder again. The Company will give reimbursement for this fee only if it was assessed through no fault of the cardholder. Prompt filing of expense accounts after charges are incurred will ensure Company reimbursement to the cardholder in order for the cardholder to make payment to VISA prior to the next billing date.

Notice that the writer buries the action in nouns, writing "place a charge" instead of "charge," "give reimbursement" instead of "reimburse," and "make payment" instead of "pay." Also notice that the writer doesn't make the primary actor the grammatical subject of the sentence: "Let it be known" and "Please be aware," although the actor is "VISA"; "Prompt filing of expense accounts . . . will insure," although the actor is "you" or "the employee."

Compare the verbose, convoluted example with this revised version:

Revised

At the beginning of the month, VISA will send you a statement. If you don't pay the total amount due before VISA bills you again, VISA will charge your account $10. To avoid this charge, file your expense accounts immediately after using the card, so the company can reimburse you before the total amount is due. If you fail to file your accounts promptly, the company will not reimburse the $10.

The revised version is shorter and concise. The writer uses verbs that express the action of the sentence directly. The writer also focuses on the primary actors—"VISA," "you," and "the company"—making them the grammatical subjects of the sentences describing their actions.

In this chapter you will learn four principles that will help you write clear, straightforward sentences. In Chapter 9 you will learn principles that will help you to use language that clearly and concisely conveys what you intend to say in your documents.

THE READER'S CORNER

Reader-Oriented Poetry

Poetry can teach us a lot about reader-oriented writing. Consider Robert Frost's "Stopping by Woods on a Snowy Evening." In sixteen lines, Frost wanted to convey to his readers how he felt when he stopped in a wintry forest. The first lines read:

Whose woods these are I think I know.
His house is in the village though:
He will not see me stopping here
To watch his woods fill up with snow.

Our first question may be, Why are you stopping in the woods like this? Frost himself sounds uncertain at first. Notice that he almost begins the poem with a question—"Whose woods these are"—and admits he's not sure about who owns the woods ("I think I know"). In the second line, however, Frost appears more confident about his decision to stop. He adds "though" at the end of line 2 to let us know that he's aware that stopping and watching these woods is strange, but nobody will see him. (The word "village" reinforces our sense of Frost being safely alone in the woods.) Still, even if he's sure nobody will see him, we ask, why watch snow falling in the woods anyway? Consider how the phrase Frost uses in the last line—the "woods fill up with snow"—makes the event sound so new and strange and compelling that his decision to stop suddenly makes sense.

FOCUS ON ACTORS AND ACTIONS[1]

In most of your writing, you will tell a story involving actors and actions. In even the most convoluted writing, you usually can find actors acting. Let's look at a passage in which the writer buries the actors and actions:

Convoluted

It is Sabrina's proposal for the adoption of the employee profile software by the personnel department. This software provides assistance in the selection of new employees.

Who are the real actors? In the first sentence, "Sabrina" and "the personnel department" are the actors, although the sentence does not describe their actions. In the second sentence, the actor seems to be "software"; but because of the structure of this sentence, we can't be sure whether the software or the personnel department is selecting the employees.

---

1. I borrow the concept of actors and action from Williams (65).

What actions does the writer of that passage mention? In the first sentence, the actions appear in the nouns "proposal" and "adoption." Again, in the second sentence, the actions appear in nouns: "assistance" and "selection." The writer buries the action in nouns instead of using verbs to describe it.

Let's look at a revised version of the passage:

Revised

Sabrina proposed that the personnel department adopt the employee profile software. The personnel department can use this software when they select new employees.

Here, the actors ("Sabrina" and "the personnel department") are the grammatical subjects, and the actions ("proposed," "adopt," "use," and "select") appear in verbs. The revised passage illustrates two powerful style principles:

- Make the actors the subjects of your sentences.
- Put the action in verbs.

PRINCIPLE 1: MAKE THE ACTORS THE SUBJECTS OF YOUR SENTENCES

Most readers expect the actor to be the grammatical subject of a sentence. When the actor isn't the subject, readers must stop to search for the actor. In the following example, the writer buries the actor in the pronoun "our." By revising to make the actor the subject of the sentence, the writer creates a more direct statement (the subjects appear in **bold type**; the symbol ≠ means "is different from"; the symbol = means "is the same as").

Actor ≠ subject	**Our expectation** was to begin the new uniform policies immediately.
Actor = subject	**We** expected to begin the new uniform policies immediately.

In some sentences, the actor doesn't appear in the sentence. The writer of the first sentence below knew what person or group selected a new organizational plan and adopted a new budget. Less informed readers, however, have no way of learning the identity of this person or group because the writer doesn't include this information. The second sentence lets readers know that the executive committee selected the plan and adopted the budget.

Actor ≠ subject	At the previous meeting, **a new organizational plan** was selected and **a new budget** was adopted.
Actor = subject	At the previous meeting, **the executive committee** selected a new organizational plan and adopted a new budget.

Use People as Subjects Whenever Possible

In your writing, try to make people the subjects of your sentences. Writing that uses few people as subjects is abstract and often has an impersonal, bureaucratic tone. Consider this passage:

People ≠ subjects

As announced earlier, the prescription drug card program will be eliminated effective at the end of the year. Effective January 1, prescriptions that are purchased from local pharmacies may be filed and will be paid at 80% after a $200 deductible. This means that all prescriptions purchased from local pharmacies must be paid for and the receipts saved. A claim form and your receipts should then be mailed in for reimbursement.

Readers of this passage must infer who is purchasing, eliminating, filing, and so on. They could confuse the actions that they are to perform (purchasing, filing, paying, saving, mailing) with the actions that the pharmacy or insurance company will perform (eliminating, paying, reimbursing). Let's look at a revision in which people are the subjects:

People = subjects

As announced earlier, **you** will begin using a new prescription drug program on January 1. Instead of using your prescription drug card, **you** may file with us any prescription that **you** purchase from local pharmacies. **We** will pay 80% of the cost of your prescriptions after **you** meet the $200 deductible. To take advantage of this new program, **you** follow four simple steps:

- Pay for all prescriptions purchased from local pharmacies.
- Save the receipts.
- Complete the attached claim forms.
- Mail the completed form in the envelope provided, so **we** can reimburse you.

Each sentence in the revised version has an actor, and the passage now clearly explains what readers must do and what the company will do. The use of human actors lessens the distance between readers and the writer and eliminates ambiguity.

Generally, Use the Active Voice

Let's look again at some of the sentences in the unrevised prescription passage. The *object* of the action is the grammatical subject of these sentences because the writer uses passive-voice verbs instead of active-voice verbs. In the **passive voice**, the subject is acted upon. In the **active voice**, the subject performs the action.

subject = object of the action

Passive voice   As announced earlier, <u>the prescription drug card program</u> **will be eliminated** effective at the end of the year.

subject = object of the action

Passive voice   Effective January 1, <u>prescriptions</u> that **are purchased** from local pharmacies **may be filed** and **will be paid** at 80% after a $200 deductible.

When writers use the passive voice, readers must search for the actors or infer their identity. When writers use the active voice, the actor is the grammatical subject of the sentence, as readers expect.

Notice how the active voice changes the two passive-voice sentences:

subject = actor

Active voice   As announced earlier, <u>we</u> **will eliminate** the prescription drug card program at the end of the year.

subject = actor

Active voice   Beginning January 1, <u>you</u> **may file** with us any prescriptions that you **purchase** from local pharmacies.

In these active-voice sentences, the actors—"we" and "you"— are in the subject position. Active-voice sentences immediately tell readers who is performing the action. Active voice also uses fewer words than does passive voice.

Now that you know what effect the passive voice can have, let's find out how to recognize it. A passive-voice sentence has these characteristics:

- The actor and the subject are not the same. The actor may be missing or may appear in a prepositional phrase beginning with *by*.
- The verb consists of a form of the verb *be* plus the past participle of the main verb. (The verb *be* has eight forms: *is, am, are, was, were, be, being,* and *been.*)
- The object of the action is the subject.

Let's look at another passive-voice sentence:

subject

Passive voice   <u>The proper procedures</u> for presenting a guest's check **must be**

prepositional phrase

actor

learned <u>by the front-desk staff</u>.

The subject and the actor aren't the same. The actor appears in a prepositional phrase. The verb consists of *be* plus the past participle of <u>learn</u>. Look now at the active-voice version of this sentence:

	subject = actor		object	

Active voice   <u>The front-desk staff</u> **must learn** <u>the proper procedures</u> for presenting a guest's check.

This and other active-voice sentences have these characteristics:

- The actor and the subject are the same.
- The verb does not consist of a form of *be* plus the past participle of the main verb.
- The object appears after the verb.

Use the active voice as much as possible because it generally is stronger, clearer, and more concise. The active voice requires fewer words and makes the actor the subject, so readers can read quickly and understand sentences easily.

To change a sentence from the passive to the active voice, follow these steps:

1. Identify the actor.
2. Make the actor the subject of the sentence.
3. Follow the actor with the action (the verb) of the sentence.
4. Follow the action (the verb) with the object or the receiver of the action.

Occasionally, Use the Passive Voice

Sometimes you may have to choose between the active and the passive voice. Let's look at two examples:

Passive voice   Samples **are gathered** every six hours except between 6:00 P.M. and 10:00 P.M.

Passive voice   During the last six months, more than 500,000 bumper stickers were **distributed**.

The writers of these sentences chose the passive voice because the actors either were unknown or were unimportant. Before you decide to use the passive voice, answer these two questions. If you answer "yes" to either one, the passive voice may be appropriate:

1. Do your readers need to know who is acting?
2. Do you want to focus attention on the object rather than on the actor? (We discuss this situation later in this chapter, in the context of Principle 4.)

PRINCIPLE 2: PUT THE ACTION IN VERBS

Readers generally expect to find the action of a sentence expressed in verbs. Many writers, however, bury the action in nouns, as in this sentence:

verb

Action in noun The fire marshal is conducting an **investigation** of the fire that occurred this morning.

Readers must look beyond the verb "is conducting" to find the primary action. The writer names this action in the noun "investigation," instead of using the verb *investigate*. The verb "is conducting" doesn't give readers any information they need. To improve this sentence, the writer needs to eliminate the verb "is conducting" and express the real action in a different verb:

Action in verb The fire marshal **is investigating** the fire that occurred this morning.

Readers of this revised version don't have to search for the primary action—it appears in the verb, where they expect to find it. Notice, too, that the revised sentence is shorter and more direct.

Identify Sentences in Which the Verb Does Not Express the Action

Most sentences in which the verb is not expressing the action have one or both of these characteristics:

- A noun expresses the primary action of the sentence.
- The verb of the sentence is a form of *be*.

If a noun expresses the primary action, you may be able to identify that noun from its suffix: *-tion*, *-ment*, *-ion*, *-ance*, *-ence*, or *-ery*. However, the noun may not end in a suffix, for some verbs (for example, *hope*, *result*, and *change*) do not change form when they are used as nouns.

Let's look at some sentences in which nouns express the primary action; see how much clearer and more concise they become when revised:

Action in noun Her **discovery** of the missing coins happened on Friday while she was cleaning the antique vase.

Action in verb She **discovered** the missing coins on Friday while she was cleaning the antique vase.

The second sentence of that pair is more direct and reader oriented and has two fewer words than the first.

When the verb is a form of *be*, check to see whether a noun is expressing the primary action:

a form of *be*

Action in noun There was a **discussion** of the zoning ordinances by the city council on Tuesday.

Action in active verb   The city council **discussed** the zoning ordinances on
Tuesday.

In the first sentence the real action appears in the noun "discussion." The
effectiveness of the sentence increases when the writer puts the real action in a
verb. The original sentence becomes more direct and more concise in the active
voice. Using the active voice—making the actor the subject—shortens the original sentence by five words.

Keep the Actor and the Action Together

Once you have successfully expressed the action in a verb, keep that verb and
the actor or subject close together in the sentence. If several words separate the
subject from the verb, readers may forget what the subject is and have to
reread the sentence. Consider this example:

Actor and action separated   **Some managers** because they have little or no
training in human relations or insufficient
managerial experience **cannot handle** insubordinate employees.

By the time you finally read the action ("cannot handle"), you may have forgotten the actor ("some managers") because fourteen words separate the actor
from the action. The sentence is easier to understand when the actor and the
action are together:

Actor and action together   Because they have little or no training in human
relations or insufficient managerial experience,
some managers cannot handle insubordinate
employees.

PRINCIPLE 3: EMPHASIZE THE IMPORTANT INFORMATION IN YOUR SENTENCES

You can convey your intended message and help readers to read your documents quickly if you emphasize the important information in your sentences.
Emphasize the most important information by

- Putting it at the end of the sentence
- Using visual cues to call attention to it

Put the Most Important Information at the End

The natural stress point of most sentences is the end. When reading a sentence
aloud, you tend to raise the pitch of your voice near the end and stress the last

ISSUES IN CONTEXT

How Are Your Editing Skills?

You probably feel relieved when you write the last word of a document. However, when you write that last word, you still aren't finished—that is, you're not finished if you want to ensure that the document is error free. You still need to edit it. If you have time, ask coworkers or friends to help edit your documents. Most writing professionals agree that "editing your own work is not the best way to go" (Hansen 16). However, often you'll write under deadlines or won't be able to find someone to edit your document. When you edit your own documents, James B. Hansen suggests these tips:

- **Use a style sheet or style guide.** If you or your company doesn't have a style sheet, start creating your own or use style guides such as *The Chicago Manual of Style*.

- **Create a checklist.** Checklists can help you locate your particular writing problems. For example, if you tend to misuse the comma, a checklist can help you to isolate comma errors.

- **Wait a day or two before editing.** Don't edit a document immediately after you write it (Hansen). A waiting period will help you to consider what the document actually says rather than what you intend it to say.

- **Edit the document on paper.** Avoid editing on a computer screen. "Reading speed can drop as much as 30 percent on a computer screen" (Hansen 16; Gomes; Krull and Hurford).

- **Read the document several times.**

few words (Williams 65). When writing, you can take advantage of this natural stress point to emphasize important information. In the examples that follow, the less important information appears in italics and the more important in bold.

You have not mailed us **your December payment** *according to our records.*
The profits in January **increased by 30 percent,** *for example.*

In both of those sentences, unimportant prepositional phrases appear at the end. Moving those phrases to the beginning of the sentence allows the writer to emphasize the more important information about the December payment and the 30 percent increase in profits:

According to our records, you have not mailed us **your December payment.**

For example, the profits in January **increased by 30 percent.**

The revised sentences flow more smoothly because the natural stress falls on the most important information.

Use Visual Cues to Emphasize Important Information

You can also emphasize important information with visual cues such as boldface type, italic type, large type, color, and dashes. In online documents, color is especially effective for emphasizing important information. On some Web sites, writers put keywords in another color to indicate links to another page, site, or topic. In this example the writer emphasizes important information with boldface and a dash:

Please destroy your American Express card after December 31, 1997—**regardless of its expiration date.**

When deciding which visual cues to use, remember these tips:

- **Boldface type** stands out more than normal type and more than *italic type.*
- Larger type stands out more than normal type or smaller type.
- Color with good contrast stands out more than boldface, uppercase letters, and most sizes of type. Remember that if you overuse color or use too many colors you'll draw attention to the color rather than to the information.
- Blinking or flashing words online annoy some readers, so instead use color for keywords.

You can use several cues to emphasize words in your sentences. However, be careful not to overuse any one cue or to use too many.

PRINCIPLE 4: TIE YOUR SENTENCES TOGETHER

When you are writing, *you* understand how your sentences relate to each other. Never assume, however, that *your readers* will share your understanding. Instead, be sure to order the information in your sentences to guide your readers. This section presents four guidelines to help you tie your sentences together.

Put Old Information Near the Beginning of a Sentence

Old information is information that has previously appeared in a paragraph. New information is information that has not yet appeared in a paragraph. In the following paragraph, the old (familiar) information is underlined. The writer consistently places it near the end of a sentence, after presenting new (unfamiliar) information. Therefore, until you reach the end of a sentence, you don't know how new information relates to old information in the previous sentence(s).

Old information misplaced

The Blood Center is exploring the possibility of reinstating a recognition program for apheresis donors. One unanimous suggestion from a 1990 <u>apheresis donor</u> group was to bring back the plaques with annual updates of <u>apheresis donation</u> totals. Below are several styles of <u>plaques</u> that have been awarded to <u>apheresis donors</u>. Small dated and numbered brass plates indicate the <u>donation</u> year and the number of units <u>donated</u>.

Did you have to read some sentences more than once to figure out how the sentences tie together? The writer could clarify the relationship between the old and the new information by moving some of the old information near the beginning of the sentences:

Revised

The Blood Center is exploring the possibility of reinstating a recognition program for apheresis donors. A 1990 <u>apheresis donor</u> group unanimously suggested bringing back the plaques with annual updates of apheresis donation totals. Pictures of <u>plaques</u> previously awarded appear below. On each <u>plaque</u>, small dated and numbered brass plates indicate the donation year and the number of units donated.

In the revised passage, the information flows logically from one sentence to another. The reader doesn't have to figure out how the sentences relate because the writer connects them by putting old information near the beginning of the sentences.

Use Topics to Tie Sentences Together

You can also relate sentences by topic. The first sentence in a paragraph introduces the topic. The second sentence comments on that topic, and the third, fourth, fifth, and subsequent sentences comment further on that topic. In a well-written paragraph, the writer signals the topic by mentioning it in the subject position of each sentence.

In the following passage, the subject of each sentence is underlined:

Shifts in topic

<u>Your Personal Identification Number (PIN)</u> should arrive within three (3) days after the card. <u>VISA</u> currently does not have the capability to permit cardholders to choose personalized PINs. <u>The company</u> selected a four-digit number for your PIN.

"Your Personal Identification Number (PIN)," the topic of the first sentence, appears as the subject, and the remainder of the sentence provides information about the topic. The second sentence, however, does not comment on that topic but instead introduces a new topic—"VISA"—in the subject position, and that topic does not relate clearly to the topic of the previous sentence. In the third sentence, the writer introduces another new topic—"the company." Because of the topic changes, readers may not be sure how the sentences tie together. The writer needs to signal the common topic in the subject of each sentence:

Revised

<u>Your Personal Identification Number (PIN)</u> should arrive within three (3) days after the card. <u>Your PIN</u> cannot be personalized because VISA currently does not have the capability to permit this. Therefore, <u>your PIN</u> is a four-digit number that VISA selected.

In the revised version, the common topic appears as the subject of each sentence, and readers can easily relate the old information to the new information in each sentence. The writer uses the passive voice in the second sentence to place the common topic in the subject position. This writer appropriately uses the passive voice to tie together related information. Sometimes, the only way you can put a common topic into the subject position is by using the passive voice.

In the revised passage discussed above, the topic of each sentence is the same, and the words used to name that topic are nearly the same. In some passages, however, you may want to vary your choice of words to signal a common topic. Consider this paragraph:

Common topic

When rocks erode, <u>they</u> break down into sediment—smaller pieces of rock and minerals. <u>These sediments</u> may eventually travel in water to new sites such as the sea or river beds. <u>The water</u> deposits the sediments in layers that become buried and compacted. In time, <u>the sediment particles</u> are cemented together to form new rocks, known as sedimentary rocks. <u>The layers of sediment</u> in these rocks are often visible without microscopes in large outcrops.

The subjects (underlined) in this passage aren't the same, but each subject relates to a common topic. None of these subjects surprises readers because the subjects contain old information and relate to the common topic: the erosion of rocks.

Use Transitions

Transitions are words, phrases, and even sentences that connect one idea or one sentence to another. Transitions indicate relationships of time, cause and effect, space, addition, comparison, and contrast. Figure 8.1 presents a list of common transitions that writers use to connect ideas.

When using transitions to tie your sentences together, put the transition at or near the beginning of the sentence. Putting a transition after the verb or near the end of the sentence weakens the effect of the transition and frequently creates an awkward sentence, as in this example:

Awkward

The results of the mayoral election concerned many of the top party officials. They asked the city for a recount, **therefore**.

Putting the transition ("therefore") at the end of the sentence prevents readers from seeing the cause-and-effect relationship until they reach the end of the

Figure 8.1

Commonly Used
Transitions

Time	before, while, during, after, next, later, first, second, then, subsequently, the next day, meanwhile, now
Cause and Effect	because, therefore, since, thus, consequently, due to, if . . . then, so
Place	below, above, inside, outside, behind, at the next level, internally, externally
Addition	furthermore, in addition, also, moreover, and
Comparison	likewise, as, like, similarly, not only . . . but also
Contrast	conversely, on the other hand, unlike, although, however, yet, nevertheless, but

sentence. In addition, with the transition at the end, the sentence fails to stress the most important information. The transition is more effective at the beginning of the sentence:

Revised

The results of the mayoral election concerned many of the top party officials. **Therefore,** the officials asked the city for a recount.

Repeat or Restate Key Words or Phrases

You can tie sentences together by repeating or restating key words or phrases. Repetition and restatement help readers to remember information and to understand the point you are making.

Repeating Words or Phrases

You can repeat keywords or phrases to tie sentences together. However, avoid overusing this technique. The following sentences illustrate effective repetition of keywords:

The accident on the space station <u>depleted</u> the oxygen <u>supply</u>. Because of the <u>depleted supply</u>, the crew had to limit its physical activities.

A variation of that technique is evident in the following example:

The city council <u>recommended</u> that the city redraw the lines of the districts. This <u>recommendation</u> upset many citizens.

The verb "recommend" in the first sentence is echoed in the second sentence by the noun "recommendation." The repetition allows the writer to put old information at the beginning of the sentence.

Restating with Pronouns

You can use pronouns to refer to nouns that appear in a previous sentence. Pronouns not only help tie your sentences together but also avoid the monotony that results when the same noun appears several times in a sentence or paragraph.

> As the <u>team</u> planned the project, <u>they</u> created a listserv for sharing information.

Restating with Summary Words

You can tie sentences together with words that summarize ideas or information presented earlier. Summary words allow you to restate information, usually in just a few words. In the example below, the subject of the second sentence ("this setup") summarizes the equipment mentioned in the first sentence:

> The computer lab purchased <u>six new laser printers and twelve new Pentium-class personal computers</u>. <u>This setup</u> will allow the lab to better serve the computer science students.

By using summary words, the writer effectively and concisely restates information from the previous sentence and puts that old information at the beginning of the new sentence.

CONCLUSION

When you follow the principles described in this chapter, you will write sentences and paragraphs that readers can read and understand quickly. As you write technical documents, be sure not only to include accurate, useful information, but also to write clear and direct sentences. Use the "Worksheet for Writing Reader-Oriented Sentences and Paragraphs" to check the style of your sentences.

WORKSHEET for Writing Reader-Oriented Sentences and Paragraphs

Principle 1: Make the Actors the Subjects of Your Sentences

- Have you put the actor(s) in the subject?
- Have you used people as the subject whenever possible?
- Have you used the active voice whenever possible and appropriate?
- If you have used passive voice, did you answer "yes" to one of the questions on page 163?

Principle 2: Put the Action in Verbs

- Have you expressed the action in verbs?
- Are the actor and the action close together in your sentences?

Principle 3: Emphasize the Important Information in Your Sentences

- Have you put the most important information at the end of your sentences?
- When appropriate, have you used visual cues to emphasize important information?

Principle 4: Tie Your Sentences Together

- Have you put the old (familiar) information near the beginning of your sentences?
- Have you put the new (unfamiliar) information near the end of your sentences?
- Have you appropriately used transitions to tie your sentences together?
- Have you appropriately used repetition and restatement to tie your sentences together?

EXERCISES

Bryan

1. Rewrite these sentences to make the actor the subject.

   a. Attempts were made by the engineering staff to assess the project.
   b. The completion of the new building will allow 30 new businesses to relocate to the downtown area.
   c. The cost of the reinspection is to be paid by the insurance company in accordance with the contract.
   d. There have been several changes to the blueprint from the previous copies we submitted.

2. Convert these sentences from the passive to the active voice. Follow the procedure described in Principle 1.

   a. The annual merit raises were approved by the board of directors last week.
   b. Employee purchases must be paid for within ninety days or in six payroll deductions by all employees.
   c. Your cash advance limit will be approved and communicated to you by your management in early December.
   d. Your department's growth figures are being reanalyzed by the accounting department to determine your budget for next year.

3. Rewrite these sentences to put the action in the verb.

   a. We must provide support for the three candidates from our district who are running for president, vice president, and secretary.
   b. Our expectation was to begin the new semester immediately.
   c. The police are conducting an extensive investigation of the armed robbery that occurred this morning.
   d. Students must make a search for time not only to study but also to relax.

4. Rewrite these sentences to put the more important information near the end of the sentence.

   a. The outcome of the election changed because of some unfortunate comments about the city founders, according to the news release.
   b. Several homeowners in the Cottonwood subdivision are suing the developer for faulty foundations and poor building materials, however.
   c. Water pipes in many older homes will freeze and possibly burst under these weather conditions.
   d. Several students in the writing seminar have not completed the business proposal assignment according to my records.

5. For each sentence listed below, do the following.

   • Identify the principle or principles that the writer has <u>not</u> followed.
   • Rewrite the sentences to make them more reader oriented. Follow the guidelines given in Principles 1, 2, and 3.
   • After your rewritten sentence, write the number of the principle or principles that you followed while rewriting.

   a. There was first a review of the evolution of the computer by the professor.
   b. Because of the clerk's inability to help us with the equipment, there was a delay in the repairs that we had to do the next day.
   c. Employee termination in companies should be avoided not only because it is expensive but also because the loss of a responsible employee could account for a reduction in productivity.
   d. Our intention is to audit the financial records of your company.
   e. A reinvestigation of the new employee's travel expenses by the accounting division is necessary before reimbursement from headquarters can be provided.
   f. The creation of an international relations committee will increase our budget requirements for the new year, however.
   g. Our international sales divisions, which are located in Germany, Japan, Canada, England, Brazil, and Sweden, have increased the company profits by 30 percent.

h. Many sales managers of the major software companies are planning to be in attendance at the annual software exposition in April.

i. The new computer network for the engineering staff will use six days for installation and training, according to the network operator.

j. According to our accountant, we find that your payments at the present time are two months late.

6. These passages do *not* follow Principle 4. Rewrite them so that the sentences fit together smoothly.

a. The company will begin using First Bank cards instead of the corporate American Express cards. A greater number of establishments accept the First Bank card. Travel accident insurance in the amount of $500,000 is provided by First Bank. The overall cost to the company is less.

b. Some animals are highly social in their behavior and will share their territory with other animals of the same species. It is not uncommon to observe small groups of dogs at street corners, apparently engaged in highly socialized behavior, for example.

c. According to the IRS, the state must consider all reimbursements for partial per diem expenses as taxable income when an employee does not stay overnight. Receipts must be submitted, and the amount reimbursed may not exceed approved limits for per diem expenses.

d. The project manager has approved the thermocouple specification and has submitted a purchase requisition form. I have enclosed a copy of the specification for your files. There will be 69 thermocouples installed.

7. The following passage is an excerpt from a report written by an engineering and environmental consulting firm. The firm has studied the effects of a planned lignite-powered plant on the environment. This passage is about the location of established residences, schools, hospitals, and other community centers near the site. Rewrite the passage to tie the sentences together. Also, correct any sentences that don't follow Principles 1, 2, or 3.

No schools or hospitals were identified within the site or its one-mile perimeter. Liberty Faith Church and cemetery are located along FM 979 approximately 0.5 mile south of the site. St. Paul's Episcopal Church is located approximately 0.5 mile north of Liberty Faith Church and 0.6 mile south of the site. No future community centers have been planned within one mile of the site.

There will be limited emergency response units located at the site, including a nurses' station, ambulance, fire truck, and fire station. The nearest hospitals off the site are

- Summit County Community Hospital
- U.S. Government Veterans' Hospital
- Brazos Memorial Hospital, Incorporated

Summit County EMS is the nearest emergency medical service located in Frisco approximately 13 miles from the site. Also located in Frisco are the nearest sheriff's station and volunteer fire department unit.

Chapter 9

Using Reader-Oriented Language

Y ou want the words in your documents to communicate what you mean. You want readers to share your understanding of the information in your documents. To ensure that they will understand, you can use the six principles discussed in this chapter.

PRINCIPLE 1: USE SPECIFIC AND UNAMBIGUOUS LANGUAGE

To understand your documents and respond appropriately, readers need specific and unambiguous language. Without such language, they may misunderstand or misinterpret what you write. When you use specific and unambiguous language, you convey your intended meaning precisely.

Using Specific Language

Readers of technical documents expect specific language, not vague language. Specific language is clear and precise; vague language is often unclear and always imprecise. Specific language clarifies the meaning and eliminates questions that readers may ask when the language is vague.

Vague   A computer in one of the labs isn't working properly.
Specific The monitor on computer 26 in the College of Arts and Sciences lab is flickering erratically.

After reading the vague sentence, a reader might wonder, Which computer? Which lab? What is wrong with the computer? The specific sentence answers all those questions. It identifies the lab where the computer is located, the specific computer, and the problem.

To make your language specific, include examples and details. You can use "such as" or "for example" to introduce the examples:

Vague   For its mission, the relief organization needs food and supplies.
Specific For its mission to the area damaged by hurricane Carlos, the relief organization needs food and supplies such as

- Canned milk
- Bottled water in 1-gallon plastic containers
- Canned meat such as tuna, chicken, or ham spread
- Ready-to-use baby formula
- Disposable diapers
- Gauze, bandages, and rubbing alcohol

Though grammatically correct, the vague sentence is imprecise. Readers of the vague sentence might not provide the relief organization with the specific food and supplies that it needs. Readers of the specific sentence know exactly what items the organization needs.

Using Unambiguous Language

In addition to being specific, your language should be unambiguous: it should convey only one meaning. Ambiguity in sentences results from:

- Misplaced modifiers
- Dangling modifiers
- Faulty word choice

Misplaced Modifiers

Misplaced modifiers appear to modify the wrong referent. These misplaced modifiers can cause ambiguity. To eliminate the ambiguity, place the modifier as close as possible to the intended referent. Misplaced modifiers are frequently phrases or clauses:

Ambiguous   Our manager suggested to the vice president that we register for the class **in San Francisco.**

After reading this sentence, can you say for certain whether the class is being held in San Francisco? The meaning is ambiguous because of the placement of the prepositional phrase "in San Francisco." To prevent the ambiguity and possible misreading, either place a prepositional phrase next to the word it modifies or rewrite to clarify your meaning:

Unambiguous   Our manager suggested to the vice president **in San Francisco** that we register for the class.

Unambiguous   Our manger suggested to the vice president that we register **in San Francisco** for the class.

Unambiguous   Our manager suggested to the vice president that we register for the **San Francisco** class.

Let's look at another example. Here the misplaced modifier occurs because the writer has incorrectly placed the modifier "growing in the sterile solution" next to the lab technicians instead of next to "bacteria," which is actually what is growing in the solution.

Ambiguous   **Growing in the sterile solution,** the lab technicians observed the bacteria.

Unambiguous   The lab technicians observed the bacteria **growing in the sterile solution.**

ISSUES IN CONTEXT

Localizing Documents for International Readers

As you write for international readers, you may want to "localize" a document. Localizing is more than translating words. When writers localize a document, they "adapt it to fit the political, economic, technical, and marketing realities of that country" (Klein 32). Technical documents can change across cultures just as body language, everyday expressions, and forms of greetings change. For example, a U.S. company that produces heart treatment equipment "introduced its products with a cartoon of happily smiling hearts" (Klein 33). Although the graphic worked for U.S. readers, the German readers were offended by this light treatment of heart disease. Likewise, to readers in the United States, the acronyms EPA (for Environmental Protection Agency) and IRS (for Internal Revenue Service) are common; however, these abbreviations don't apply outside the United States. (Klein 32). As you write for international readers, remember that readers in various "locales" will have different rules, data, and cultural expectations. For example, the United States is a locale, China is a locale, and India is a locale—each has its own set of rules, data, and cultural expectations.

To localize documents, some companies hire translation/localization agencies. If your company hires one of these companies, make sure the company has ISO 9001 certification covering localization services (Klein 33). You can also consult the following sources to help you localize documents.

Hall, Edward. *Understanding Cultural Differences*. Yarmouth, ME: Intercultural Press, 1990.

Hoft, Nancy L. *International Technical Communication*. New York: John Wiley & Sons, 1995.

Uren, Emmanuel, Robert Howard, and Tiziana Perinotti. *Software Internationalization and Localization—An Introduction*. New York: Van Nostrand Reinhold, 1993.

Dangling Modifiers

Dangling modifiers have no referent in the sentence:

Dangling   **Trying to put out the fire,** the fire extinguisher broke.

In this sentence, the writer has not identified who is putting out the fire. To eliminate the dangling modifier, rewrite the sentence to add the person in either the main clause or in the modifier:

Correct	**Trying to put out the fire,** I broke the fire extinguisher.
Correct	**As I was trying to put out the fire,** the fire extinguisher broke.

You can also create dangling modifiers when switching from the indicative mood (a statement of fact) to the imperative mood (a command or request usually with an understood "you" subject). To identify dangling modifiers in those situations, you can often look for a passive voice construction following the dangling modifier, as in the following example:

Dangling	**To link to other Web sites and topics,** the green keywords should be clicked on.
Correct	**To link to other Web sites and topics,** click on the green keywords.

To correct the dangling modifier, the writer simply puts the passive voice into active voice with an understood referent—in this case "you."

Faulty Word Choice

Let's look at another ambiguous sentence. In this one, the ambiguity occurs because of the word choice:

Ambiguous	We were **held up** at the bank.
Unambiguous	We were **delayed** at the bank.

The ambiguous sentence has two possible meanings: "We" were either delayed or robbed. To eliminate the ambiguity, the writer selects the verb *delay*, which can have only one meaning in the sentence. Carefully select the words in your sentences, making sure that readers will understand them in only one way.

PRINCIPLE 2: USE ONLY THE WORDS YOUR READERS NEED

Readers want to read your documents without wading through unnecessary words. Therefore, use only the words that your readers need to understand what you mean. You can write concisely if you

- Eliminate redundancy
- Eliminate unnecessary words

Eliminating Redundancy

Redundancy occurs when you use words or phrases that unnecessarily repeat the meaning of other words in the sentence:

Redundant	Your **counsel** and **advice** will **help** and **benefit** each youth in the Kids Plus program.
Concise	Your advice will help each youth in the Kids Plus program.

Each redundant pair ("counsel" and "advice" and "help" and "benefit") uses two words although just one word will do. The words "counsel" and "advice" have the same meaning, and so do "help" and "benefit." Thus, to be concise, the writer needs to use only one of the words in each pair. Redundancies frequently occur in pairs. Figure 9.1 is a list of common redundant pairs. When you see these pairs in your writing, revise to use only one word in the pair and delete the "and."

Redundancy also results from modifiers that repeat all or part of the meaning of other words in a sentence. Examples of redundant modifiers include the following (the redundant words appear in bold type):

Redundant	**end** result, **very** unique, **absolutely** free, **completely** eliminate

For more examples, see Figure 9.2.

The sentences below illustrate the positive effect of eliminating redundant modifiers:

Redundant	The proposed budget cuts will not affect the **final** outcome of our current demographic study or our **future** plans for improving the street drainage.
Concise	The proposed budget cuts will not affect the outcome of our current demographic study or our plans for improving the street drainage.

In the redundant sentence, the modifier "final" is unnecessary because it repeats the meaning of "outcome" (an outcome is always final), and the modi-

Figure 9.1
Common Redundant Pairs

advice and counsel	full and complete
agreeable and satisfactory	help and cooperation
any and all	hope and trust
assist and help	if and when
basic and fundamental	null and void
due and payable	opinion and belief
each and every	prompt and immediate
fair and equitable	thought and consideration
first and foremost	

absolutely essential	past memories
absolutely free	personal opinion
close proximity	reduce down
decrease down	repeat again
end result	quite unique
final outcome	rarely ever
free gift	round (square, oblong, etc.) in shape
future plans	seldom ever
green (purple, red, black, yellow, etc.) in color	true facts
human volunteer	twenty (thirty, two, etc.) in number
mail out	very latest
past experience	very unique

Figure 9.2 Redundant Modifiers

fier "future" is unnecessary because it repeats the meaning of "plans" (all plans involve the future). Let's look at another example:

Redundant	We asked the research team to analyze a rock that was pink **in color**, cylindrical **in shape**, and 61 pounds **in weight**.
Concise	We asked the research team to analyze a pink, cylindrical rock that weighed 61 pounds.

The prepositional phrases in the redundant sentence repeat the meaning of "pink," "cylindrical," and "61 pounds": pink is a color, cylindrical is a shape, and 61 pounds is a weight.

Eliminating Unnecessary Words

Wordy phrases make documents unnecessarily long. Even when readers understand a wordy phrase, they prefer clear, concise writing. Readers want to read technical documents as quickly as possible, so eliminate any words not absolutely necessary to convey your meaning and purpose. Figure 9.3 lists some wordy phrases and suggests concise alternatives.

At first you may not notice the wordy phrases that appear in your writing, because you have used them for a long time or have read them in so many technical documents. Thus, you may have to make a special effort to spot these phrases and then to replace them with more concise and effective words.

You can also simply eliminate a wordy phrase instead of replacing it with something more concise. Figure 9.4 lists several expressions that you usually can eliminate.

Let's look at the effect of wordy phrases on sentence length and clarity:

Figure 9.3
Revising Wordy
Phrases

Instead of These Wordy Phrases . . .	Use These Concise Alternatives
according to our records	we find
a limited number	a few
a majority of	most
a number of	many
at a later time (date)	later
at the conclusion of	after, following
at this point and time	now, currently
by means of	by
conduct an investigation	investigate
conduct a study	study
despite the fact that	although
due to the fact that	because
have the capability to	can
in accordance with your request	as you requested
in connection with	about, concerning
in order that	so that
in order to	to
in reference to	about
in regard to	about
in the near future	soon
in this day and age	today
in view of the fact that	because
it is my (our) belief that	I believe that, we believe that
it is my (our) opinion that	I think that, we think that
it is my (our) understanding that	I understand that, we understand that
it is our recommendation that	we recommend
make reference to	refer to
on a weekly (daily, monthly) basis	weekly, daily, monthly
prior to	before
relative to	about
so as to	to
subsequent to	after
take into consideration	consider
until such time as	until
we are not in a position to	we cannot
will you be kind enough to	please
without further delay	now, immediately
with reference to	about
with regard to	about
with respect to	about

Figure 9.4

Unnecessary Phrases

as a matter of fact	it is evident
I beg to inform you	it is interesting to note that
I believe	it is significant (important) that
I hope	it should be noted that
in my opinion	it should be pointed out that
in other words	thanking you in advance
I should point out that	the fact that
I think	there are (is)
it is essential	to the extent that

Wordy   **As a matter of fact, there is** an old warehouse that the emergency relief groups can use to house the tornado victims **at this point in time.**

Concise   The emergency relief groups can now use the old warehouse to house the tornado victims.

Wordy   **It should be pointed out that there are** three candidates that our organization will endorse **without further delay, despite the fact that we are not in a position** to contribute any money to their campaigns.

Concise   Our organization will endorse three candidates now although we cannot contribute any money to their campaigns.

Wordy   **It should be noted that** mercury levels in the river have increased this year, and **in accordance with your request** our department will **take into consideration** whether **it is essential** to **conduct a study with regard to** possible sources of this pollution.

Concise   Mercury levels in the river have increased this year, and as you requested, our department will consider whether to study possible sources of this pollution.

PRINCIPLE 3: USE SIMPLE WORDS

When you want to impress your reader, resist the temptation to use words that you don't normally use—words that you rarely if ever use when talking. Many writers believe that they will impress readers by using fancy words such as those listed in Figure 9.5. In technical writing, however, you are more likely to impress readers not with these fancy words with more than one syllable but with simple, clear, everyday words.

Fancy words   The race officials **anticipate** that the race will **commence** at 8:00 A.M.

Simple words   The race officials **expect** the race to **begin** at 8:00 A.M.

Figure 9.5

Fancy and Simple Words

Instead of These Fancy Words . . .	Use These Simple Words
accelerate	speed up
accompany	go with
accumulate	gather
acquaint	tell
advise	tell
anticipate	foresee
apparent	clear
approximately	about
ascertain	learn, find out
assist	help
attempt	try
cognizant	know
commence	begin, start
commitment	promise
compensation	pay
complete	fill out
construct	build
contribute	give
demonstrate	show
endeavor	try
equivalent	equal
expedite	speed up
explicit	plain
facilitate	help, ease

Fancy words   Our office assistants will **accompany** you to **endeavor** to get our **compensation** checks.

Simple words   Our office assistants will **go** with you to **try** to get our **pay** checks.

Most readers of technical documents want to gather the information they need as quickly and effortlessly as possible. Documents that contain many fancy words take longer to read than documents written in the language of everyday speech.

PRINCIPLE 4: USE POSITIVE LANGUAGE

Whenever possible, tell readers what something is, instead of what it is not. Readers comprehend positive language more easily and quickly than they

Figure 9.5 (cont.)

Instead of These Fancy Words . . .	Use These Simple Words
furnish	give, provide
herewith is	here is
indebtedness	debt
indicate	show
initiate	begin
initial	first
legislation	law
locality	place
maintenance	upkeep
modify	change
objective	aim, goal
optimum	best, most
perform	do
prioritize	rank
prior to	before
proceed	go
procure	buy, get
purchase	buy
reimburse	pay back, repay
subsequent to	after, next, later
sufficient	enough
terminate	end
transmit	send
utilize	use

comprehend negative language. The presence of several negative constructions in a sentence or paragraph slows the pace of reading, because readers have to work harder to gather information and meaning from negative language. Figure 9.6 lists some negative phrases and their positive counterparts; you'll discover more as you write.

As the following examples show, using positive rather than negative language leads to clearer and often to more concise sentences:

Negative   **Do not discontinue taking** the medicine until **none** of the medicine is left.

Positive   **Continue taking** the medicine until it is **all** gone.

or

Take all the medicine.

Figure 9.6
Negative Phrases
and Their Positive
Counterparts

Instead of Saying What Something Is Not . . .	Say What It Is
not many	few
not all	most
not on time	late, delayed
not late, not delayed	on time
not continue	discontinue
not discontinue	continue
not efficient	inefficient
not sad	happy
not accurate	inaccurate
not approve	disapprove
not disapprove	approve
not now	later
not familiar	unfamiliar

Negative	**Not all** of the team members could attend the meeting.
Positive	**Most of** the team members could attend the meeting.
Negative	Because the engineering department **was not unaware** of the change in scheduling for the project, they could not meet the deadline for the *beta* testing.
Positive	Because the engineering department **was aware** of the change in scheduling for the project, they could have met the deadline for the *beta* testing.

PRINCIPLE 5: USE TECHNICAL TERMINOLOGY CONSISTENTLY AND APPROPRIATELY

Readers of technical documents expect writers to use consistently the words that refer to technical concepts, instructions, and equipment. For instance, readers of a computer maintenance manual may be confused if the writer uses *screen* and *monitor* interchangeably. The writer should pick one term or the other and use it consistently. Using words consistently is especially important when writing instructions and when describing equipment. For example, if a software manual explains how to select "typefaces" but the software itself uses the word "fonts," readers who don't know that *typefaces* and *fonts* are synonyms will be confused.

As you write, consider whether you can use more than one term to refer to a concept, instruction, piece of equipment, and so on. Then decide which word or words you will use, and use them consistently. Also consider which words readers prefer, and, if possible, use those words—perhaps, for example, choosing *e-mail* instead of *electronic mail.*

Technical terminology—or jargon—is the specialized vocabulary of a particular field, profession, or workplace. For instance, professionals in the restaurant business may use the term "back server" for the employees who clear guests' tables during and after meals. Horticulturalists may use the scientific rather than the common name for plants—for example, referring to a pecan tree as *Carya illinoinensis* or a day lily as *Hemerocallis*. Technical terminology is useful. It offers a concise way to convey technical information. However, readers who are unfamiliar with the technical terms may find them confusing or may misinterpret them. You can solve this problem for some readers by defining technical terms in parentheses the first time you use them or defining them in a glossary. Other readers, however, will be uncomfortable with this solution and will prefer that you use nontechnical language whenever possible.

How will you know whether to use technical terminology in your documents? Ask yourself these questions:

- Will all of my readers understand the technical terminology and abbreviations? Will they understand any of the technical terms and abbreviations?
- How can I help readers who don't understand the technical terminology and abbreviations? Will I define terminology and explain abbreviations in parentheses the first time I use them, or will I refer readers to a separate technical-terms glossary?
- Will my readers expect me to use technical terminology and abbreviations?

Use technical terminology only if your readers have detailed knowledge of the topic. You can assume, for example, that an engineer knows what the abbreviation *psi* (pounds per square inch) means; someone without an engineering background may not understand the abbreviation. Expert readers expect technical terminology. If your readers have casual or scant knowledge of your topic or of your field, avoid using technical terminology that they don't understand. If you cannot avoid using it, define the terminology that you use.

PRINCIPLE 6: USE GENDER-FREE LANGUAGE

Gender-free language is inclusive; it doesn't restrict ways of thinking about men or women and their roles in the world around us. Gender-specific language can distract or mislead readers, so eliminate all unnecessary references to gender in your writing.

This section describes several ways to eliminate gender-specific language.[1] Personal pronouns are especially troublesome. Many writers use *he/she* or *s/he* to eliminate gender, but these expressions are awkward, especially when they appear several times in a paragraph. Use the following techniques to avoid *he/she* and *s/he* and to avoid associating gender with a person's role or job:

- **Avoid gender-specific nouns when referring to job functions or occupations.** Gender-specific nouns such as *anchorman* exclude one gender or the other.

---

1. Adapted from Guidelines developed by the National Council of Teachers of English.

Figure 9.7
Alternatives to
Gender-Specific
Nouns

Gender-Specific Noun	Gender-Free Noun
chairman, chairwoman	chair, chairperson
policeman, policewoman	police, police officer
postman, mailman	postal worker, mail carrier
fireman	firefighter
waitress	server
stewardess	flight attendant

Figure 9.7 lists gender-free alternatives to some gender-specific nouns that refer to job functions or occupations.

- **Use plural nouns to eliminate gender-specific pronouns.** The following examples illustrate how using plural nouns results in gender-free language:

Gender-specific	**Each employee** should maintain **his** equipment and uniforms.
Gender-free	**Employees** should maintain **their** equipment and uniforms.
Gender-specific	**Each teacher** must live in the city where **she** teaches.
Gender-free	**Teachers** must live in the city where **they** teach.

- **To eliminate gender-specific pronouns, use *you* and *your*.** Often you can avoid gender-specific language by using second-person pronouns (*you, your*) instead of singular nouns. Use second-person pronouns to address your readers directly. Notice how using second-person pronouns results in gender-free language:

Gender-specific	The user should read the troubleshooting section of the manual before **she** calls the help line.
Gender-free	**You** should read the troubleshooting section of the manual before **you** call the help line.

or

Read the troubleshooting section of the manual before **you** call the help line.

- **Avoid using *man* and words that contain *man* to refer to all human beings.** Words such as *mankind* and *man-made* are inaccurate. Instead, you might use *people* for *mankind* and *synthetic* for *man-made*.

- **Use *he or she* or *she or he* when you must use gender-specific pronouns.** Whenever possible, use plural nouns or second-person pronouns to avoid gender-specific pronouns. However, when you can't avoid gender-specific pronouns, use *he or she* or *she or he*. These constructions are clear and inclusive.

A SPECIAL NOTE: LANGUAGE AND INTERNATIONAL READERS

With computer networks and the global marketplace, many companies are doing business with people and companies abroad. When communicating with people from other countries, companies encounter two problems: cultural differences and language interference (Mirshafiei 280). For example, miscommunication often occurs when people in the United States communicate with people whose cultures value "detailed, subjective analyses" and "philosophical argumentation" (Mirshafiei 281). In Middle Eastern cultures, writers often use what people in the United States regard as overstatement and exaggeration; these writers are "highly rhetorical and use a highly complex and decorative language" that people in the United States often find bewildering (Mirshafiei 281). Likewise, many Middle Eastern readers may not understand the tendency for directness and individualism. Such misunderstanding and miscommunication can result when readers and writers don't understand the cultures that drive and dictate communication styles.

Similarly, Japanese writers often use "telepathic communication," an indirect communication style that avoids direct confrontation. Telepathic communication allows writers to imply conflicting opinions and keep the communication smooth (Mirshafiei 281). When the Japanese communicate with people in cultures that expect and value direct, not vague language, miscommunication often occurs. For example, communication problems frequently occur between people in the United States and people in Japan because the telepathic communication style conflicts with the direct style expected by readers in the United States.

As you communicate with international readers, remember that their culture shapes their communication style just as your culture shapes yours. A communication that is unfamiliar to you is not inherently wrong or right; it is only different from the style to which you are accustomed. Your international readers probably have as much difficulty with your communication style as you do with theirs. Do your best to minimize this difference and to eliminate possible miscommunication by learning as much as you can about your readers' expectations and culture.

Along with cultural differences, consider language interference. Your international readers may not understand the idioms and technical or workplace language that you might use with other readers in your country or at your workplace. Idioms are expressions whose meaning is different from the literal or standard meaning of the words they contain. Examples of idioms in the

THE READER'S CORNER

Artificial Languages

Some natural languages—English and French especially—dominate international communication; but most experts doubt that any one of them could ever become *the* single international language. The association of natural languages with their particular cultures is just too strong. For this reason, artificial languages have seemed to many the best candidates for an international language. Dreams of such a language began during the period in the 1700s known as the Enlightenment. Since then hundreds of artificial languages have been proposed. A recent example is Hans Freudenthal's Lincos, or Lingua Cosmica, intended for communicating with extraterrestrials. However, the most successful attempt at establishing an international language has involved one based on several natural languages.

Drawing on French, English, German, and other Indo-European languages, a Polish ophthalmologist developed Esperanto in 1887. More than a century later, an international movement to promote its use still flourishes in more than eighty countries throughout South America and Asia. The 1 million people who use Esperanto work in specialized fields, as translators, and radio broadcasters (the most popular Esperanto program is broadcast from Beijing, China). Esperanto is a highly logical language. Spelling is completely regular. A consistent set of endings indicates grammatical functions of words (every noun ends in *o*, every adjective in *a*, every infinitive verb in *i*). Esperanto has a productive system of constructing new words from old: *ami* means "to love"; *malami,* "to hate"; and *malemo,* "the tendency to hate."

United States include *put up with, turn over a new leaf,* and *know the ropes.* International readers can't understand idioms logically; international readers must memorize what they mean. For example, you might say to your roommate: "Let's run down to McDonald's and grab a burger." You don't literally mean that the two of you should run to the restaurant and snatch a sandwich from the server. What you mean is "Let's get in the car, and drive to McDonald's, and buy something to eat."

When you write for international readers, consider the words and phrases you use, so that your readers will understand what you mean. Even international readers who speak English may not understand some of the expressions you use. For instance, in the United States, people say "line up" outside a theater box office, but people in England say "queue up." In everyday speech, you use many words and phrases that international readers may not understand. Likewise, you might use workplace language or technical terminology that is clear to others in your workplace but is baffling to international readers—especially to people who have never been to your country or to your workplace. For example, the expression *boot up,* referring to turning on a computer and starting a software package, may be unclear and even humorous to a reader in some countries.

When writing for international readers, try to find out as much as possible about their knowledge of your language and your country and about their language and customs. These tips can help you to minimize language interference:

- **Avoid idioms—expressions whose meaning is different from the standard or literal meaning of the words they contain.** Most U.S. readers, for example, would realize what "dig their heels in" means—that people stubbornly refuse to change their positions. International readers might interpret the expression literally and think that people dig holes in the ground with their feet.

- **Use workplace and technical language that international readers will be familiar or comfortable with.** Avoid using any terminology that is likely to be unfamiliar to your readers. For example, when writing to readers in England and Europe, use metric measurements, such as kilometers rather than miles.

- **Avoid localisms—phrases familiar only to people living in a specific area.** For example, many people in the southern part of the United States use the phrase *fixing to,* as in "I am fixing to go to the store." This phrase sounds odd to people not from the South and certainly would sound odd to an international reader. Brand names are another type of localism. Many people in the United States mistakenly use the brand name "Kleenex" to refer to all facial tissues and the brand name "Xerox" to refer to all copying machines. Such brand names will baffle many international readers.

- **Avoid metaphors and allusions that may refer to or imply a concept or information that is familiar to readers in the United States but probably is unfamiliar to international readers.**

- **If you must use expressions and terminology that international readers may not understand, explain what the language means, to avoid misinterpretation or misunderstanding.** Perhaps you also can find and use the corresponding word or phrase in the native language of your readers. You can also have the document you are writing translated into their native language. If you select this option, be sure that the translator knows the readers' language and country well enough to translate idioms and workplace and technical language correctly, not just literally.

- **Write simple, clear, complete sentences.** Divide long sentences into two or more shorter sentences. International readers or readers who aren't native speakers of your language will comprehend information more easily in a short sentence than in a long one.

CONCLUSION

Language is a powerful communication tool when used accurately. You can use this tool to persuade, inform, and instruct. However, to use this tool to your advantage, follow the guidelines in this chapter to write with clarity, conciseness, and precision. Your words will speak for you. Your readers will not be able to ask you to explain what you mean.

WORKSHEET for Using Reader-Oriented Language

Principle 1: Use Specific and Unambiguous Language

- Have you used specific language?
- Have you given readers enough examples and details to understand your sentences?
- Have you used unambiguous language?

Principle 2: Use Only the Words Your Readers Need

- Do your sentences contain redundant pairs?
- Do your sentences contain redundant modifiers?
- Have you used any unnecessary words or phrases?

Principle 3: Use Simple Words

- Have you used any fancy words that you could replace with simple words?

Principle 4: Use Positive Language

- Whenever possible, have you told readers what something is, instead of what it is not?

Principle 5: Use Technical Terminology Consistently and Appropriately

- Have you used technical terminology consistently?
- Will all readers understand the terminology and abbreviations you have used?

Principle 6: Use Gender-Free Language

- Have you used any gender-specific nouns to refer to job functions or occupations?

- Have you used plural nouns to eliminate gender-specific pronouns?
- When possible, have you used *you* and *your* instead of gender-specific pronouns?
- Have you avoided using *man* and words that contain *man* to refer to all people?

EXERCISES

1. Rewrite these sentences, substituting specific language for vague language. Add details and examples to make the language specific.

   a. The dryers in the laundry room are acting funny.

   b. The results of the survey will be available soon.

   c. Our analysis of the drinking water revealed a number of items that we can consider.

   d. The hurricane victims need building supplies.

2. Rewrite these sentences to eliminate ambiguous language.

   a. A brochure about the cost-sharing program is enclosed with the application that gives complete details.

   b. The study suggests that we should continue the recycling program to the city and the council.

   c. After the seminar, the citizens were revolting.

   d. Frozen solid, she removed the ice sculpture from the freezer for the banquet.

   e. After two months as an exchange student in India, the United States was a wonderful sight.

   f. We watched them perform the final experiment from the room with a one-way mirror.

3. Revise these sentences to eliminate redundant words and phrases.

   a. This important and significant jobs program should help each and every youth dedicated to improving himself or herself.

   b. If and when you complete the programming, we will document the program fully and completely.

   c. To enhance the marketing of our new line of computers, we are offering free gifts to the first 100 customers.

   d. The pipe to the main generator rarely ever leaks.

   e. The decorator plans to paint the auditorium walls green in color and to repeat the color again in the foyer.

   f. We have a very unique opportunity to see the future plans for the space center at the convention in May.

4. Rewrite these sentences, eliminating all unnecessary words and phrases and condensing wordy phrases. Correct any other style errors that you find in the sentences.

   a. There are several scientists who are uneasy about the research results.

   b. There are many children who need warm clothing for the winter.

   c. It is important that we turn in our applications by the deadline.

   d. As a matter of fact, we will be offering the internship program next semester.

   e. You should check the roof for damage on a monthly basis.

   f. The majority of the candidates support the tax rollback but have not taken into consideration the cost to education and social programs.

   g. It is our opinion that the architects should redesign the kitchen area to include a buffet serving area.

   h. It is interesting to note that at the conclusion of the council meeting, most of the opponents of the new taxi policy were gone.

   i. Until such time as the new health plan goes into effect, all employees should continue to file claims according to the current plan without further delay.

5. Revise these sentences, replacing fancy words with simple words. Correct any other style errors that you find in the sentences.

   a. The new health plan will commence on January 1 of next year.

   b. Subsequent to the organizational meeting, we will terminate the current compensation program and begin the new program.

   c. To obtain optimum performance from your

automobile, you should endeavor to follow the maintenance program furnished in the owner's manual.

d. We are cognizant of the fact that you are attempting to facilitate our reimbursement for the incorrect pipe fittings that we purchased from your organization.

6. Change the negative constructions to positive constructions in these sentences.

   a. As lab employees, you should not treat any student or faculty member unprofessionally and discourteously.

   b. Since the repair team did not know of the crack when they began their work, they could not repair the wall according to their original estimate.

   c. Not many of the competitors finished the marathon because of the extreme heat and humidity.

   d. Even though the plane was delayed because of fog, we were not late to the conference.

7. These sentences contain gender-specific language. Revise the sentences, replacing the gender-specific language with gender-free language. You may

change singular nouns to plural nouns when appropriate.

   a. Before the plane made an emergency landing, the stewardess checked the children's seatbelts.

   b. Each student should discuss his degree plan with his adviser at least two years before he graduates.

   c. The network operator should read all instructions before she updates the network.

   d. Many athletic shoes and equipment contain man-made materials.

8. Assume that international readers or non-native speakers of English will read these sentences. Eliminate any language that these readers may not understand.

   a. During the debate, the adviser told the candidates to stick to their guns when answering questions about their political views.

   b. After the midterm examination, we walked to our apartment and crashed.

   c. The victims of the hurricane need medical supplies such as Band-Aids, Kleenex, and alcohol.

CASE STUDY	Changing Old Habits

Background

Your company has decided to talk to employees about using gender-free language. In the past, the company has used the gender-specific pronoun *he* to refer to all employees, except when addressing a female employee by name. The company uses *she* when referring to administrative assistants and clerical staff, although several of the assistants and members of the clerical staff are males. The company also uses the terms *chairman of the board* and *chairman of the committee.*

Several of the employees—male and female— have complained about the gender-specific language. Other employees, however, don't see a problem with the language. They say that *he* is the universal pronoun and refers to males or females when talking or writing about a group such as employees of the company. They say that using another pronoun is unnecessary because they aren't really excluding anyone.

Despite resistance from many employees, the vice president, Jon Rowland, wants to make all employees—even the company executives— aware of the power of gender-specific language. Jon wants employees to use gender-free language when they speak, write, and refer to other employees and their job functions. He has asked you to write for his signature a memo explaining the power and problems of gender-specific language and presenting ways of eliminating such language.

Assignment

Your instructor will tell you whether you will write the memo individually or with a team.

1. Write a draft of the memo, remembering to keep the goodwill of all your readers as much as possible while still making the point that gender-specific language excludes and stating that the company and all employees will use gender-free language.

2. Bring your draft to class for peer evaluation.

3. Revise the draft as necessary, and give it to your instructor.

4. Be prepared to discuss your memo and this case in class.

Chapter 10

Designing Documents for Your Readers

R eaders form an impression of your document before they begin to read it. They draw this impression in part from the design elements—or lack of design elements. These elements help to create a favorable or unfavorable picture of your document and possibly you and your company. Design elements such as headings, type size, color, page layout, and white space affect the success of a document. These elements also help readers to locate information and motivate readers to read. In this chapter, you will learn four principles to help you design documents that will favorably impress your readers.

HOW DESIGN MAKES DOCUMENTS MORE READABLE

Before we examine those principles, let's compare the presentation of information about canine epilepsy in Figures 10.1 and 10.2. The document shown in Figure 10.1 has no design elements other than the title and paragraph breaks. It doesn't have headings or lists to help readers locate information, so the readers can't read selectively. Readers who are interested in specific information must read until they find that information. For example, someone who wants to know how to medicate and treat an epileptic dog must read six paragraphs before finding that information. In contrast, the document shown in Figure 10.2 contains visual clues to the organization of the text and the information it provides. Readers of that document can locate specific information about types of canine epilepsy and about treating epilepsy.

Readers process a document from top to bottom unless the writer gives them some clues about the content of the document (Duin). Without these clues, readers may assume that information near the beginning is more important than information near the end, and they may read the information near the beginning of a document especially closely and generally recall it better than they recall information at the end. If readers are likely to need information that appears in the middle or near the end, the writer can give clues through the document design to help readers find that information. The format of the document in Figure 10.2 gives readers clues through headings and lists. The headings visually categorize information and make it unnecessary for readers to process the document from top to bottom. Instead, readers can scan through the document for the information that interests them. The format of the document in Figure 10.1 gives readers no clues about content and forces readers to process the document in a top-down manner.

PRINCIPLE 1: CONSIDER THE DESIGN AS YOU PLAN YOUR DOCUMENTS

To save yourself time and frustration, consider design elements when you identify your readers and their purpose for reading. If you wait until you have written one or more drafts, you may not have time to incorporate the design elements you want, or you may have to unnecessarily spend time reformatting the text to fit your design. Before you begin writing, decide on the page size, page layout, typefaces, type sizes, and heading style. By deciding on these elements early, you can format your document as you write; or you can create a

Figure 10.1 A Document with No Design Elements

Canine Epilepsy

Epilepsy is a disorder characterized by recurrent seizures. Seizures, also known as fits or convulsions, occur when an area of nerve cells in the brain becomes overexcitable. This area is often called a seizure focus. The mechanism responsible for developing this focus is unknown.

A dog can inherit or acquire canine epilepsy. Inherited epilepsy affects about 1% of the canine population. Breeds which may inherit epilepsy include the beagle, Belgian shepherd, German shepherd, dachshund, and keeshond. Researchers also suspect a genetic factor in the following breeds: cocker spaniel, collie, golden retriever, Labrador retriever, Irish setter, miniature schnauzer, poodle, Saint Bernard, Siberian husky, and wire-haired fox terrier.

Acquired epilepsy may occur months to years after an injury or illness that causes brain damage. In many cases, the dog is completely normal except for occasional seizures. Causes of acquired epilepsy include trauma, infection, poisons, hypoxia (lack of oxygen), and low blood sugar concentrations.

A dog with inherited epilepsy has generalized seizures that affect its entire brain and body. The dog usually falls on its side and displays paddling motions with all four limbs. During or immediately after the seizures, the dog may also exhibit loss of consciousness (i.e., the dog will not respond when you call its name), excessive drooling, and urinating or passing of feces. The seizure usually lasts no longer than 1 or 2 minutes. The first seizure of inherited epilepsy usually occurs between the ages of 1 and 3 years. Seizures that occur before 6 months or after 5 years of age probably result from acquired epilepsy.

A dog with acquired epilepsy has partial seizures. A partial seizure affects only one part of the body, and the dog may not lose consciousness. During a partial seizure, the dog may exhibit turning of the head to one side, muscular contractions of one or both legs on the same side of the body, or bending of the body to one side. These signs are localizing because they help to determine the location of the seizure focus in the brain. The localizing sign may occur only briefly, after which the seizure becomes generalized. If the seizure becomes generalized, you or your veterinarian may have difficulty distinguishing between acquired and inherited epilepsy. The first seizure may occur at any age.

You can treat epilepsy by giving anticonvulsant medication orally several times a day. This treatment is effective in 60 to 70% of epileptic dogs. Unfortunately, the medication will not completely eliminate the seizures. Instead, the medication reduces the frequency, severity, and duration of the seizures. Most veterinarians recommend that dogs receive the anticonvulsant medication when the seizures occur more often than once every 6 weeks or when severe clusters of seizures occur more often than once every 2 months. To successfully treat epilepsy, you must consistently give the medication as directed by the veterinarian and continue the medication without interruption. If you discontinue the medication, status epilepticus could occur, resulting in the dog's death. Status epilepticus is a series of seizures without periods of consciousness. If this condition occurs, contact a veterinarian immediately.

Source: Adapted from S. Dru Forrester and Bruce Lawhorn, *Canine Epilepsy* (College Station: Texas Agricultural Extension Service, n.d.). Reprinted by permission.

Figure 10.2 A Document with Design Elements

Canine Epilepsy

Epilepsy is a disorder characterized by recurrent seizures. Seizures, also known as fits or convulsions, occur when an area of nerve cells in the brain becomes overexcitable. This area is often called a seizure focus. The mechanism responsible for developing this focus is unknown.

Types of Canine Epilepsy

A dog can inherit or acquire canine epilepsy. Inherited epilepsy affects about 1% of the canine population. Breeds which may inherit epilepsy include the beagle, Belgian shepherd, German shepherd, dachshund, and keeshond. Researchers also suspect a genetic factor in the following breeds: cocker spaniel, collie, golden retriever, Labrador retriever, Irish setter, miniature schnauzer, poodle, Saint Bernard, Siberian husky, and wire-haired fox terrier.

Acquired epilepsy may occur months to years after an injury or illness that causes brain damage. In many cases, the dog is completely normal except for occasional seizures. Causes of acquired epilepsy include trauma, infection, poisons, hypoxia (lack of oxygen), and low blood sugar concentrations.

Characteristics of Inherited Epilepsy

A dog with inherited epilepsy has generalized seizures that affect its entire brain and body. The dog usually falls on its side and displays paddling motions with all four limbs. During or immediately after the seizures, the dog may also exhibit some or all of the following signs:

- loss of consciousness (i.e., the dog will not respond when you call its name)
- excessive drooling
- urinating or passing of feces.

The seizure usually lasts no longer than 1 or 2 minutes. The first seizure of inherited epilepsy usually occurs between the ages of 1 and 3 years. Seizures that occur before 6 months or after 5 years of age probably result from acquired epilepsy.

Characteristics of Acquired Epilepsy

A dog with acquired epilepsy has partial seizures. A partial seizure affects only one part of the body, and the dog may not lose consciousness. During a partial seizure, the dog may exhibit one or more of the following localizing signs:

- turning of the head to one side
- muscular contractions of one or both legs on the same side of the body
- bending of the body to one side.

These signs are localizing because they help to determine the location of the seizure focus in the brain. The localizing sign may occur only briefly, after which the seizure becomes generalized. If the seizure becomes generalized, you or your veterinarian may have difficulty distinguishing between acquired and inherited epilepsy. The first seizure may occur at any age.

Treatment of Canine Epilepsy

You can treat epilepsy by giving anticonvulsant medication orally several times a day. This treatment is effective in 60 to 70% of epileptic dogs. Unfortunately, the medication will not completely eliminate the seizures. Instead, the medication reduces the frequency, severity, and duration of the seizures. Most veterinarians recommend that dogs receive the anticonvulsant medication when the seizures occur

Figure 10.2 (cont.)

> more often than once every 6 weeks or when severe clusters of seizures occur more often than once every 2 months.
>
> To successfully treat epilepsy, you must
> - consistently give the medication as directed by the veterinarian
> - continue the medication without interruption.
>
> If you discontinue the medication, status epilepticus could occur, resulting in the dog's death. Status epilepticus is a series of seizures without periods of consciousness. If this condition occurs, contact a veterinarian immediately.

Source: Adapted from S. Dru Forrester and Bruce Lawhorn, *Canine Epilepsy* (College Station: Texas Agricultural Extension Service, n.d.).

template or master pages with your word-processing or desktop publishing software to help you create consistent page designs.

As you decide on the design elements, you also can develop a prototype page and a style sheet. A prototype page shows the layout of a typical page of the document. A prototype page is especially important for documents that instruct, such as manuals, software documentation, and online help. (A sample prototype page appears in Chapter 2 on p. 27). A style sheet is a tool to help writers and designers maintain consistency throughout a document. A style sheet might include language choices such as those discussed in Chapter 9; it also can serve as a plan for designing a document. Figure 10.3 shows a simple style sheet for the design elements of a software manual written by a team of students. The team put the style sheet in a public directory on the local area network (LAN) in their computer lab, so each team member could easily access it.

A style sheet can help you maintain consistency in several situations. When you are working on a long document, a style sheet can help you remember the design decisions that you made at the start of the project. For example, it can tell you that first-level headings are to be in 14-point green Helvetica type. Style sheets also can help you give a consistent appearance to similar documents or to all of the documents written for a specific organization or company.

Many companies have their own style guides or specific design requirements for their documents. For example, a regional telecommunications company in the southwestern United States requires the company logo always to appear in the same typeface, type size, and color. This company also has specific page layout requirements for business letters and certain types of reports. As you prepare documents for your company, group, or organization, find out whether it has a style sheet or specific design requirements.

When you are working as part of a team, a style sheet helps you and other team members to use the same design elements and to format consistently.

Figure 10.3

Sample Style Sheet

Team 3
Style Sheet for Software Manual

Page Elements	Page size	9" x 6"
	Margins	$^3/_4$"
	Layout	two uneven columns, the left column for marginal comments and headings
		left column 1$^1/_2$"
		right column 3"
	Spacing	single-space for text
		double-space between paragraphs
	Visual aids	no captions for screen captures placed at point of reference
	Headings	left-hanging
Type Elements	Typeface	Bookman
	Size	10 point for text
		12 point for headings
		10 point for subheadings
	Style	bold for subheadings
	Color	color 13 for major headings

Keep the style sheet simple, so team members can easily follow it. The style sheet should list at least these design elements:

- Typefaces
- Type sizes
- Margins
- Heading style
- Line spacing

If team members follow the guidelines spelled out in the style sheet, the team can easily combine each member's section to create one document.

 You also can use electronic templates available in most word-processing software. These templates provide page layouts that you can use for your documents. You also can customize or create your own templates. If collaborating, you can copy these templates for each team member.

PRINCIPLE 2: CHOOSE DESIGN ELEMENTS TO MOTIVATE READERS TO READ

 As you plan your document, think about design elements that will prompt people to read and use your document. For example, if you are creating a home page for your company on the World Wide Web, you want to motivate readers to stop "surfing the Net" and read your page and then possibly to link to other Web sites about your company and its services or products. Readers generally notice the design or appearance of the elements on the page before they actually read the text, visual aids, or headings. Readers often are first attracted to a document by its packaging: the cover, binding, paper, and layout.

An Engaging, Appropriate Cover

The cover is the part of a document that many readers see first. It could be the first page of a Web site, the first screen of an online document, or the outside of a paper document. An effective cover makes a good first impression and invites readers to read and use the document. It will feature a clear, legible title or opening headline. If you use graphics, select ones that do not detract from or overpower the title or headline. If you are creating a cover for a paper document, select good-quality paper. If you have the budget, have the cover professionally laminated. For paper documents, select a cover material and style that are appropriate for the document and that will enhance your document. You will learn more about covers in Chapter 12.

If you are creating a cover or home page for a Web site, consider these design tips to motivate readers to stop and read it:

- **Use color to draw the readers to the page.**
- **Use ample "white space" or empty space which highlights and unifies the information you want to highlight.** Be sure to surround the name of the site or the company with ample "white space." The white space creates a frame that keeps the related information together.
- **Include information about the contents of the site.** You might use icons with explanatory phrases that invite readers to read beyond the cover or home page.
- **Avoid using paragraphs of text to describe the site.** Instead use lists, phrases, and visual aids.

Appropriate Binding

For long paper documents, several types of binding are available: three-ring binders, spiral binding, and traditional book binding. If readers will be using the document to complete a task or to follow instructions, select spiral binding or a three-ring binder; so the document will stay open to a specific page. If you will be updating the document frequently, use a three-ring binder; so you can update sections without reprinting the entire document. If you use traditional book binding, think of the spine of the book as a locating device: include at least the title of the document and possibly the writer's or the company's name.

Good-Quality Paper

For a paper document, select 20- or 30-pound bond paper. If you will be printing on both sides of the paper, make sure that the printing will not bleed through from one side to the other. When selecting the color of the paper, consider how easily readers will be able to read the print on the color you prefer.

Consistent Page Layout

As readers move beyond the external packaging, they look at the page layout to determine whether and what to read. Page layout can attract readers to your document. A consistent layout helps readers to locate information. To create consistent page layouts, follow these guidelines:

- **Use the same top, bottom, left, and right margins on each page.** For example, if you use 1-inch margins for one section of the document, use 1-inch margins for every section.

- **Use typefaces, type sizes, and type styles for headings and text consistently throughout the document.** For example, if you use a 14-point boldface serif typeface for the first-level headings in the first chapter of the document, use the same 14-point boldface serif typeface for first-level headings in every chapter.

- **Put page numbers in the same place on every page.** If you include a header or a footer with the page numbers, include that same style of header or footer on every page (see Figure 10.4). A **header** is a word or phrase that

Figure 10.4 Examples of a Header and a Footer

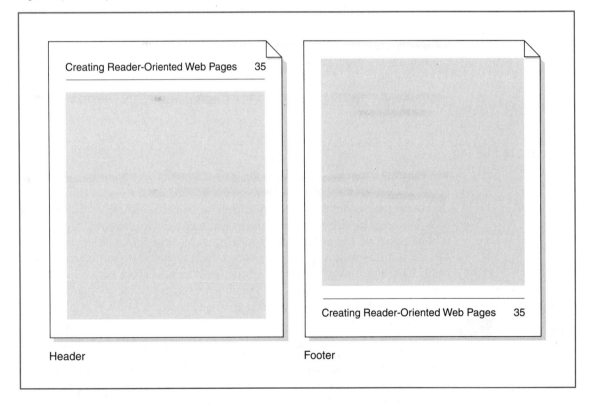

Creating Reader-Oriented Web Pages   35

Creating Reader-Oriented Web Pages   35

Header

Footer

you put at the top of each page to identify a document or specific sections of a document (a **footer** serves the same purpose but appears at the bottom of each page). The wording of the header or footer may change from chapter to chapter or from section to section.

- **Use consistent paragraph indents and spacing between columns, within lists, and before and after headings.** For example, if you use a 3-space indent for the first paragraph, use the same indent for all paragraphs.

PRINCIPLE 3: CHOOSE DESIGN ELEMENTS TO HELP READERS LOCATE INFORMATION

As you plan page layouts, remember that most readers have a goal when reading your document. They may be reading to

- Answer a question
- Gather information
- Complete a task or procedure
- Learn how to do something

To help readers reach any of these goals, you can include various design elements to help readers locate information. Such locating devices can appear at the document, chapter or division, and page or screen levels.

Document-Level Locating Devices

Document-level locating devices include the following:

- Table of contents
- Navigation tools
- Index

The table of contents appears at the beginning of a document. It offers an overview of the document by listing the headings and subheadings in the order in which they appear in the text (see Chapter 12). The table of contents also tells the number of the page where a heading appears. Even when writing online documents, provide readers with a table of contents or an overview of the contents. To overview the contents, you can include a menu or a list of the topics covered in the document.

Figure 10.5 is the table of contents for online help in WordPerfect® software. This table of contents lists the categories of information and tells readers how to access each topic. In an electronic table of contents, be sure to tell readers how to navigate through the online document since online documents don't have page numbers and aren't organized like paper documents.

To help readers locate information in paper documents, you also can provide an index. An index is an alphabetical listing of topics and includes more information than the table of contents. The index goes at the end of a document. You can find an example of an index at the end of this book.

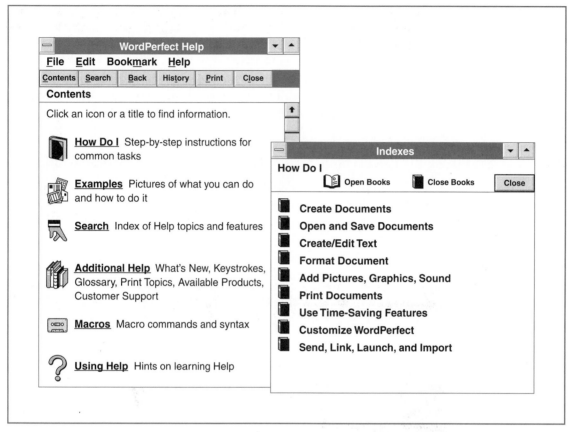

Figure 10.5 Table of Contents for an Online Document

Source: WordPerfect 6.0. Used by permission of Corel Corporation.

Chapter- or Division-Level Locating Devices

You might break a long document into chapters, divisions, or parts. For example, you might group the chapters of a long document into divisions. When you use chapters or divisions, be sure to use tabs or divider pages to indicate where each chapter or division begins.

Tabs—frequently used in manuals, procedures, and proposals—allow readers to quickly and easily locate chapters and divisions. If you decide to use tabs in your documents, select tabs with a professional appearance, and print a shortened version of the chapter or division title on the tab.

Divider pages help readers to locate chapters and major divisions. Divider pages appear before chapters, divisions, or chapter groupings. In this book, for example, divider pages appear at the beginning of Parts I, II, and so on. These pages list the title of the part and the chapters included in that part. Each divider page that appears before a chapter usually lists a brief table of contents for that chapter.

Page- and Screen-Level Locating Devices

Page- and screen-level devices that you can use to help readers locate information include:

- Headers and footers
- Headings
- Color
- White space
- Navigation tools

Figure 10.6

Three Positions for Headings

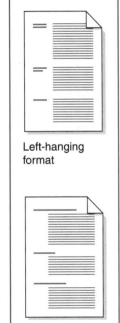

Left-hanging format

Modified hanging format

Flush-left format

Headers and Footers

Headers and footers help readers locate specific pages; they also may tell readers the chapter title and the division or part title. Figure 10.4 illustrates a header and a footer. Headers and footers can contain page numbers, chapter titles, chapter subtitles, division titles, and book titles. You can also use a header or footer on a screen or Web page. An effective screen or Web page will include an "identifying graphic banner" such as a header with the title of the Web site or the grouping of pages (Yeo 13–14). This information helps readers to navigate through the pages and locate information.

Headings

Look again at Figures 10.1 and 10.2. When information is grouped, or "chunked"—as it is in Figure 10.2—readers can easily locate the information they need. In the absence of "chunking"—as in Figure 10.1—readers have to read down from the top of a page or a screen until they find the information they want.

The device most often used to "chunk" information is headings. Headings help readers locate information on a page or screen and show the organization of information. Figure 10.6 shows three ways of positioning headings.

As you create headings, follow these design guidelines:

- **Generally, use no more than four levels of headings in one document.** Too many levels can clutter a document and even confuse readers.

- **Use more lines of space above your headings than after your headings.** For instance, in a double-spaced document, use three lines of space above the heading and two lines of space after. In a single-spaced document, use two lines of space above and one line after.

- **Always put a heading with at least two lines of text below it.** Don't leave a heading without at least two lines of text at the bottom of a page. Headings without these lines appear to float at the bottom of a page (see Figure 10.7).

- **Use different type size—and possibly color and type style—to indicate levels of headings.** Readers associate size of type with importance—the larger the type, the more important the information (White 95). (See page 212 of this chapter for information about type size and headings.)

Figure 10.7
A Floating Heading

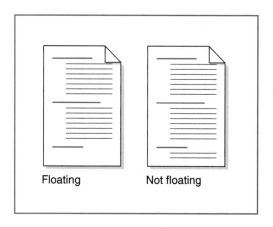

Floating   Not floating

Color

Color can guide readers through your document. Figure 10.8 illustrates ways you can use color to help readers locate information and guide them. You can use color with locating devices at the document as well as the page level. You can use color for the following locating devices:

- Headings
- Headers and footers
- Tabs
- Divider pages
- Navigational tools in online documents

Figure 10.8 Using Color to Help Readers Locate Information

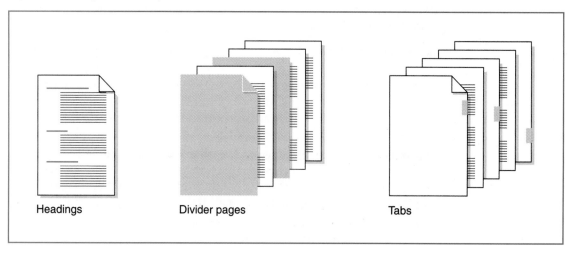

Headings   Divider pages   Tabs

Because color attracts readers' attention, use color to emphasize and highlight information, as shown in Figure 10.9. For example, you can

- Use colored bullets to highlight a list
- Put keywords in color to draw readers' attention to them, especially in online documents
- Use horizontal rules to highlight blocks of text or sections of a document
- Use shading within or colored rules around boxes that highlight a warning or a special note

When you use color, follow these guidelines:

- **Use the same color throughout the document for the same type of information.** For example, if you use green for the first-level headings in the first chapter, use green for the first-level headings in all chapters. If you use different colors for the same type of information, the colors will serve merely to decorate rather than to help readers locate information.

- **Use color along with other devices, such as white space, boldface, or type size.** Colorblind readers or readers with computer monitors that display only 8-bit color need clues other than color to help them locate information. If you indicate a locating device with color only, some readers may not be able to use that device.

- **Use colors primarily to communicate, not to decorate.** With relatively inexpensive printers, you can now easily add color to any document. Color attracts readers' eyes. If the color merely decorates, it may distract readers from the information you are trying to communicate. Color that is only decorative is likely to overpower the information.

- **Consider readers when selecting colors.** Some colors have different meanings in different contexts (Horton; White). For example, when many U.S.

Figure 10.9 Using Color to Emphasize and Highlight

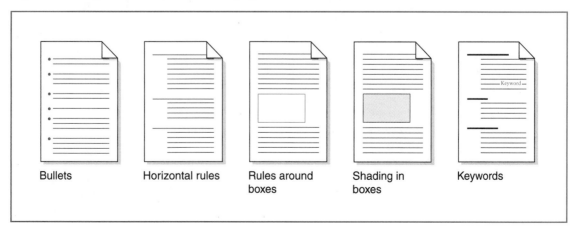

| Bullets | Horizontal rules | Rules around boxes | Shading in boxes | Keywords |

ISSUES IN CONTEXT

Using Color to Structure Information

Many writers think primarily about what and how much color to use, yet color may have even greater power in terms of where writers use it. When used as a key to information structure, color can help readers to handle more information and process it more efficiently (Horton). When studying how color interacts with the structure of documents, researchers have discovered that

- Color can help readers group objects, "taking precedence over other visual" cues (Keyes). Readers group by color before they group by shape, size, or other visual attributes (Keyes; Horton; Martinez and Block). In other words, readers see color as taking precedence over size, shape, or location.
- Color grabs a "reader's attention first *before* the reader has understood the surrounding informational context—where it is in the hierarchy, what type of information it is, or its relation to other text" (Keyes 647). Readers , then, perceive a color element independently of its surrounding text.
- Color creates a separate "visual plane" that differentiates and consolidates visual information (Keyes 649). For example, readers might separate color type from noncolor type. This separation helps readers to scan documents.
- Multiple colors distract readers because each color group forms a separate category that competes for the reader's attention (Krull and Rubens). Therefore, when selecting color, "less is definitely more" (Keyes 648).

When selecting color for your documents,

- Think carefully about what you want to highlight with color. Regardless of the information that you select, the readers will perceive that information first.
- Use different shades of one color rather than several different colors.

readers see instructions printed in red, they associate the red with danger. However, when they see the color red while driving, they know to stop. In business, red is often associated with power. In the United States and other Western cultures, people associate black with death and mourning. In some contexts, black connotes formality and power. People in China associate white with death. As you select colors for your document, consider what the color may connote for your readers, especially those readers from other cultures.

White space doesn't highlight the bullets.

White space highlights the bullets.

Figure 10.10
Using White Space in Bulleted Lists

- **Use color to unify a document or a series of documents.** Used consistently, color can unify a document or a series of documents. Throughout one document or a series, use the same color for the same types of information or visuals. For example, if you use blue for the headers, footers, and bullets of the first document in a series, use the same shade of blue in all other documents in the series.

White Space

Readers look for relationships among the elements on a page—text, visual aids, headings. Those elements should look as though they belong together; otherwise, readers may be confused. To create a unified layout, frame the page or screen elements with white space (Lay; Yeo). To use white space effectively, follow these guidelines:

- **Push related elements together with white space.** White space "pushes" page elements together (Lay 73–75), helping readers to see what elements belong together. For example, leave more white space before a heading than you leave after it, so readers can see clearly what text the heading describes.
- **Surround with white space any elements that you want to emphasize.** Simply surrounding elements with white space will emphasize them. For example, notice that white space surrounds the bullets in this textbook. The text aligns to the right of the bullet, not under the bullet, and the white space highlights the bullet. If the text aligned under the bullet (see Figure 10.10), the displayed list would be less visible on the page or screen. Set off elements such as headings, bullets, and graphics with white space to increase their visibility and allow readers to locate them easily.

Navigation Tools

For online documents, include navigation tools to help readers move from page to page and to locate information and pages. The most commonly used navigation tools are buttons and text. Place these tools at the top or bottom of the screen. They should provide relevant, descriptive links to other places in the document (Yeo 13). You can also include a button that brings readers back to the home page or the main menu page. Always place these tools in the same position on the screen, and be sure that they have the same design throughout the document.

PRINCIPLE 4: CHOOSE DESIGN ELEMENTS TO HELP READERS READ YOUR DOCUMENTS

As you plan, consider design elements that will make your document easy for readers to read. When you select the type in which your text will appear, consider the typeface, type size, and type style of each text element. The type that you select can "help or hinder" the readability of your document (Parker 47).

Appropriate Typefaces

Figure 10.11

Examples of Serif and Sans-Serif Typefaces

N

Times Roman
Bookman
Palatino

Serif Type

N

Univers
Gill Sans
Helvetica

Sans-Serif Type

When selecting the appropriate type for your documents, you can select from two different groupings of typefaces: serif and sans-serif (see Figure 10.11). A **serif** is a short stroke or line at the top or bottom of a letter. In serif type, the thickness of some of the lines of a letter may vary, helping readers to distinguish the shapes of letters. In sans-serif type—type without serifs (*sans* means "without" in French)—no small strokes project from the top or bottom of the letters, and, generally, the thickness of the lines of a letter is uniform.

Follow these guidelines to select the appropriate serif or sans-serif typeface:

- **Use serif typefaces for paper text.** Use serif type for most paper text because the serifs guide readers' eyes from letter to letter; the serifs help readers to see the text "in terms of words and sentences instead of as individual letters" (Parker 60). Serifs and the variations in line thickness help readers to distinguish between letters with similar shapes (*l* and *I* for example) and to recognize the shapes of all letters.

- **Use sans-serif typefaces for titles and headings in paper documents and for online documents.** In paper documents, sans-serif type is difficult to read in long blocks of text and in small sizes, but small amounts of it can "add impact to a document," especially when plenty of white space surrounds the elements printed in it (Parker 61–62). Sans-serif type is effective for the text, headings, and titles of online documents. It creates a more readable screen than does serif type.

- **Use no more than two typefaces in a paper document.** Word-processing and desktop publishing programs offer many typefaces. Avoid the temptation of using more than two of them in one document. Limit the number of typefaces in your documents to two: a serif typeface for the text and a sans-serif typeface for the titles and headings. You can use a different, perhaps more decorative typeface for title pages, chapter titles, covers, or divider pages.

- **Select a typeface that is easy to read.** Your word-processing or desktop publishing software may offer decorative or script typefaces. You can use them for logos, title pages, chapter titles, divider pages, and covers. However, text set in these typefaces is uninviting and hard to read (see Figure 10.12).

Appropriate Type Sizes for Text and Headings

Type size is measured in points; 72 points equal one inch. Most word-processing and desktop publishing programs allow you to adjust the type size up to 72 points. When deciding what sizes of type to use in your documents, follow these guidelines:

- **For text, use 10- or 12-point type.**
- **For headings, use type that is no more than twice the size of the type in the text.** For instance, if using 12-point type for the text, you can use a maximum heading size of 24 points and a minimum of 12 points. If your docu-

Figure 10.12

An Example of Text Set in a Hard-to-Read Typeface

> What is your procedure if someone is out sick and do you have a substitute list? The school has a skeleton list of substitutes. Since good substitutes are hard to find, we see how the other classrooms look as far as ratios go. The younger the child the higher the priority—the younger the child the lower the ratio. We also would like to have a permanent floater that goes from classroom to classroom on an as need basis. We can also call the Springfield school to see how the situation looks over there. If necessary, we can bring someone over from Springfield.

ment has three levels of headings, you might use 24-point type for the first level, 18-point type for the second level, and 14-point type for the third level.

- **Make sure that the size of the headings is appropriate for the page.** Headings should stand out from the text but should not overpower the page.

Appropriate Type Styles

 With word processing and desktop publishing programs, you can modify the appearance of the type to create different looks in your document. With most word-processing software, you can use boldface, italics, underlining, shadowing, outlining, and reversed type. To use these type styles effectively, follow these guidelines:

- **Use boldface type to add emphasis.** Boldface type increases the visibility of headings and individual words and phrases. In paper documents, use boldface for headings and, sparingly, to emphasize isolated words in blocks of text; do not use it for entire paragraphs or more than two or three lines of type. In online documents, designers recommend that you reserve boldface type for headings (Yeo 14).

- **Use italics to add emphasis.** Italics also increase the visibility of isolated words and short phrases, though less dramatically than boldface. Avoid overusing italic type. Use it for isolated words and short phrases, not for entire paragraphs or large blocks of text.

- **Use shadowed, outlined, and reversed type sparingly.** These type styles can "seriously hinder legibility" and are especially hard to read in small sizes and in uppercase letters (Parker 67). If you use reversed type, use a sans-serif typeface in a relatively large size.

- **Avoid underlining.** Underlining interferes with readers' ability to recognize the shapes of some letters. It can distort letters with descenders—*y, j, p, q,*

THE READER'S CORNER

Typography

Typography—the design and selection of letter forms—began with the ability to print from movable type around 1450. The three major type families—gothic, roman, and italic—all were based on the Latin script used by calligraphers. During the Middle Ages, scribes throughout Europe had developed a convenient single-stroke approach. Dominant when the first printing presses emerged in Germany, this major calligraphic form served as the basis of the typeface known as gothic. In Italy, however, where the humanist movement celebrated the ancient classical writers and their emphasis on individual dignity, the dark, imposing gothic letters seemed inappropriate for new editions of classical authors such as Cicero. Admiring the rounded calligraphy used by the classical authors themselves, Italian printers developed a type they called "antiqua" to distinguish it from the "modern" gothic. Known today as "roman," this typeface spread with humanist thought throughout western Europe; Germany alone continued to favor the gothic typeface. The third major type family, italic, replicated the fast, informal cursive used by chancellery clerks; when it debuted early in the 1500s, printers used it, like gothic and roman, for entire texts. Within a few decades, however, printers judged italic more appropriate for specific situations (such as foreign words), a judgment with which most contemporary typographers would agree.

g—and marks of punctuation such as commas and semicolons. Instead of underlining, use boldface, italics, or color.

- **Avoid using text in uppercase (capital) letters.** A line of uppercase letters is hard to read (see Figure 10.13). If you want to emphasize a portion of text, don't use all uppercase letters. Instead, use upper- and lowercase letters in boldface, italic, or color. Text in upper- and lowercase letters is easier to read than text printed in uppercase letters. Lowercase letters take up less space, so readers can "take in more words as they scan a line of text"; and lowercase letters give each word a distinct shape, which helps readers to recognize and recall (Benson 41). Shape helps readers distinguish letters and identify words (Felker et al. 87). As Figure 10.13 shows, all words set in uppercase letters have the same basic shape or outline, but words set in lowercase or in both upper- and lowercase letters have different shapes. The uniform shape of words set in uppercase letters slows readers' ability to recognize each word. Figure 10.13 also shows that text set in uppercase letters takes up more space than does text set in both upper- and lowercase letters.

Figure 10.13

A Comparison of Text Set in Uppercase Letters and Text Set in Upper- and Lowercase Letters

> IF YOU WANT TO EMPHASIZE A PORTION OF TEXT, DON'T USE ALL UPPERCASE LETTERS. INSTEAD, USE UPPER- AND LOWERCASE LETTERS IN BOLDFACE, ITALICS, OR COLOR. TEXT PRINTED IN UPPERCASE LETTERS IS HARDER TO READ.
>
> If you want to emphasize a portion of text, don't use all uppercase letters. Instead, use upper- and lowercase letters in boldface, italic, or color. Text printed in uppercase letters is harder to read.

Change type style with discretion and consistency. These styles can improve your documents' appearance by providing "visual relief in an otherwise uniform page of text" (Felker et al. 72). However, if overused, these type styles can clutter the page or screen, confuse readers, and fail to focus readers' attention on what you intended to communicate.

Unjustified Text and Ragged Right Margins

When lines of text are of different lengths and do not align on the right, the text is *unjustified* or *ragged*. When lines of text are equal in length, the text is said to be *justified*, and the right margin *even* (see Figure 10.14). Readers generally find unjustified text easier to read (Benson 41). Moving from one line to the next is easier when line lengths vary. When text is justified, the lines all look the same, and readers can't easily distinguish one line from the next and may find their eyes moving to the wrong line as they read down a page or screen.

The space between words in justified text is inconsistent. From one line to the next, the space between words varies so that all lines will align evenly on

Figure 10.14

A Comparison of Justified and Unjustified Text

> **Justified Text**
>
> Justified text gives documents a formal look; but it is harder to read than unjustified text, and the inconsistent spacing between words may bother your readers. Unjustified text gives documents a more open look. The unequal line lengths of unjustified text help readers to move smoothly from line to line and eliminate the inconsistent spacing associated with justified text.
>
> **Unjustified Text**
>
> Justified text gives documents a formal look; but it is harder to read than unjustified text, and the inconsistent spacing between words may bother your readers. Unjustified text gives documents a more open look. The unequal line lengths of unjustified text help readers to move smoothly from line to line and eliminate the inconsistent spacing associated with justified text.

the right side of the page or screen. This inconsistent spacing can slow reading and make readers wonder whether a word is missing. In the justified example in Figure 10.14, notice the inconsistent spacing between words and the uniformity in line lengths. In the unjustified example in the figure, notice the uniform spacing between words and the open look that results when the text is unjustified and the right margin is ragged.

CONCLUSION

With the tremendous options available for designing documents with word-processing and desktop publishing programs, you may want to use a wide assortment of design options such as various page layouts, heading styles, typefaces, type appearances, and type sizes in one document. However, if you use too many of these options or overuse any one of them, you will weaken your document and perhaps even cause your document not to achieve its intended purpose.

Good design does not call attention to itself; it is invisible to readers. You want readers to notice what you are trying to communicate. If readers primarily notice your design, then your design may not be simple enough. To create simple, effective designs, consistently use a carefully selected page layout with appropriate "white space" and select effective and appropriate heading styles, typefaces, and type sizes.

WORKSHEET for Designing Reader-Oriented Documents

Principle 1: Consider the Design as You Plan Your Documents

- Have you developed a style sheet and a prototype page, especially for collaborative documents?
- Have you appropriately planned for visual categories to help readers scan the document?

Principle 2: Choose Design Elements to Motivate Readers to Read

- Have you selected an engaging, appropriate cover for a paper document, opening page for a Web site, or first screen for an online document?
- Have you selected an appropriate binding for long paper documents?
- Have you used good-quality paper?
- Have you used the same top, bottom, left, and right margins on each page or screen?

- Have you used typefaces, type sizes, and type styles for headings and text consistently throughout the document?
- Have you put page numbers in the same place on every page?
- Have you used the same paragraph indents and spacing between columns, within lists, and before and after headings?

Principle 3: Choose Design Elements to Help Readers Locate Information

- In long documents, have you used document-level locating devices such as a table of contents, index, or main menu?
- Have you used chapter- or division-level locating devices such as tabs or divider pages?
- Have you used page- or screen-level locating devices such as headers, footers, headings, color, white space, or navigation tools?
- On the page or screen level, have you used headings, lists, and paragraphs to "chunk" the information for readers?
- Have you used the same color throughout the document for the same type of information?
- Have you used elements besides color to emphasize the information so colorblind readers or readers with computer monitors that display only 8-bit color can locate information?
- Have you emphasized page or screen items by surrounding them with white space?

Principle 4: Choose Design Elements to Help Readers Read Your Documents

- Have you used a serif typeface for the text of paper documents? Have you used a sans-serif typeface for online documents?
- Have you used no more than two typefaces in paper documents?
- Have you selected a typeface that is easy to read?
- Have you used 10- or 12-point type for the text?
- Have you used type styles, such as boldface and italics, effectively and consistently?
- Have you used unjustified text and ragged right margins?

EXERCISES

1. Find a paper or online document that has an *ineffective* design. Look for such documents on the Internet, on campus, at home, or at work. Write a memo to your instructor explaining the problems with the design. With your memo, include a photocopy or printout of the document.

2. Revise two pages of the ineffective document that you found for Exercise 1. Be sure to correct the design problems that you identified in your memo for Exercise 1.

3. Write a memo to your instructor describing and then evaluating the design of the technical report "What You Can Do About Lyme Disease," reproduced in Figure 10.15.

4. Revise the page design of "What You Can Do About Lyme Disease." Rewrite any passages necessary to improve the report. Be sure to correct any of the problems that you identified in your memo for Exercise 3 and any style errors.

5. Write a memo to your classmates describing the typeface, type size, type style, color, and other design options available on the word-processing software that you use or that is available for students at your college or university.

6. Working with a team assigned by your instructor, redesign the format of "The Disabled Student in the Classroom: A Faculty Guide," reproduced in Figure 10.16, or the format of a document that your instructor gives you. Your instructor has a disk copy of the document in Figure 10.16. To complete this exercise, follow these steps:

- Step 1: Organize your team.
  - a. Select a team leader to serve as managing editor of the project. The managing editor is responsible for communicating with your instructor, handing in the final document, assigning tasks when necessary, and proofreading the final document.
  - b. Exchange telephone numbers and/or e-mail addresses.
- Step 2: Plan the design of the document.
  - a. Make a list of the design problems that you need to solve.
  - b. Create a style sheet for redesigning the document.
  - c. Create a prototype page for the redesigned document. Ask your instructor to critique this page. Then revise the design as needed.
- Step 3: Using the style sheet, rewrite the document.
  - a. Correct any style errors in the original document. Be sure to eliminate inappropriate or insensitive language. (If you are unsure of the language, check with the disability accommodation office on your campus.)
  - b. Hand in your rewritten document to your instructor.

Figure 10.15 The Document for Exercises 3 and 4

WHAT YOU CAN DO ABOUT LYME DISEASE

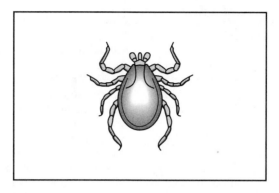

Figure 1. *Ixodes scapularis, the black-legged tick, is a suspected vector of Lyme disease in Texas.*

Like buckling up when you enter a car, there are certain positive safety measures you can take to reduce the probability of being exposed to ticks and the new summertime disease known as Lyme disease. Use of repellents, wearing proper clothing, and knowing how to spot and remove ticks before they become firmly attached, are all effective methods of reducing the possibility of being exposed to Lyme disease.

Lyme disease, so named because it was first identified near the town of Lyme, Connecticut, causes symptoms that often include a circular rash and accompanying flu-like symptoms. If left untreated, symptoms can include painfully stiff joints and other neurological complications.

Lyme disease is transmitted primarily, if not exclusively, by ticks. Ticks are small arachnids, related to insects, and can be identified by having eight legs and a flattened, leathery body (Fig. 1).

Ticks feed on blood from a variety of animals such as birds, reptiles, raccoons, deer, dogs, cattle and man. Unfortunately, in the process of feeding on more than one host during its lifetime, ticks can act as carriers of disease organisms, carrying germs from infected to healthy animals. In the northeastern states, Lyme disease is transmitted by the deer tick, *Ixodes dammini*, from mice, deer, and other wild and domestic animals. Little is yet known about the wild carriers of the disease in Texas.

Although the number of cases in Texas is on the rise, the Lyme disease problem hasn't become as serious as in the Northeast and Great Lakes regions. Eighty-two confirmed cases of Lyme disease were reported by the Texas Department of Health, with the majority of these cases being reported from the eastern and northeastern portions of the state.

The best way to deal with this disease is to take measures to avoid being bitten by ticks. This means wearing appropriate protective clothing outdoors, avoiding tick-infested sites, and using tick repellents. When in wooded areas it is best to wear long pants with the cuffs tucked into the socks. Ticks typically hitch rides on humans from their perches on grass blades or low brush. Once picked up on a shoe, sock, or pants leg they climb upwards until they find a suitable place to attach. Tucking pants legs into the sock eliminates

Figure 10.15 (cont.)

one of the most popular sites for ticks to gain access to the skin. Use of repellents such as diethyl toluamide (DEET), the active ingredient in OFF® and most other commercial insect repellents, will give some protection from ticks. Newer repellents containing permethrin, which are applied to the clothing, both repel and kill ticks before they can attach.

You should carefully examine yourself and other family members following an outdoor activity in potentially tick-infested sites. Carrying a roll of masking tape on outings is handy for removing ticks that have not yet attached to the skin. Pressing the sticky side of the tape on the crawling tick should easily remove it from the skin.

Should you find a tick attached to the skin, the following procedures should be used for removal:

Use blunt tweezers or disposable gloves to handle the tick. If fingers must be used, shield them with a tissue or paper towel. Infectious agents may be picked up through mucous membranes or breaks in the skin by handling infected ticks. This is especially important for people who "detick" pets or other domestic animals, as ticks infesting dogs and other domestic animals can carry Lyme disease or several other diseases capable of infecting humans.

Grasp the tick as close to the skin surface as possible. This reduces the possibility of the head detaching from the body upon removal.

Pull the tick straight out with a steady, even pressure. Do not twist or jerk the tick as this may cause the mouthparts to break off and remain in the skin, increasing the chances of infection.

Continue the steady pressure even if the tick does not release immediately—it may take a minute or so of pulling to cause the tick to release.

After removing the tick, thoroughly disinfect the bite site and wash your hands with soap and water. Home remedies such as applying Vaseline®, grease, or a hot match to the rear of the tick are not recommended. These practices cause the tick to salivate and can actually increase the chance of getting the disease.

After removing the tick, you may wish to preserve it in alcohol—plain old rubbing alcohol will do. Be sure to label the container with information about the time and place where the tick bite occurred. This activity will help you to remember details of the incident if the rash or other symptoms associated with Lyme disease appear later. This information will also be of help to a physician in diagnosing the illness.

Fortunately, prompt treatment with antibiotics is very effective in curing Lyme and other tick-borne diseases, but most people agree that protecting yourself from tick bites in the first place is the best approach.

Note: The information given herein is for educational purposes only. Reference to commercial products or trade names is made with the understanding that no discrimination is intended and no endorsement by the Cooperative Extension Service is implied.
D4 Misc. Leaflet D4001   4-92

Source: Michael Merchant, *What You Can Do About Lyme Disease* (College Station: Texas Agricultural Extension Service, n.d.). Used by permission of the author.

Figure 10.16 The Document for Exercise 6

THE DISABLED STUDENT IN THE CLASSROOM: A FACULTY GUIDE

FOREWORD
      Faculty response is crucial to the success of qualified disabled students who seek a college education. The extent to which faculty members provide reasonable accommodation for special needs—in effect, to make what is taught in the classroom accessible—is the determining factor in whether or not a student is able to complete a course or a program of study. Equally important, a student's future employment depends upon acquisition of a degree.

      Laws have been passed which require equal access to a college education for disabled individuals who meet admission criteria; in addition, the University has issued a policy which supports these laws. By law, the University must make reasonable accommodations for qualified disabled students. Individual faculty members must assist in making these accommodations in the classroom. Unfortunately, faculty members sometimes feel confused as to how to respond to a disabled student or overwhelmed by the responsibility of having a student with special needs in the classroom.

      In most instances responding to the needs of a disabled student requires little adjustment to the environment or to teaching style. With some flexibility and a genuine willingness to help, instructors and academic departments can find ways to accommodate special needs. The information in this GUIDE is designed to facilitate that process. Additional procedural help is available from the Office of Disability Accommodation, which provides a liaison between students with special needs and other areas of the University. Please feel free to call upon the office whenever we may be of assistance.

QUESTIONS FREQUENTLY ASKED ABOUT
ACADEMIC MODIFICATIONS FOR DISABLED STUDENTS

WHAT IS MY RESPONSIBILITY IN ACCOMMODATING THE NEEDS OF DISABLED STUDENTS?
      Academic departments (and the individual faculty members who make up those departments) are responsible for ensuring that their programs are accessible to disabled students. This responsibility covers physical access to the location where the activity will occur and modifications necessary in the format or delivery of information which would make it accessible to an individual with a specific disability. Each academic department should have in place a contingency plan which faculty members can follow

Figure 10.16 (cont.)

when disabled individuals request accommodation. Help is available both in understanding what is required by law and in devising ways to make the necessary accommodations through the Equal Opportunity Office and the Office of Disability Accommodation.

HOW WILL I KNOW IF THERE ARE DISABLED PERSONS NEEDING ACCOMMODATION IN MY CLASS?

Request that disabled individuals requiring special accommodation contact you after class or during office hours. Print this information in your syllabus. In this way you give students "permission" to approach you with their needs.

HOW DO I KNOW THAT THE ACCOMMODATION THE STUDENT HAS REQUESTED IS APPROPRIATE AND LEGITIMATE?

If the student presents to you a Special Accommodation Request Form, prepared by Disability Accommodation, you can be assured the student has provided the University with proof of a disability under the legal definition of the word. The type of special accommodation requested on the form will be one which has legitimacy in relation to the disability listed.

A student not presenting such a form or any other type of proof of disbility and whose outward appearance does not make existence of a disability apparent can be referred to our office to complete a request for service.

HOW CAN I BE SURE I AM DOING WHAT IS NECESSARY TO PROVIDE ACADEMIC ACCESS?

The most successful way to ensure academic access is to discuss with the student what his/her needs are. No two disabled students are alike. Only a personal conference with the student in which you discuss both the course demands and the student's accommodation needs is likely to provide both parties with a satisfactory outcome.

It is a good idea to put into writing what you and the student agree will be done so that there can be no confusion. If you have questions as to why the student needs a particular accommodation, feel free to call Disability Accommodation for more information.

SUPPOSE I DON'T AGREE TO PROVIDE ACCOMMODATION IN THE EXACT WAY THE STUDENT IS REQUESTING IT?

There are usually several ways to ensure that a student's special needs are met. All federal law requires is "reasonable" accommodation. If your way meets that criterion in light of the student's handicapping condition, you have complied with the law. However, if the objection stems from the student's use of an assistive device necessary to compensate for his/her disability (tape recorder, etc.), federal law may require that it be allowed. You may, however, require the student to complete an agreement which covers problems you envision with the device (such as not releasing the tape recording or transcription, allowing you to erase tapes, etc.). A model form for such an agreement is available in the Office of Disability Accommodation.

AM I BEING ASKED TO COMPROMISE ACADEMIC STANDARDS OR GIVE THE DISABLED STUDENT AN ADVANTAGE?

Definitely not. If the existence of the disability has been verified, the accommodation should have the purpose of providing an equal opportunity to the student, in effect starting the student on equal footing with others. To compromise standards or "water down" the requirements would not assist the student to acquire a competitive degree. The disabled student should fulfill all the essential course-related requirements; however, altering the format, substituting an equivalent requirement, or changing the method of meeting requirements may provide the student a more equitable chance at success.

Figure 10.16 (cont.)

BY MAKING CERTAIN ACCOMMODATIONS TO DISABLED STUDENTS, AM I NOT DISCRIMINATING AGAINST THE OTHER STUDENTS WHO WOULD PROBABLY PREFER SUCH THINGS AS EXTENDED TIME FOR TESTS, ETC.?

Technically, it may appear that preferential treatment is being given to disabled students; however, the objective of the legal requirement is to help the disabled student to compensate for a life function which is not the same as that of other students in the class. Through the accommodation we attempt to provide the student with the same opportunity that other class members have without special measures. The law allows, and in fact requires, that special needs be met.

WHERE DO I GO FOR ASSISTANCE IN MAKING ACCOMMODATIONS?

Disability Accommodation, Suite 318, Union, can provide information and assistance in dealing with many of the concerns you may have about accommodating students. While the office is not budgeted to fund in-class aids or assistants, we have information on many creative ways to accommodate students and can provide the instructor with information about how other institutions have solved access problems. The following sources also provide help:

* when the class must be moved to accommodate a mobility-impaired individual, contact the department chair and/or the Registrar's Office for available accessible classrooms. If rescheduling will solve the problem, refer the student to our office.
* when a special table or desk is needed, contact the building supervisor or call Inventory Control.
* when special equipment or special arrangements are needed, contact your department chair or our office. [Vocational rehabilitation services can frequently provide such equipment.]
* when copies of class notes or assistance with manipulating equipment is needed, ask a classmate to share a copy of class notes or partner the student (NCR carbonless paper is available from our office).
* if you and your department chair cannot find a way to solve the problem, contact our office for ideas and added assistance in seeking help from other sources.

WHAT SPECIFIC HELP DOES DISABILITY ACCOMMODATION OFFER TO FACULTY MEMBERS?

The specific charge of Disability Accommodation is to assist disabled students. However, the office serves as a resource/liaison for any and all concerns which may arise in relation to disabled students. For faculty members, the office provides informational pamphlets describing each of the major disabilities with suggestions on making classroom material more accessible for the student. In addition, the office offers limited adaptive testing resources as a service both to the student and to the faculty member.

EXACTLY WHAT DOES THE LAW SAY IN REGARD TO ACADEMIC ACCOMMODATION?

Section 504, Rehabilitation Act of 1973 (Public Law 93-112 and subsequent regulations), has several sections which deal specifically with academic accommodations. Part 104.43, Treatment of Students, states:

"No qualified handicapped student shall, on the basis of handicap, be excluded from participation in, be denied the benefits of, or otherwise be subjected to discrimination under any academic, research, occupational training, . . . counseling, . . . physical education, . . . or other postsecondary education program or activity." The regulations further state that students must be educated in the most integrated setting appropriate to the individual's needs.

Part 104.44, Modification of Requirements, states that modifications must be made to academic requirements to ensure that they do not discriminate against a qualified disabled student. "Academic requirements which can be demonstrated to be essential to the program of instruction being pursued [i.e. to the degree] or to any directly related licensing requirement are not considered discriminatory.

Figure 10.16 (cont.)

Modifications such as changes in the length of time permitted for the completion of degree requirements, substitution of specific courses required for the completion of degree requirements, and adaptation of the manner in which specific courses are conducted may be necessary." The regulations further state that tape recorders, guide dogs, braillers, interpreters, notetakers, or other "aids or adaptations which may be necessary to provide equality of access may not be prohibited from the classroom." Course examinations or other evaluations must be provided by methods or in formats which will best ensure that the results of the evaluation represent the student's achievement in the course, rather than reflecting the impairment.

Finally, the regulations state that "auxiliary aids or adaptations must be provided to ensure participation of students with impaired sensory, manual or speaking skills in classroom instruction or to ensure that such students are able to benefit from the instruction." These may include taped textbooks, readers, interpreters, notetakers, typewritten transcripts, adapted equipment, or other effective methods of making classroom presentations accessible to the student. The institution has flexibility in choosing the methods by which the aids will be supplied and can opt to use resources already available through state vocational rehabilitation agencies, private charitable organizations, textbook taping services, etc. Within the classroom, partnering the student with a classmate for lab situations and using volunteer notetakers, etc., are legitimate methods of making accommodation. It is not necessary to provide attendants, individually prescribed devices, readers for personal use or study, or other devices or services of a personal nature.

The Americans With Disabilities Act of 1990, signed by President Bush in July, is a civil rights act enlarging the scope of Section 504. It protects individuals with disabilities from discrimination by certain employers, by providers of public services (such as housing, transportation, communication), and by States, agencies, political subdivisions of States, or boards, commissions or other instrumentalities of States and political subdivisions. It provides legal recourse whenever disabled persons are denied equal opportunity to gain the same benefit, obtain the same result, or reach the same level of achievement as nondisabled individuals in the most integrated setting appropriate to the individual's needs. Qualification standards, selection criteria, performance standards or eligibility criteria that exclude or deny services, programs, activities, benefits, jobs or other opportunities to an individual with a disability must have been demonstrated to be both necessary and substantially related to the ability of an individual to perform or participate or take advantage of the essential components of the particular program, activity, job or other opportunity.

WHAT IS THE UNIVERSITY POLICY ON ACCOMMODATION FOR DISABLED PERSONS?

The policy states: "In accordance with Section 504 of the federal Rehabilitation Act of 1973, the University will make reasonable adjustments in its policies, practices, services and facilities to ensure equal opportunity for qualified disabled persons to participate in all educational programs and activities." The cooperation and support of all faculty and staff members is necessary in implementing and maintaining the policy, and in this regard, physical access to at least one section of course offerings must be provided as necessary; academic requirements which have not been demonstrated as essential to the program of instruction being pursued nor to any directly related licensing requirement are subject to reasonable modification (such as extension of time limits, substitutions, adaptations in format or presentation, etc.); and auxiliary aids must be permitted when they are required to ensure full participation and equal educational opportunity for disabled students.

SUGGESTIONS FOR MEASURING STUDENT PROGRESS IN THE CLASSROOM**

**Hartmann and Redden, Higher Education and the Handicapped Resource Center, National Clearinghouse on Postsecondary Education for Handicapped Individuals, Washington, D.C.

Figure 10.16 (cont.)

[NOTE: Suggested adaptations for day-to-day classroom situations are outlined in pamphlets for each disability area. Request the specific pamphlet you need from Disability Accommodation.]

Taking a test under standard conditions requires certain skills and abilities which are not a part of what is being measured by the test instrument. For some disabled students, the format of the test itself or the physical location in which the test is to be administered will constitute a discriminatory barrier to performance. The suggestions below (listed by disability categories) provide guidelines for adapting examinations to eliminate discrimination against disabled students. A discussion of changes appropriate for many students (adaptations in the test environment, extra time, proctors, etc.) is also included.

HEARING IMPAIRMENT

A hearing impairment may be caused by a physical diminution or loss of hearing ability or by a perceptual problem that causes the brain to process incorrectly what is heard. Such an impairment may cause the student not to hear or to comprehend rapidly spoken information such as procedural instructions, descriptive background, or questions posed by other students and answers given before the actual test begins.

ADAPTATIONS
* Student may be given written instructions or information ordinarily read aloud by examiner.
* Oral or sign language interpreter may translate oral instruction and information.

VISUAL IMPAIRMENT

A visual impairment may represent a physical diminution or complete loss of vision or the inability of a person to perceive what is viewed through the eye. Such an impairment may cause a student not to see or to comprehend written material which may include announcement of test dates, procedural information, and content of the examination itself. In addition, visual perceptual problems (which may include inability to discriminate figure or ground, sequencing and letter reversals, and similar shaped letters) may preclude comprehension of printed test materials and/or completion of a standard answer sheet or essay exam in the usual manner.

ADAPTATIONS
* Arrange for a special edition of the exam, i.e. on tape, individually read, larger print, or braille.
* Student may use electronic optical aids, such as a Visual-tek, which enlarge the print; or non-optical aids, such as an Opticon or a Kurzweil Reading Machine, which change the form of the print to be usable for people with visual impairments.
* Student may record answers by typing or taping.
* Student may dictate answers to a proctor who marks the answer sheet or writes the essay.
* Where spelling and punctuation are related to course objectives, student and instructor may determine a way for grammar to be evaluated within the parameters of the adaptation.

* * *

MOTOR IMPAIRMENT

Motor impairment broadly describes any disability which limits functional movement of any limb or fine motor ability. It may involve limitations in performing certain acts such as reaching and entering the exam site, sitting for long time periods, manipulating test materials (i.e., scratch paper, pencils, calculators, etc.), and transcribing responses.

ADAPTATIONS
* Arrange for exam to be given in accessible building and classroom; arrange for a lab assistant, etc.
* Arrange for a proctor to assist manipulation of test materials, marking exams, and writing numbers and/or symbols as directed by student.
* Arrange for alternative methods of recording answers such as typing or taping.

Figure 10.16 (cont.)

SPEECH IMPAIRMENT

A speech impairment may cause a student to be unable to speak, to mispronounce certain words, to speak slowly or in a manner hard to understand. Such an impairment rarely restricts a student in a written examination; however, depending upon the extent of the impairment, it may have a great influence on oral recitation types of examinations.

ADAPTATIONS

* Written examinations might be substituted for oral recitation exams.
* Student may write his/her response for an oral recitation and have that presentation read by an interpreter.
* Student may use an auxiliary aid such as a word board or interpreter for classroom participation.

EMOTIONAL IMPAIRMENT

An emotional impairment may cause the student problems in waiting patiently, controlling anxiety, remaining quiet in a testing situation, or exhibiting appropriate behavior during the exam. Most people have test anxieties which sometimes can enhance exam results. For some, however, stress is so severe that it not only seriously distracts other candidates but also prevents normal functioning on the part of the disabled student.

ADAPTATIONS

* Administer regular exam individually within the regular time limit.
* Determine an alternative task to be completed so long as requirements and objectives are suitably met.
* Refer student to study skills center or learning center to develop experience with various test formats for future exam taking competency.

HIDDEN DISABILITIES

Among the vast range of disabling conditions which are not usually visible or readily detectable to the casual onlooker are seizure disorders and other problems related to brain injury or neurological dysfunction; cardiovascular diseases; musculo-skeletal problems (from arthritis to back injury); respiratory disease or dysfunction (such as asthma and chemical or environmental allergies); systemic diseases or dysfunctions (such as lupus, diabetes, cancer, etc.); and learning disabilities. Some students with hidden disabilities must cope daily with constant severe pain, a high level of fatigue, or medications which may affect classroom performance. Because needs will differ widely, adaptations should be made in close consultation with the student. Specific information follows on the most common hidden handicap, a learning disability.

LEARNING DISABILITY

Learning disability is a documented perceptual handicap which affects the ability to process information in people of average to above average intelligence. Different individuals may have difficulties in one or more areas of receiving or sending information. These may include spelling, reading, handwriting, short-term memory, attending, organizing, following directions, spatial relations, math, even translating aural cues.

ADAPTATIONS

* Arrange for alternate methods of recording answers such as taping, typing, or dictating answers to a proctor who marks the answer sheet or writes the essay.
* Arrange for special edition of the exam, i.e. on tape, individually read, in large print, in essay form as opposed to short-answer or in short-answer form as opposed to essay.
* Where spelling and punctuation are related to course objectives, student and instructor may determine a way for grammar to be evaluated within the parameters of the adaptation.

Figure 10.16 (cont.)

* Allow student to use a dictionary and provide additional time.
* Allow use of a word processor with spell-check/grammar-check capability, etc.
* Permit test to be given individually in a quiet room without distractions.

ADAPTATIONS WHICH AID STUDENTS WITH A VARIETY OF DISABILITIES

TIMING

Some adaptations to conventional test formats require that the examinee be granted additional time to complete the exam. The act of reading braille or large print takes longer than reading a standard typed page, as does use of print enlargers. Similarly, listening to a tape or dictating an answer takes longer than writing answers in longhand. Extended time is frequently necessary, but there are no rigid rules for determining how much additional time should be given; extended time should flexibly permit reasonable progress without dawdling. Many instructors find that allowing the disabled student twice as long as other students to complete a test will fit most situations. Factors to be considered in determining a reasonable time extension include:
* type of accommodation (device? personal aide? other?)
* exam format (short answer? multiple choice? open book? essay? paper?)
* experience of the student (prior education or onset of disability?)
* purpose of the course (personal development? career preparation?)

TEST ENVIRONMENT

Ideally, students should be allowed to take an adapted test in the same classroom at the same time with the other students. However, if adaptation requires the exam to be administered in a place other than the regular exam site, efforts should be made to provide a setting which is equally conducive to concentration. Considerations include:
* free from interruptions and distractions
* adequate privacy for working with a reader, writer or such devices as a typewriter, talking calculator, or brailler.
* sensible and sensitive proctoring

A student should not be expected to cope with taking the exam in a hallway, library main reading room, or department office if phone, visits, or other distractions will be allowed.

EXAM PROCTORS AND ADMINISTRATORS

Objective test administration may best be assured by arranging for a proctor other than the student's instructor, reader, or interpreter. Having one's instructor administer the exam individually can be an intimidating experience for some students and could put the student at a disadvantage as compared to the relative anonymity of group administration of a test in large classes. It may be difficult to ascertain that a vision impaired student's regular reader or that an interpreter has maintained objectivity. Proctors who will administer exams adapted for various functional limitations may need:
* orientation in ways to read aloud
* practice in writing exactly what is dictated
* discussion of methods of maintaining integrity and ethics of the test situation

TEACHING APPROACHES

The following teaching approaches facilitate learning on the part of all students:
* Provide a course syllabus or other clear structure for course materials and assignments, preferably with due dates.

Figure 10.16 (cont.)

* Present material in more than one mode (e.g., visual as well as aural).
* Monitor the class to see how well students understand the concepts being presented, providing opportunities for students to clarify unclear points.
* Delineate for students an appropriate learning methodology for your discipline.

WHEN YOU NEED HELP WITH TEST ACCOMMODATION . . .

Most teachers prefer to administer their own tests for security reasons, and it is always desirable to test in the most integrated setting possible. However, it may sometimes be impossible for you to respond to a student's request for altered testing format, location, or extended time. When it is not possible to accommodate the student's special needs in a classroom setting and your department cannot assist you, Disability Accommodation can provide a proctored alternative site for testing.

Our staff is limited (two persons) and the space we use is borrowed from other areas. Thus, we must know in advance if you will need our services in order to arrange for an appropriate test site, a proctor, or to allow time to reproduce the test in another format. If you need our services, please give us as much advance warning as possible and complete an <u>Alternative Testing Permit Form,</u> giving us specific instructions, as follows:

a. Student name and social security number
b. Class and section number
c. Class meeting days and time (Tests will be administered as nearly as possible at these times; evening and Saturday tests must be arranged between 8 and 5, M–F.)
d. Dates for all tests during the semester for which you require our assistance (if known).
e. Special instructions for administration of the test, such as permission to use calculator, tables, reference materials; length of time the student may have to complete the test; etc.
f. Instructions for returning the test: (Can the student return the test sealed in an envelope immediately upon its completion? [We sign and seal it.] Will the test be picked up by a staff member?)

Since our staff is so small, we are unable to pick up tests. (Some professors hand carry their own tests; others send them by departmental secretary.) Once a Testing Permit Form has been filed with the test dates, however, you may wish to have the student bring over his or her own tests [sealed in an envelope] a few minutes before the exam time, if no special test preparation is required.

We want to provide as much assistance as we can both to disabled students and their professors. We are limited, however, by the size of our staff and must request your cooperation in order to serve you.

A FINAL WORD ABOUT . . .

<u>CONFIDENTIALITY:</u>

Information that a student does or does not have a disability for which special accommodation must be made is not a part of public information and must be treated as confidential. Every effort must be made to preserve the privacy of the student who needs special accommodation and to treat the individual with the same dignity and courtesy accorded to all other students in the classroom. Confidentiality requirements are dictated by federal and state law. Questions regarding confidentiality may be directed to the General Counsel's Office.

<u>EMERGENCY PROCEDURES:</u>

Consult the student involved for information on emergency medical procedures if a high likelihood exists that a medical emergency may occur in class. The student will be the best guide for what to

Figure 10.16 (cont.)

do. In any medical emergency, remain calm. If you need medical assistance, send a student to the nearest telephone and contact the University Police for help (dial 3000 or 911).

IN THE EVENT OF AN EMERGENCY SITUATION REQUIRING EVACUATION, the safe exit of every individual from the building will naturally be a priority for all university personnel. Students in wheelchairs and others with mobility disabilities should move toward the nearest marked exit. As a first choice, the wheelchair occupant or other disabled person may attempt to use the elevator, although in a fire, elevators will be inoperable. The disabled person may request help from others. If this is the case, ask the individual for instructions on lifting or moving [Must the individual be moved in the wheelchair or with other support? If so, where can the chair be safely grasped for lifting, i.e., handlebars, wheel rims, etc.?] If a power wheelchair must be moved downstairs, remove batteries before attempting to transport it. Make sure the foot rests and arm rests are locked. If a seatbelt is available, secure the person in the chair. A relay team arrangement may be needed. If it is not possible to carry the individual downstairs, the wheelchair occupant or other disabled person should stay in the exit corridor or on the landing in the stairwell. Exit corridors and stairwells are marked with exit signs and are protected with self-closing fire-rated doors. These are the safest areas during an emergency. Rescue personnel (Fire and Police) are trained procedurally to check first all exit corridors and exit stairwells for any trapped persons.

BIBLIOGRAPHY

Shaw, Robert A. "Dyslexic Students Possess the Characteristics of Self-Awareness and Deliberation That Are Hallmarks of a Liberal Education." The Chronicle of Higher Education, 09/19/1990.

Smith, Lynn M. The College Student With A Disability: A Faculty Handbook. U.S. Government Printing Office. 1982.

Source: Office of Disability Accommodation, *The Disabled Student in the Classroom: A Faculty Guide* (Denton: University of North Texas, n.d.). Reprinted by permission of the University of North Texas Office of Disability Accommodation.

CASE STUDY A "Disastrous" Design

Background

You are the manager of a large computing facility at a university. The facility employs approximately 150 employees spread over several buildings on campus and has equipment worth millions of dollars. You are responsible for the safety of the employees and the equipment. Recently, the facility lost some important equipment because of flooding after spring rains. During the flooding, some employees were injured and taken to a local hospital.

You want to prevent such damage and injury in the future, not only when flooding occurs but also when other emergencies—fires, tornadoes, bomb threats—arise. You decide to review and revise the "emergency situations" instructions that all your employees receive. As you read these instructions, you notice some design and style problems:

- Readers can't easily scan and find information.
- The instructions contain unnecessary information.
- The instructions contain many sentence and language problems.

Assignment

The "emergency situation" instructions for your computing facility appear in Figure 10.17. Your instructor has a disk copy of these instructions. Revise and redesign the instructions, creating a format appropriate for readers who will use the instructions in emergency situtations. As you revise, eliminate all unnecessary information and improve the style.

Figure 10.17 The Document for the Case Study "A 'Disastrous' Design"

EMERGENCY SITUATIONS

Emergency situations can occur from natural or man created circumstances. Prior consideration of actions to be taken during emergencies can help reduce the confusion caused by such disruptions. It is not possible to attempt to cover all potential disaster situations. The situations that will be addressed by this procedure are fire, flood, tornado, and bomb threats. This procedure is only intended to be a guide. Each person will be expected to use common sense in addition to this procedure to insure their own personal safety, and the safety of other personnel in the Computing Center as well.

ASSISTANCE NOTIFICATION

During any emergency situation, Computing Center personnel will probably need assistance from some other group in dealing with contingency problems. In order to ease personnel tension and help avoid confusion for all departments on campus, the Police Department has been designated to be the initial contact for all emergency services. Therefore, any time an emergency situation occurs (fire, flood, tornado, bomb threat, etc.), the first thing to do will be to notify the Police. In order to expedite a request for assistance, the Police Department suggests that the following procedure be used:

(1) Call Emergency Number 113
(2) State the situation. Example: "We have a fire."
(3) State the location of the emergency. Example: "In room 617 of the Administration Building."
(4) Reaffirm your desire for assistance. Example: "Please send help."
(5) Stay on phone as long as possible to give additional information.

EVACUATION RALLY POINT

Whenever it may be necessary or advantageous to evacuate a building, the problem of determining whether or not everyone gets safely out of the building arises. In order to verify that everyone does evacuate, Rally Points have been established for Computing Center personnel. When you evacuate a building because of an emergency situation, please go to the Rally Point as quickly as possible and check in so you can be accounted for. If you fail to follow this procedure, a decision may be made for someone to reenter the building to make a search for you. Needless to say, if you have evacuated the building safely, your failure to check in may cause injury or loss of life to the personnel trying to find you.

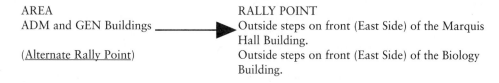

AREA	RALLY POINT
ADM and GEN Buildings	Outside steps on front (East Side) of the Marquis Hall Building.
(Alternate Rally Point)	Outside steps on front (East Side) of the Biology Building.

If you are at work but plan to be away from your work-station for an extended period, you should notify a coworker to that effect. That way, your absence may be accounted for at the Rally Point. Additionally, if you are at some other location on campus and hear of an emergency at the Computing Center, you should go to your designated Rally Point and check in.

FIRE CONTROL

In all probability, a fire from either accident or civil disturbance is the most likely emergency situation to occur. Most buildings on campus should have fire and smoke detection systems installed. These systems are tied in with the buildings' electrical system with battery backup for operation during power outages. In addition to fire and smoke sensors located throughout a building, fire alarms can be

Figure 10.17 (cont.)

signaled by activating the emergency pull switches located in strategic places such as main entrance ways and designated exits. The alarm system should provide for automatic notification of a fire to the Police Department. However, for safety measures, a fire in the Computing Center should be reported by phone (113) to the Police Department, who will in turn notify the fire department. The Fire Department estimates a response time within seven (7) minutes from time of notification.

PERSONNEL SAFETY
        The most important resource the Computing Center has is the people that work here. Some of the activities listed below have employees taking action against a fire. The employees involved are expected to exercise individual discretion when making decisions on the proper course of action to take against a fire. The rule to live by should be, "When in Doubt, Shout, and Get Out" (i.e., evacuate to the designated Rally Point).

CONTROLLING SMALL FIRES
        Small fires usually do not need the expertise of professional firefighters to put them out. For our purpose, a small fire is defined as a fire that has not spread beyond its point of origin. When possible, an attempt should be made to control small fires by utilizing the portable hand held fire extinguishers, which are located in strategic areas of the Computing Center. Usually, a small fire can be controlled in less than sixty (60) seconds. The hand held fire extinguisher will usually be empty after one (1) minute of continuous usage.

In the Computing Building, there are three (3) portable fire extinguishers strategically located in the Input/Output Area in Room 633B. One is kept on the wall in the Forms Storage Area immediate adjacent to the main entrance door to the Input/Output Area. A second one is kept in the wall cabinet opposite the electrical panels that are installed beside the main entrance hall to the Input/Output Area. A third portable fire extinguisher is kept on the South wall adjacent to the East end of the Air Conditioning Unit in the Input/Output Area.

In Control Center, there are seven (7) portable fire extinguishers strategically located in the High Security Computer Room. One is kept in the wall cabinet on the South wall, adjacent to the HALON Fire Control Panel. One is kept on the outside corner wall of the Communications Room, across from the UPS Electrical Closet. One is kept on the East wall in the Lounge Area, adjacent to the Microwave Oven. One is kept on the North wall, adjacent to the West wall of the Forms Storage Room. One is kept on the North wall, adjacent to the East wall of the Disk Room. One is kept midway on the West wall in the Disk Room. Another is kept midway on the East wall in the Disk Room.

        In order to keep confusion to a minimum in the event of a fire, each individual must routinely practice fire prevention when on the job, keep informed of fire extinguisher locations and operation, know both primary and alternate evacuation routes, and always give top priority to personnel safety when taking action against any fire. If and when a fire occurs, the person first noticing the fire should take the responsibility to obtain the closest extinguisher and attempt to control the fire. Simultaneously, this person should ask another coworker for assistance in either controlling the fire, sounding a fire alarm, notifying the Police, and/or assisting in evacuating the building.

FIRE CONTROL PROCEDURE FOR COMPUTING BUILDING PERSONNEL
        The senior (I/O) operator will be the person expected to determine the appropriate action to take against a fire. If the senior operator decides not to fight the fire, or if an attempt to control a fire fails:

Figure 10.17 (cont.)

(1) Notify the Police Department (Phone 113).
(2) Sound building fire alarm.
(3) Evacuate the building.
(4) Wait at Rally Point for further instructions.

FIRE CONTROL PROCEDURE FOR CONTROL CENTER PERSONNEL

    The Console Operator will be the person expected to determine the appropriate action to take against a fire. However, even if the operator does decide to try controlling a fire with a portable fire extinguisher, this action must be taken within the guidelines of the Official Fire Plan for the Control Center, due to the HALON 1301 Fire Detection and Suppression System that is installed. The Official Fire Plan for the HALON 1301 protected zones follows:

OFFICIAL CONTROL CENTER FIRE PLAN (For the HALON 1301 Protected Zones)

In the event that the HALON 1301 Fire Extinguishing Agent has been released, the following steps are to be followed:

1. Personnel should not re-enter an area where the HALON 1301 has been discharged until the Police or Physical Plant personnel has given permission, even though the HALON 1301 is considered to be a non-toxic gas.
2. When notifying the Police Department, please be specific and state, "There has been a fire in the Control Center, Room _____, and the HALON Fire Extinguishing Agent has been discharged."
3. Notify the Physical Plant or Stand-by Maintenance to alert the Electrical and Heating/Air Conditioning Shops that the HALON 1301 has been discharged. Personnel at these shops have been advised that a HALON 1301 discharge is a priority item.
4. DO NOT ATTEMPT TO RESET THE BREAKER PANELS. The breakers on several electrical panels MUST be reset only by Electrical Shop employees.
5. DO NOT ATTEMPT TO RESET THE FIRE DAMPERS. The fire dampers MUST be reset by Electrical Shop and/or HVAC employees to restore air conditioning and return air to the affected HALON Zone(s).
6. DO NOT ATTEMPT TO RESTART ANY COMPUTER SYSTEM. All computer equipment MUST be checked for damage before restoring electrical power.

Source: Adapted from Computing Center, *Emergency Situations* (Denton: University of North Texas, n.d.). Reprinted courtesy of the University of North Texas Computing Center.

Chapter 11

Creating Effective Visual Aids for Your Readers

CHAPTER OUTLINE

You've heard the expression "A picture is worth a thousand words." Indeed, you can often convey information in technical documents more effectively and efficiently with pictures than with words. You can often use "pictures"—visual aids—to explain abstract concepts; those same concepts described with words alone may be difficult for readers to understand. How can visual aids help readers?

- Visual aids can support and supplement words. Visual aids especially help readers who are unfamiliar with the concepts or who want to gather information at a glance.
- Visual aids can summarize the information in the text and present the information in a different way to help readers understand it.
- Visual aids can present some types of information more quickly and efficiently than words. For instance, using a map to show the locations of coral reefs is more efficient than using words for conveying the locations.

Visual aids can support the words and purpose of your documents. For instance, if your purpose is to show readers how to exit a building during a fire, diagrams of the building with arrows marking the exits will be much more effective than a paragraph describing the location of the exits. In fact, many readers expect visual aids. Many expert readers, for example, expect tables and graphs summarizing the results of testing. Tables help readers to see relationships among test results or to spot trends.

Your readers are bombarded with visual information through television, advertising in all media, video games, movies, and the World Wide Web. Because readers are so accustomed to receiving information visually, they will respond best to technical documents that use not only words but also visuals to convey information. Many of your readers may demand a visual as well as verbal presentation of some concepts and data. Without the visuals, many readers may abandon a document or miss important information because they may not read page after page of text.

In most documents, however, you can't rely solely on visual aids to communicate information. For example, in Figure 11.1, the writers rely primarily on pictures to tell the readers how to open the window exits and the airstair door exit. The readers neither need nor want a detailed verbal explanation of these procedures. Nevertheless, the writers do include brief step-by-step instructions for these procedures. The pictures alone convey the message, but the written instructions serve to clarify if a reader needs more information.

To balance the visual and verbal elements, consider the needs of your readers and what you want to communicate. This chapter will help you to choose the most appropriate visual aids for readers and to strike the proper balance between visual and verbal elements.

PRINCIPLE 1: LOOK FOR AREAS WHERE VISUAL AIDS WILL HELP YOU COMMUNICATE

Think about the various documents that you have read or that you might write at work. Many of them probably contain visual aids. Visual aids can help you

Emergency and General Information

Window exits

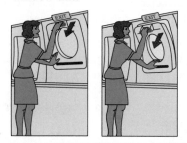
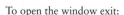

To open the window exit:

1. Pull the red handle down.
2. Pull the window toward you.
3. Throw the window out of the exit.

Airstair door exit

To open the airstair door exit:

1. Pull the red handle.
2. Turn the handle in the direction indicated by the arrow.
3. Push away from you to open the door.

Figure 11.1 Effective Drawings with Few Words

convey part or all of a message. Before you select a visual aid, consider what readers expect from your document and what they know about the topic.

Plan the visual aids early in the writing process. If you wait too late, you may not have the time or resources to create the visual aids that you need, or you may find that to add visual aids you will need to reformat the entire document (reformatting long documents or documents with intricate page design can be quite time-consuming). Instead, think about the visual aids as you decide what information to include in the document. Then you can prepare and plan for them before you write the rough draft.

Think about the different ways in which you can present information visually. As you learned in Chapter 10, you can use design elements, such as headings, lists, and page layout, to present information visually. In addition, visual aids help readers to understand information and concepts that would be difficult to understand if presented with words alone. Visual aids let you do the following:

- Show how to follow instructions or explain a process
- Show what something looks like
- Show and summarize relationships among data
- Emphasize and reinforce information
- Show how something is organized
- Simplify complicated concepts, discussions, processes, or data
- Add interest to your document

Show How to Follow Instructions or Explain a Process

Visual aids are excellent tools for giving readers instructions or for explaining a process. Many instructions without visual aids are hard to follow. For example, imagine trying to learn how to do a partial curl-up (sometimes called a crunch) for the first time without a visual demonstration or pictures. Without a demonstration or pictures, these curl-ups—for most of us—would be difficult to do correctly. With pictures, it is relatively easy to learn (see Figure 11.2). Many readers could follow most of the instructions without referring to the written instructions.

Visual aids also help readers to visualize processes. Figure 11.3 illustrates the launch sequence of the Centaur shuttle. This diagram helps readers to visualize events that they cannot see from Earth.

Show What Something Looks Like

Visual aids such as photographs and drawings are excellent techniques for helping readers to see what something looks like. Often, including a visual aid is the only way to help readers visualize a concept, theory, or object. For example, Figure 11.4 is a digitized color photograph of an erupting volcano on Io, one of Jupiter's moons. This photograph helps scientists to study the amount of gas and dust in the eruption. The drawings easily illustrate differences for the amateur. Figure 11.5 shows a photograph of Whip coral. Each of these visual aids helps readers to quickly grasp a concept or to visualize something.

Figure 11.2
Drawings That Help
Readers Follow
Instructions

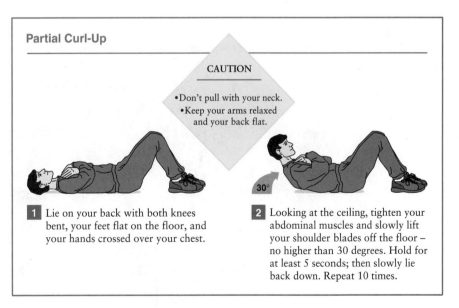

Source: Adapted from *The Fit Back Workout* (Daly City, CA: Krames Communications, 1990) 10.

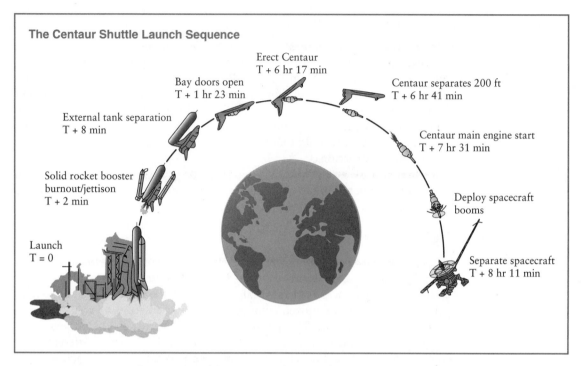

Figure 11.3
A Diagram That
Shows a Process

Source: National Aeronautics and Space Administration, *Galileo: Exploration of Jupiter's System* (Washington: GPO, 1985) 8.

Figure 11.4
An Illustration That
Shows What
Something Looks Like

Volcano Erupting on Io *(Photri)*

Figure 11.5
A Photograph That
Shows What
Something Looks Like

Red Whip Coral *(Peter/Stef Lamberti/Tony Stone Images)*

Show and Summarize Relationships Among Data

In some documents, you may want to display numerical data or show how one set of data relates to another. Perhaps you want to show the results of a laboratory test, a survey, or a trend or other changes over time. Visual aids permit readers to quickly see the relationships among the data.

You can use several types of visual aids to show relationships among numerical data. Figure 11.6 is a line graph that illustrates the dramatic change in enrollment at Baylor University after the signing of the GI Bill in 1944. Simply mentioning the numbers in a paragraph would not adequately convey the scope of the change. Figure 11.7 is a table that shows the dropout and retention rates among sixteen- to twenty-four-year-olds in the United States. The table allows readers to see the dropout and retention data divided according to family income.

Figure 11.6

A Line Graph That
Shows Relationships
Among Numerical
Data

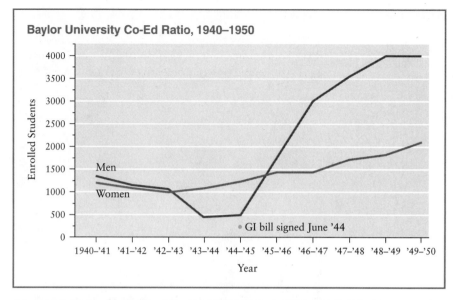

Source: Judy Henderson Prather, "The G.I. Bill," *The Baylor Line* 57.1 (1995): 36. Reprinted by permission of *The Baylor Line*.

Figure 11.7

A Table Summarizing
Numerical Data

Dropout and Retention Rates of 16- to 24-Year-Olds, by Family Income: 1992

Student characteristic	Percent retained in one or more grades	Total	Dropout rate[1] Never retained	Retained
Total	11.5	11.0	9.4	19.8
Family Income[2]				
Low	16.5	24.6	22.6	33.2
Middle	11.3	10.1	8.6	16.6
High	7.8	2.3	1.5	8.5

[1]The percentage who are not enrolled in school and who have not received a high school diploma or equivalency credential.
[2]Low income is the bottom 20 percent of all family incomes; high income is the top 20 percent of all family incomes; and middle income is the 60 percent in-between.

Source: Dept. of Education, Office of Educational Research and Improvement, *The Condition of Education*, NCES 94–149 (Washington: GPO, 1994) 30.

Emphasize and Reinforce Information

You can use any type of visual aid to emphasize information presented in the text. Your choice will depend on the information that you want to emphasize or reinforce and on your objectives. For example, if you want to emphasize the findings of a series of tests on airbags, you might first discuss the data in a paragraph and then present the data in a horizontal bar graph or a line graph to visually reinforce the discussion. You might also display the data in a table and then reinforce the data in a bar graph or line graph. Let's look at a specific example.

In *Drugs, Crime, and the Justice System,* the Bureau of Justice Statistics uses visual aids to reinforce and to emphasize the text discussion. In their discussion of the handling of drug cases, the Bureau uses bar graphs showing that drug cases, like other criminal cases, drop out of the criminal justice system at various stages (see Figure 11.8). These bar graphs visually compare drug cases with other types of criminal offenses.

Figure 11.8 Bar Graphs That Emphasize and Reinforce Text Information

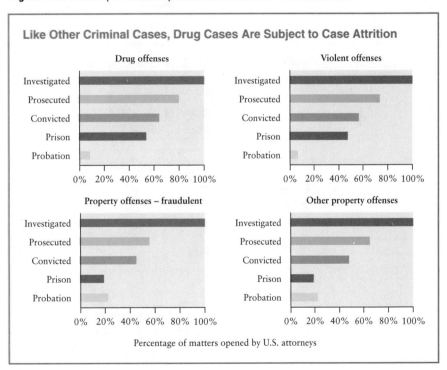

Source: Dept. of Justice, Bureau of Justice Statistics, *Drugs, Crime, and the Justice System* (Washington: GPO, Dec. 1992) 65.

Show How Something Is Organized

Often, readers need to know how something is organized; but they may have trouble making sense of verbal descriptions of organizational structure. Visual aids can make the organization clear. For example, the annual report of the chief counsel of the Internal Revenue Service (IRS) contains an organizational chart that shows readers the scope of the chief counsel's authority and responsibility (see Figure 11.9). The chart quickly identifies the three deputy chief counsels and the divisions for which each deputy chief counsel is responsible. Without this visual aid, readers of the annual report would have difficulty following a paragraph describing this organization.

Simplify Complicated Concepts, Discussions, Processes, or Data

Complicated information presented in prose is often difficult for readers to understand and analyze. The same information presented in a visual aid may be much easier to understand and analyze. For example, the scientists working on the Galileo mission wanted to show the stages of a probe's descent into Jupiter's atmosphere after being launched from the Galileo satellite. They used a graph to plot and briefly describe the probe's descent (see Figure 11.10).

Figure 11.9 A Chart That Shows How Something Is Organized

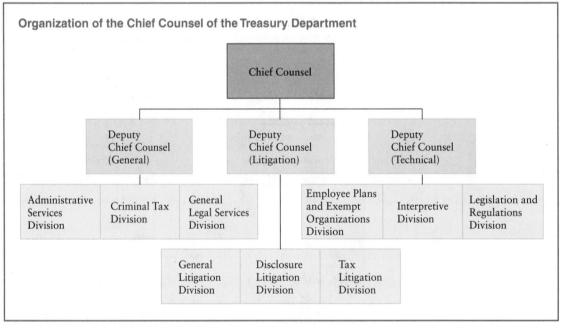

Source: Dept. of the Treasury, Internal Revenue Service, *Annual Report of the Chief Counsel for the Internal Revenue Service,* Publ. 1076 (Washington: GPO, 1980) 5.

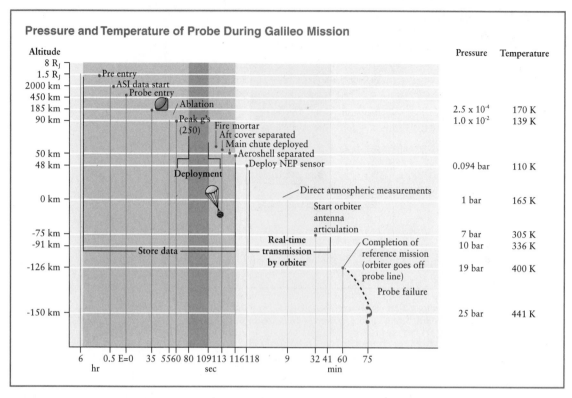

Figure 11.10 A Graph That Simplifies Complicated Information

Source: National Aeronautics and Space Administration, *Galileo: Exploration of Jupiter's System* (Washington: GPO, 1985) 87.

Figure 11.11 is another example of a visual aid that simplifies information. Writers at the National Science Foundation created this graph to show how the U.S. Department of Defense spent its budget from 1980 to 1994. The information displayed in Figure 11.11 would be cumbersome to present and hard to follow in paragraph form. The graph clarifies the information on the Department of Defense's budget and makes it easier to understand.

Add Interest to a Document

When used appropriately, visual aids such as photographs, pictographs, and decorative graphics can make your document more interesting and visually appealing. For example, when scientists discuss volcanic eruptions, they use visual aids—especially photographs—to show the eruptions and lava flows. To add interest to their discussion of these volcanoes, the scientists might include a photograph of Mount Etna, a volcano in Sicily, erupting (see Figure 11.12).

Figure 11.11
A Line Graph That
Simplifies
Complicated Data

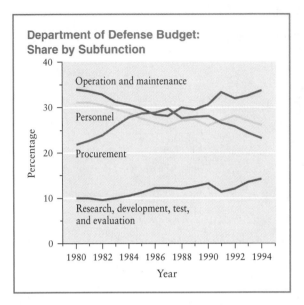

Source: National Science Foundation, National Science
Board, *Science and Engineering Indicators* (Washington:
GPO, 1993) 113.

Figure 11.12
A Photograph That
Adds Interest

Eruption of Mount Etna, Sicily *(Giampiccolo Images/FPG)*

Figure 11.13
A Pictograph That
Adds Interest and
Informs

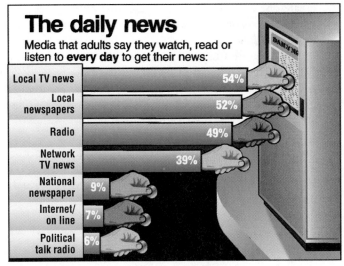

Source: USA Today 14 Aug. 1997: 1A. Courtesy of *USA Today.*

Some visual aids not only add interest but also convey important information. For example, Figure 11.13 compares the media that adults say they watch, read, or listen to for the daily news. The artist used bars proportioned to show the percentages for each media. On each bar, the artist added a hand holding a coin. This pictograph clearly adds interest to the document, but it also informs.

PRINCIPLE 2: DESIGN VISUAL AIDS THAT ARE CLEAR

Once you have found places where visual aids will help you to achieve the purpose of your document and you have determined the most appropriate visual aid for your purpose and your readers, you can begin to design effective visual aids. As you design, follow these guidelines:

- Use simple, uncluttered visual aids.
- Give each visual aid a number and a specific title.
- Consider whether international readers will read the visual aids.

Use Simple, Uncluttered Visual Aids

Your visual aids will be effective if your readers can quickly and easily understand them. Readers will quickly and easily understand your visual aids when the aids are simple and uncluttered. Therefore, include only the information your readers need; avoid including too much information. If you can't create one clear visual aid, try creating two or more visual aids to avoid overwhelming readers with one complicated, unclear aid containing too much information.

You can often use diagrams and drawings to eliminate unnecessary detail. Drawings are quite effective for showing the parts of equipment. Photographs generally have too much detail and clutter. Figure 11.14 compares a photograph and a drawing of the Mir space station. The drawing more clearly shows the parts of the space station.

Sometimes a photographer can take a clear picture by consciously excluding unnecessary visual information. Compare the photos reproduced in Figure 11.15. One of them is ineffective because it includes distracting information. In the other, the photographer has clarified the visual aid by eliminating the distracting information.

Give Each Visual Aid a Number and a Specific Title

Include a number (such as "Table 16" or "Figure 2.6") and a title with your visual aids. Numbers help readers locate the aids. Titles, or captions, identify the information in the visual aid. The titles should be brief yet informative phrases describing the content of the visual aid. Compare these examples:

Figure 11.14 A Comparison of a Photograph and Drawing of the Same Equipment

Mir Space Station *(Photo: NASA/SPL/Photo Researchers, Inc.)*

Figure 11.15
A Comparison of
Backgrounds in
Photographs

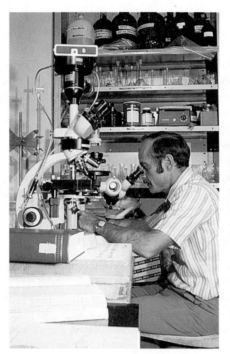 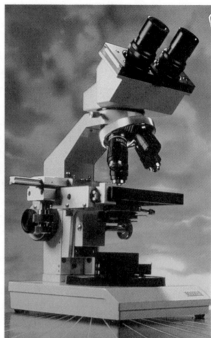

(left: Michael Collier/Stock Boston; right: Michael Tcherevkoff/The Image Bank)

Vague title   Figure 6. A figure showing inflation
Specific title   Figure 6. A comparison of inflation rates from 1984 to 1994

The vague title needlessly repeats "figure." The writer of the specific title uses "comparison" to indicate what the visual aid shows about inflation. The specific title also identifies the years that the visual aid covers, and it gives readers the information they need to locate a specific visual aid and to identify the information in it.

Within each document, number the visual aids consecutively. If you don't divide your document into chapters, number the visual aids consecutively from the beginning to the end of the document. If you divide your document into chapters, number the visual aids in each chapter separately, starting with number 1. The numbering of the visual aids starts over with each new chapter. In addition, include the chapter number with the document number. For example, you would number the visual aids in chapter 2 as 2.1, 2.2, 2.3, and so on, and those in chapter 3 as 3.1, 3.2, 3.3, and so on.

In most technical documents, use separate numbering sequences for figures and tables. Figures are all visual aids that are not tables. A document might have a Figure 1 and a Table I. Use Arabic numerals (1, 2, 3, etc.) for figures and either Arabic numerals or Roman numerals (I, II, III, etc.) for tables (Table 1 or Table I).

You have several options for the location of the numbers and titles. In the past when writers prepared documents with a typewriter, figure numbers and titles always appeared below the figure, and table numbers and titles always appeared above the table. However, with the widespread use of graphics software programs, the ground rules for placement are changing. Now, the placement of numbers and titles may vary from document to document. Decide where your readers are likely to look for the numbers and titles, or learn and follow the conventions of your company. Once you decide where to put the numbers and titles in a document, *consistently* put the titles in the same place throughout the document.

Consider Whether International Readers Will Use the Visual Aids

Because of the increase in international companies and the World Wide Web, you may create visual aids for international readers. Approach these visual aids keeping in mind principles similar to those discussed in Chapter 9, "Using Reader-Oriented Language." Visual language, like verbal language, differs from nation to nation and culture to culture. Don't assume, for example, that a visual aid that is effective for your U.S. coworkers will be appropriate for workers in Japan. Differences among international readers make drawings, photographs, and symbols especially problematic. Ordinary objects depicted in drawings and photographs for U.S. readers may not be so ordinary for international readers. Technical symbols that most U.S. citizens understand may be unclear or have a different meaning in another culture.

Before you put visual aids into a final document, consider how readers in other countries and cultures will "read" them. When feasible, ask people of the same nationality as your readers to look at the visual aids you plan to use. These people can help you predict the success of a visual aid or can suggest ways to change it so international readers will read it as you intend.

PRINCIPLE 3: SELECT THE APPROPRIATE VISUAL AID

Some visual aids are more appropriate for certain types of information and data than are others. Line graphs, for example, are more appropriate than pie charts for showing trends. You can use visual aids to achieve any of these purposes:

- Showing what something looks like (drawings, photographs)
- Showing how to follow instructions (drawings, photographs)
- Explaining a process (flow charts, diagrams)
- Showing or summarizing relationships among data (tables, bar graphs, line graphs, pie charts, pictographs)
- Showing how something is organized (organizational charts)

You also can use visual aids to emphasize and reinforce information; to simplify concepts, discussions, processes, or data; and to add interest to a document. For these uses, you can select any type of visual aid appropriate to the information and to your readers.

In this section, you will learn about ten types of visual aids and the uses most appropriate for each one. Figure 11.16 summarizes the most appropriate uses for each of the visual aids discussed in this section.

Bar Graphs

Bar graphs are excellent for comparing numerical data. Bar graphs help readers to compare and see relationships among data. Bar graphs use horizontal or vertical rectangles—bars—to show numerical data. The taller or longer the bar, the larger or greater is the quantity of the numerical data. Use bar graphs when you want to do any of the following:

- **Show the parts of a whole.** Each bar in Figure 11.17 show preferences among types of retirement investments by the age of the investor. Each bar is subdivided to show the percentage invested in stocks, bonds, and cash by each age group. You can also use a multiple-bar graph to show the parts of a whole. In Figure 11.18, multiple bars show the total amount of funding and the percentage of federal and non-federal funding for health research

Figure 11.16

Uses of Visual Aids

Type of Visual Aid	Uses
Bar graph	Showing relationships among data Summarizing relationships among data
Diagram	Explaining a process
Drawing	Showing what something looks like Showing how to follow instructions
Flow chart	Explaining a process
Line graph	Showing relationships among data Summarizing relationships among data
Organizational chart	Showing how something is organized
Photograph	Showing what something looks like Showing how to follow instructions
Pictograph	Showing relationships among data Summarizing relationships among data
Pie chart	Showing relationships among data Summarizing relationships among data
Table	Showing relationships among data Summarizing relationships among data

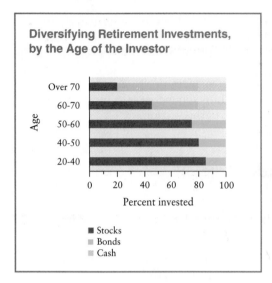

Figure 11.17 A Divided Bar Graph

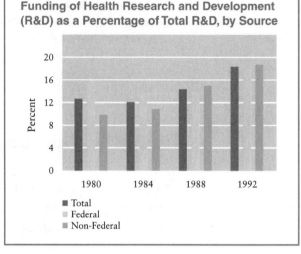

Figure 11.18 A Multiple-Bar Graph

Source: National Science Foundation, National Science Board, *Science and Engineering Indicators* (Washington: GPO, 1993) 105.

and development in the United States by year. In other words, data for each year appears in three bars.

- **Compare numerical data.** Bar graphs help readers to compare numerical data, as in Figures 11.17 and 11.18.
- **Show trends.** Bar graphs can show trends over time. For example, Figure 11.18 shows the changes in funding for health research and development from 1980 to 1992. (Although bar graphs can show trends, line graphs generally are more effective for showing changes over time.)

Tips for Creating Bar Graphs

- **Begin by creating the horizontal and vertical axes for the graph.**
- **Put tick (or hash) marks at regular intervals on the appropriate axis.** The tick marks should indicate quantities, such as percentages or amounts of money. Most graphics programs will automatically position the tick marks.
- **Use an appropriate scale.** As a rule of thumb, extend the longest bar nearly to the end of its parallel axis, as in Figure 11.18 (see the 1992 non-federal funding bar).
- **Label the bars appropriately.** Most readers prefer the labels at the beginning of the bar next to the appropriate axis. You can place the labels in a separate key (as in Figures 11.17 and 11.18), but this arrangement takes more time to read. If you decide to use a separate key, make the key easy to understand.

Diagrams

Diagrams are an excellent choice for showing a sequence of events or actions. Figure 11.19 shows the sequence of events in the criminal justice system after a felony has occurred.

Tips for Creating Diagrams

- **Sketch several rough drafts of the diagram.** Don't be afraid to make several preliminary drafts to determine exactly what you want in the diagram. Whether you use computer software or draw diagrams by hand, diagrams take a lot of time to create; so before you begin the final draft, you need to have a clear idea of what you want the diagram to show.
- **Use labels and explanations that explain the process clearly.** Labels should be easy to read. You can place explanations in the diagram if they won't interfere. If the explanations will be more confusing than helpful, you can explain the diagram in a paragraph that precedes or follows it.

Drawings

Drawings are excellent visual aids for showing readers what something looks like and for instructing. Many writers select drawings instead of photographs

Figure 11.19 A Diagram That Shows a Sequence of Events

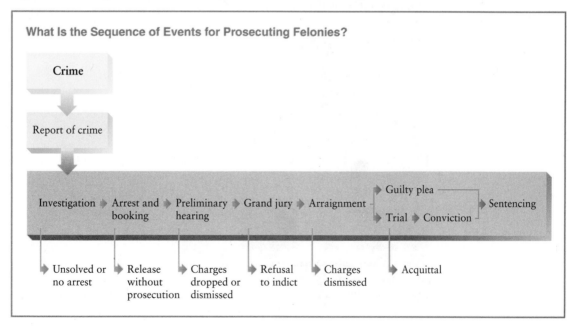

to help readers see how something is put together. Drawings can emphasize important details or parts that are not apparent in a photograph. Drawings also allow you to explode (make larger) a particular detail. Figures 11.20, 21, 22, and 23 present drawings that help readers to see details.

Tips for Creating Drawings

You can use computer software to create drawings. Learning how to use most of the drawing software takes time and training, especially if you are creating complex drawings like those in Figures 11.20, 21, 22, and 23. If you plan to use computer software, allow time to learn how to use it. If you intend to create drawings by hand, make sure that you have the tools and training to create drawings with a professional appearance. Also, follow these tips:

- **Render your drawing from the same angle that readers will have when they work with or observe the object shown in the drawing,** especially when readers will use the drawing to follow instructions. Figures 11.20, 21, 22, and 23 illustrate four angles or vantage points: a cross section, an exploded view, a cutaway, and an external view.

- **Use labels to point out significant features or details.**

- **When appropriate, make the feature or detail that you want to emphasize larger than it really is.**

Figure 11.20
A Drawing That
Shows a Cross
Section

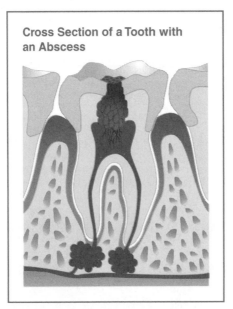

Source: "Tooth Repair" (n.p.: Whittle Communications, 1993) 2.

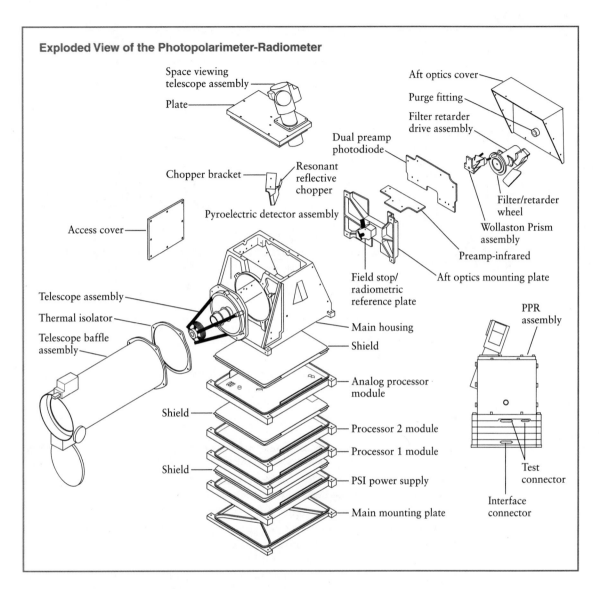

Figure 11.21 A Drawing That Shows an Exploded View

Source: National Aeronautics and Space Administration, *Galileo: Exploration of Jupiter's System* (Washington: GPO, 1985) 129.

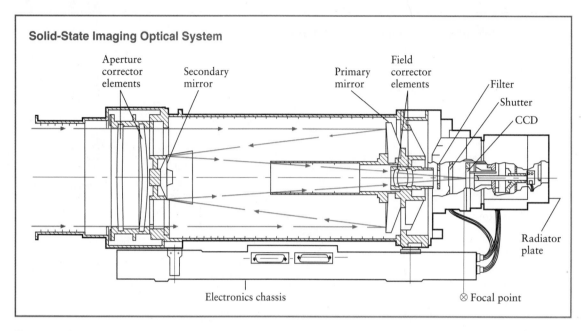

Solid-State Imaging Optical System

Figure 11.22 A Drawing That Shows a Cutaway

Source: National Aeronautics and Space Administration, *Galileo: Exploration of Jupiter's System* (Washington: GPO, 1985) 122.

Flow Charts

You can use flow charts to explain a process or to show a sequence of steps or events. Flow charts are especially useful for explaining a complex process that has conditional (if/then) steps. Flow charts generally work best for processes that have a definite beginning and a definite end (diagrams often work well for ongoing processes, such as recycling).

Flow charts usually consist of circles, rectangles, diamonds, and other geometric shapes that indicate the steps of a process. In some fields, various geometric shapes have specific meanings, and people in those fields understand that certain shapes represent specific outcomes and events. If the shapes that you use in your flow chart have specific meanings, make sure your readers will know what the shapes represent, or use a key (see Figure 11.24).

Tips for Creating Flow Charts

- **Make a rough draft of the flow chart.** By making a preliminary draft, you can make sure that the labels will fit inside the geometric shapes and that you have included all the steps. You may have to sketch several drafts to make sure that the flow chart is accurate and that the shapes are the right size.

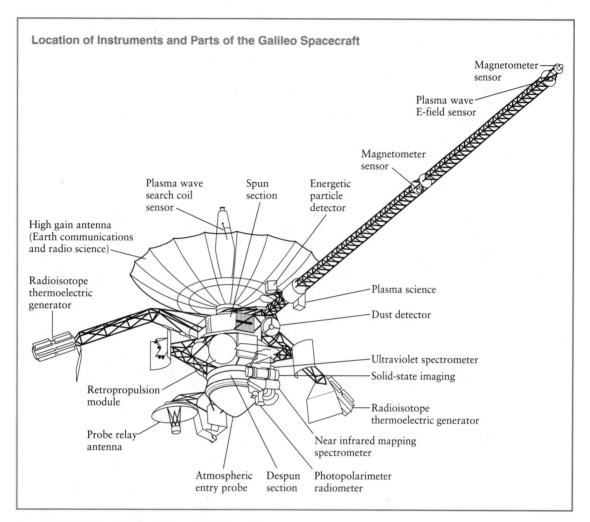

Figure 11.23 A Drawing That Shows an External View

Source: National Aeronautics and Space Administration, *Galileo: Exploration of Jupiter's System* (Washington: GPO, 1985) 120.

- **Put all labels identifying a step inside the geometric shapes.** The labels will distract and possibly confuse the reader if you place them outside the shapes. Make sure that the shapes are large enough to contain the labels, as in Figure 11.24.
- **Sequence the shapes so that the action flows from left to right or from top to bottom.** When the action flows from left to right and takes more than one line, begin the next line at the left margin.

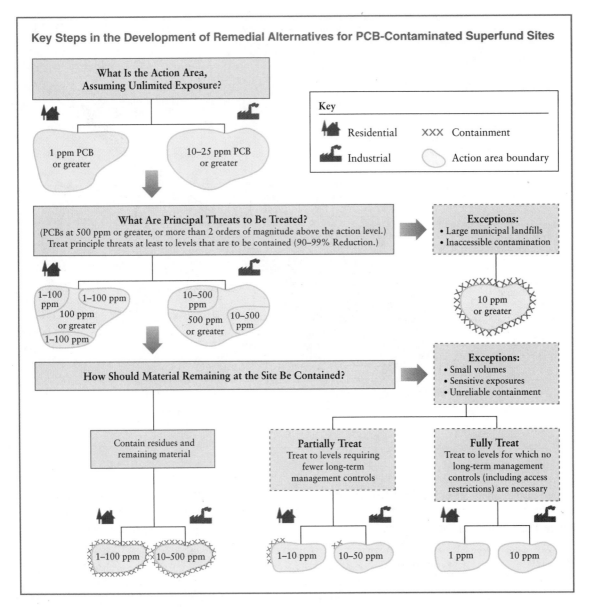

Figure 11.24 A Flow Chart That Illustrates a Process

Source: Environmental Protection Agency, *A Guide on Remedial Actions at Superfund Sites with PCB Contamination* (Washington: GPO, Aug. 1990).

THE READER'S CORNER

Visual Aids in Space

Launched in 1972 and 1973, Pioneer 10 and Pioneer 11 were unmanned space satellites designed to explore Jupiter and Saturn—missions they completed successfully. In 1986, Pioneer 10 became the first man-made object to travel beyond the solar system; it will reach the nearest star in 100,000 years or so. Would Pioneer 10 encounter intelligent life during its voyage; and, if so, what message should Earth send?

Together, Frank Drake, Carl Sagan, and Linda Salzan Sagan designed a plaque carried aboard the Pioneer spacecraft. Etched into a 6-inch-by-9-inch gold-anodized aluminum plate, the plaque tells of human life—where and when the species lived and its biological form. The top left of the plaque depicts a schematic of a universal "yardstick"; it serves as the primary code for two of the three major representations: one of the solar system and another of the Sun in relation to fourteen pulsars and the center of the galaxy. The third representation is of a man and a woman alongside the silhouette of the satellite (to provide readers with a sense of scale). The man is waving, a friendly gesture for humans that also clearly displays our all-important opposable thumb. The designers carefully drew the figures and physiognomy of the man and woman to be ethnically neutral, yet they didn't attempt to explain what may be a very mysterious difference between the two physical types shown on the plaque.

Line Graphs

Line graphs show relationships among data with more precision than bar graphs. Like bar graphs, line graphs use a horizontal and a vertical axis; but line graphs use lines instead of bars to indicate relationships. Line graphs are especially effective when you want to do either of the following:

- **Show or compare trends.** Line graphs show patterns of change over time. Figure 11.25 shows enrollment in pre-kindergarten over about a twenty-year period. Tables can present the same numerical data as line graphs; but, as Figure 11.26 shows, readers can identify trends from a line graph more easily than from a table of numbers. The table in Figure 11.26 contains the same numerical data as the line graph in the figure, but the trends are much easier to spot in the line graph.

- **Compare variables.** Line graphs can show readers how two or more variables compare under similar situations. For example, the line graph in Figure 11.27 compares the rocks at various depths in the Piedmont in Virginia.

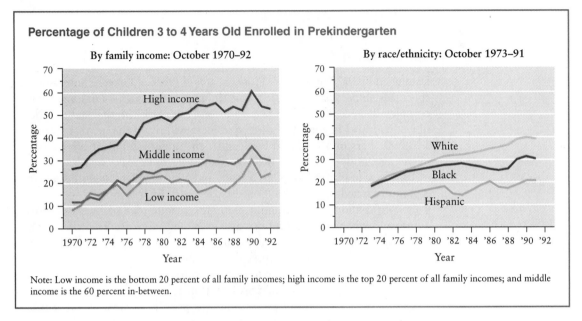

Figure 11.25 A Line Graph That Shows a Trend

Source: Dept. of Education, Office of Educational Research and Improvement, *The Condition of Education,* NCES 94-149 (Washington: GPO, 1994) 27.

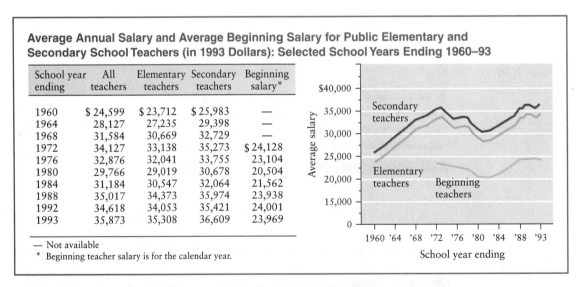

Figure 11.26 A Comparison of a Table and a Line Graph Based on the Same Numerical Data

Source: Dept. of Education, *The Condition of Education 1994,* NCES 94-149 (Washington: GPO, 1994) 154, 155.

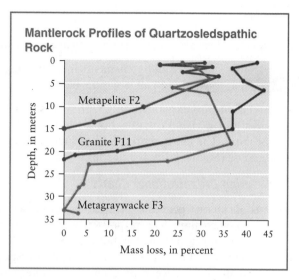

Figure 11.27 A Line Graph That Compares Variables

Source: M. J. Pavich, G. W. Leo, S. F. Obermeier, and J. R. Estabrook, *Investigations of the Characteristics, Origin, and Residence Time of the Upland Residual Mantle of the Piedmont of Fairfax County, Virginia,* U.S. Geological Survey Professional Paper 1352 (Reston: U.S. Geological Survey, 1989) 27.

Tips for Creating Line Graphs

Line graphs generally show how changes in one variable (the independent variable) affect changes in another variable (the dependent variable). For example, Figure 11.27 shows how three dependent variables are affected when the percentage of mass loss (the independent variable) varies. The independent variable always appears on the horizontal axis. Once you have determined the dependent and independent variables, follow these tips when creating line graphs:

- **Put the independent variable on the horizontal axis.** When time is a variable, treat it as an independent variable and put it on the horizontal axis.

- **Place tick marks at regular intervals on each axis.** Use the appropriate scale for each interval. Generally, make the tick marks short; longer tick marks can clutter the graph. The vertical axis should begin with zero. If it doesn't begin with zero, use hash marks or breaks to show your readers that the axis begins some place other than zero.

- **Label each axis.** Most readers prefer the labels centered along each axis.

Organizational Charts

Organizational charts are an efficient and clear way to show

- the hierarchy of people and departments in an organization
- the lines of responsibility in an organization

The same relationships explained only with words may be difficult for readers to grasp. Without a visual organizational chart, readers may misunderstand the relationships. The chart reproduced in Figure 11.28 shows the organization and lines of responsibility for one university.

Tips for Creating Organizational Charts

Organizational charts generally are shaped like a pyramid. The person or department with the most responsibility is at the top, and those with the least responsibility are at the bottom. Figure 11.28 indicates that the Board of Regents and Chancellor have the highest responsibility and that the heads of Payroll, Public Relations, and the College of Sciences have less responsibility.

Figure 11.28 An Organizational Chart

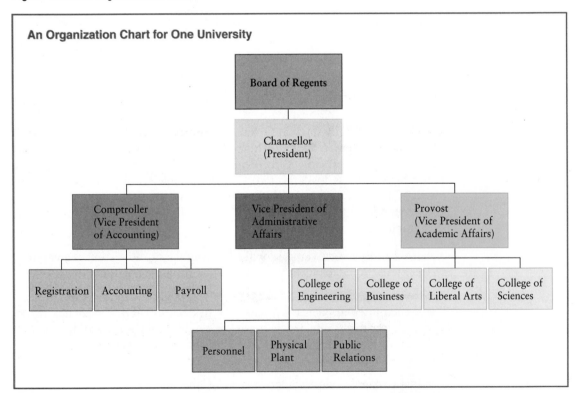

As you create organizational charts, remember that you don't have to include every person or department in the organization—only the people or departments that the reader needs to see. The chart shown in Figure 11.9, for example, just shows the organization of the deputy chief counsels and various divisions under the IRS chief counsel; it doesn't include all the people and divisions in the IRS.

Photographs

Photographs are excellent visual aids when you want to do any of the following:

- **Show what something looks like.** Often words are not enough to help readers know what something looks like, especially if they have never seen what you are describing. For example, if you are describing a piece of equipment that readers may need for an experiment, a photograph is an effective tool. If you are cataloging various types of sea life, you might use photographs (see Figure 11.29). Guides to various types of sea life in oceans around the world contain pictures of each type of sea life discussed. The authors want readers to be able to recognize the sea life, and photographs are the only practical means of helping readers to do this.

Figure 11.29
A Photograph That
Shows What
Something Looks Like

Leafy Sea Dragon *(Darryl Torckler/Tony Stone Images)*

- **Show where something is located.** You may want to show readers where something is located on a machine, a piece of equipment, and so on. A computer company used a photograph with labels to help readers locate and identify the parts of a personal computer (see Figure 11.30).

- **Show how something is done.** If you want to show readers how something is done, photographs are excellent. For instance, you might use photographs to show readers how a steelworker takes the temperature of a furnace (see Figure 11.31).

Figure 11.30
A Photograph That
Helps Readers Locate
Something

(Weinberg/Clark/the Image Bank)

Figure 11.31
A Photograph That
Shows How
Something Is Done

Steelworker Taking Temperature of Furnace *(Charles Thatcher)*

Tips for Taking and Using Photographs

- **Eliminate as much unnecessary detail as possible.** Show only the necessary parts and details.
- **Use an appropriate angle.** Take the photograph from the angle at which readers will actually view the object.

- **Use scanners and digital cameras to reproduce photographs or drawings for your documents.** With a scanner and its software, you can size photographs, eliminate distracting details that you were unable to avoid when taking the photograph, and integrate the photographs into your document.

Pictographs

Pictographs are similar to bar graphs, but use pictures or drawings instead of bars. For example, in Figure 11.32, lines of writing on a legal document serve the same purpose as the bars in a bar graph. As in bar graphs, the measurements in pictographs may not be as exact as those in a line graph. In fact, many pictographs don't have a visible vertical or horizontal axis or tick marks. Some pictographs are similar to divided bar graphs, but a picture or drawing replaces the bars. For example, the pictograph shown in Figure 11.33 uses a pyramid shape instead of bars.

Pictographs make your document visually interesting. They are especially helpful to nontechnical readers or when projected onto a screen during an oral presentation.

Figure 11.32
A Pictograph

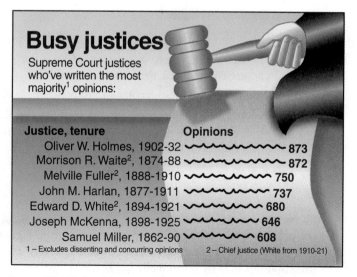

Source: USA Today 6 Oct. 1997: 1A. Courtesy of *USA Today.*

Figure 11.33
A Pictograph Similar to a Divided Bar Graph

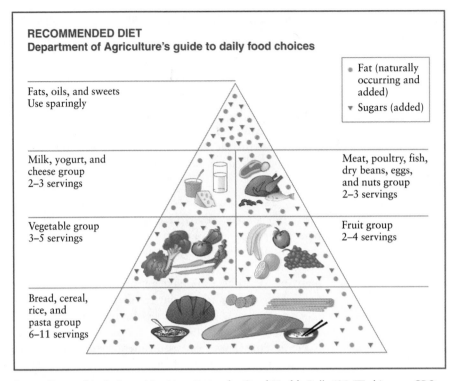

Source: Dept. of Agriculture, *Nutrition: Eating for Good Health,* Bull. 685 (Washington: GPO, 1994) 3.

Tips for Creating Pictographs

- **Use pictures and drawings that are meaningful to your readers.**
- **Use drawings rather than photographs.** Photographs contain too much detail and are too realistic for most pictographs.
- **Use color to enhance pictographs and to make them visually interesting.**
- **Label pictographs.** Even though pictographs are simpler and less exact than some other visual aids, they are not merely decorative. Pictographs need appropriate, readable labels.

Pie Charts

Pie charts are circles divided into wedges—like pieces of pie. Each wedge represents a part of the whole. The pie chart shown in Figure 11.34 demonstrates how a county spends tax dollars. You can effectively use pie charts during oral presentations and with nontechnical readers.

Figure 11.34
A Pie Chart

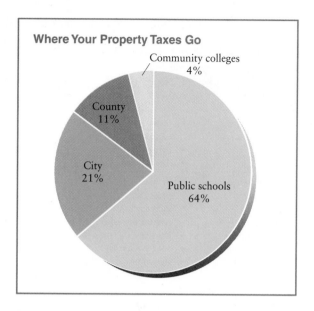

Where Your Property Taxes Go

Community colleges
4%

County
11%

City
21%

Public schools
64%

Tips for Creating Pie Charts

You can easily create pie charts with computer software. You can make them three-dimensional, or you can rotate them for a professional look. Also, follow these tips:

• **Label each wedge of the "pie."** Place the labels inside the wedges. If the labels won't fit, use callouts—lines drawn out to each label. Depending on your computer software, you may be able to pull out or explode some of the small wedges so that the labels will fit inside them.

• **Sequence the wedges from the largest to the smallest.** Place the largest wedge in the 12-o'clock position, and move to the smallest wedge as you work around the "clock."

• **Use color to make pie charts visually interesting.**

Tables

Tables present detailed information arranged in vertical columns and horizontal rows. You can find tables in many types of technical and consumer writing. For example, the labels of most food products now have a table describing their nutritional value. Many manuals use tables to present troubleshooting information, and many technical reports include tables.

Although writers most frequently use tables to display numerical data, tables are also effective for presenting information in words (see Figure 11.35). Whether your tables consist of words or numbers, they are likely to be effective when you want to do either of the following:

Figure 11.35 A Table Consisting of Words Rather Than Numerical Data

Drug type	Short-term effects Desired	Other	Duration of acute effects	Risk of dependence
Heroin	• euphoria • pain reduction	• respiratory depression • nausea • drowsiness	• 3 to 6 hours	• physical-high • psychological-high
Cocaine	• excitement • euphoria • increased alertness, wakefulness	• increased blood pressure • increased respiratory rate • nausea • cold sweats • twitching • headache	• 1 to 2 hours	• physical-possible • psychological-high
Crack cocaine	• same as cocaine • more rapid high than cocaine	• same as cocaine	• about 5 minutes	• same as cocaine
Marijuana	• euphoria • relaxation	• accelerated heartbeat • impairment of perception, judgment, fine motor skills, and memory	• 2 to 4 hours	• physical-unknown • psychological-moderate
Amphetamines	• euphoria • excitement • increased alertness	• increased blood pressure • increased pulse rate • insomnia • loss of appetite	• 2 to 4 hours	• physical-possible • psychological-high
LSD	• illusions and hallucinations • excitement • euphoria	• poor perception of time and distance • acute anxiety, restlessness, sleeplessness • sometimes depression	• 8 to 12 hours	• physical-none • psychological-unknown

What Are Some of the Effects of Illegal Drugs?

Sources: NIDA, "Heroin," *NIDA capsules,* August 1986: DEA, *Drugs of abuse,* 1989: G. R. Gay, "Clinical management of acute and chronic cocaine poisoning: Concepts, components and configuration," *Annals of emergency medicine,* (1982) 11(10): 562–572 as cited in NIDA. Dale D. Chitwood, "Patterns and consequences of cocaine use," in *Cocaine use in America:* *Epidemiologic and clinical perspectives,* Nicholas J. Kozel and Edgar H. Adams, eds., NIDA research monograph 61, 1985; NIDA, James A. Inciardi, "Crack-cocaine in Miami," in *The epidemiology of cocaine use and abuse,* Susan Schober and Charles Schade, eds., NIDA research monograph 110, 1991; and NIDA, "Marijuana," *NIDA capsules,* August 1986.

Source: Dept. of Justice, Bureau of Justice Statistics, *Drugs, Crime, and the Justice System* (Washington: GPO, Dec. 1992) 20.

- **Present detailed information in a concise, readable format.** With tables, you can present dense information in a format that readers can quickly read and understand.

- **Help readers locate information.** When you want to help readers locate information quickly and easily, you often can use a table. Confronted with paragraphs of prose, readers have to keep on reading until they find the information they need; in contrast, a table lets readers locate key words and information quickly.

Tips for Creating Tables

To create a table, put the information into vertical columns topped with appropriate headings, as in the tables shown in Figure 11.35. Figure 11.36 shows a common structure for a table. Some of the items in the table will not appear in all tables. You can use rules to separate the column heads from the table number and title (discussed earlier, in the context of Principle 2) and from the data in the body of the table. Rules can help readers to read across a table to find specific information. Place rules (or leave a blank line) after each grouping of information or after every five rows of information. Also, as you create tables, follow these tips:

- **Use computer software to create tables.** Creating tables with computer software is relatively easy, whether you use specialized graphics software or word-processing software. The software will generally ask you for the number of rows and columns you need. You simply insert the information into the rows and columns, and the software automatically formats the table.

- **Align the numbers and words correctly.** Vertically align columns of numerical data at the right or on the decimal points if the numbers are decimals:

Right-aligned column

$$7$$
$$11,890$$
$$789$$
$$8,900$$

Figure 11.36
The Structure of a Table

Table number →	**Table 2.2: Commission Option One**			
Title →				
Stub → Column headings →	**Year**	**Rate**	**Average commission** (month)	**Average commission** (year)
Row headings	1	19.5%	$3,295.50	$53,546.00*
	2–5	19.5%	$3,295.00	$39,546.00
Footnote →	*Includes signing bonus			

Source: Courtesy of Tonya McKinney.

Decimal-aligned column   0.23
203.78
33.90
3.00

If the table contains words rather than numbers, align the words at the left.

- **Label all units in a table containing numerical data.** For example, if you use percentages, dollars, pounds, kilometers, and so on, identify these units in the appropriate column head or in the table title.
- **Use letters rather than numbers for table footnotes if numbers may confuse readers.** In tables of numerical data, readers can mistake footnote numbers for mathematical notation. For example, 14^2 could mean "14 squared" rather than "footnote 2." If you think readers might misinterpret a footnote number, use letters: 14^b instead of 14^2.

PRINCIPLE 4: INTEGRATE VISUAL AIDS INTO THE TEXT

When you have designed and created your visual aid, integrate it into the text of your document. Think about how the visual aid supports and reinforces the text to create a meaningful document. To effectively integrate visual aids into the text, do the following:

- Introduce and refer to each visual aid by number.
- Tell readers what is important about each visual aid.
- Place each visual aid as close as possible to its text discussion.

Introduce and Refer to Each Visual Aid by Number

When you want readers to look at a visual aid, introduce and refer to it by number. Many readers will know that you want them to look at a visual aid, or know what you expect them to learn from the visual aid, only if you refer them to it. You can introduce and refer to visual aids in one or two sentences or in a parenthetical reference:

One-sentence introduction	As Figure 17 illustrates, heart disease kills more U.S. women than the next four causes of death combined.
Two-sentence introduction	Heart disease kills more U.S. women than the next four causes of death combined. Figure 17 shows the five leading causes of death among U.S. women.
Parenthetical reference	Heart disease kills more U.S. women than the next four causes of death combined (see Figure 17).

In each example, the writer introduces the figure by number and by content. Readers need both types of reference.

Sometimes you will want to tell readers how to use or read a visual aid or give them information they need to understand an aid. The following introduction tells the reader when and how to use a table:

> If you get an error message when installing the software, use Table 16. Read down the first column until you find the error message that you received. When you find the message, go to the second column, labeled "What to do when you receive this message."

Be sure to introduce and refer to each visual aid at the place in the document where you want the reader to look at it.

Tell Readers What Is Important About Each Visual Aid

Briefly explain the purpose of each visual aid, or tell readers what they should notice in each one. Readers may not draw the same conclusions that you drew, so state those conclusions to make sure that the readers understand the purpose and meaning of the visual aid.

For example, the writers of a scientific paper on women and cardiovascular diseases wanted readers to understand the urgency of studying these diseases specifically in women; so they wrote the following explanation of two bar graphs, one showing the causes of death among U.S. women and another the causes among U.S. men:

> Once a neglected field of research, cardiovascular diseases in women have rapidly become a major topic of scientific investigation. In 1994, cardiovascular disease killed more U.S. women than U.S. men and was the leading cause of death among women. Cardiovascular disease kills more U.S. women than the next four causes of death combined.[1]

The writers clearly state two important pieces of information that they want readers to understand after reading the bar graphs: cardiovascular diseases kill more U.S. women than men, and the diseases kill more U.S. women than the next four causes of death combined.

Place Each Visual Aid As Close As Possible to Its Text Discussion

Visual aids are most effective when they appear either on the same page as the text that refers to them or on a facing page. Readers may ignore a visual aid if they have to flip from the discussion to hunt for the visual aid elsewhere in the document. If you cannot avoid placing a visual aid at some distance away from its text discussion, be sure to refer to the visual aid and tell readers where to find it. For example, if a visual aid appears in an appendix, you might write the following:

---

[1] Beil, Laura. "Change of Heart: New Insights Gained as Cardiovascular Research Shifts More to Women." *Dallas Morning News* 6 Feb. 1995: 6D.

ISSUES IN CONTEXT

The International Language of Graphics

In the coming years, companies will increasingly use graphics due to the globalization of markets and of more widely used graphical user interfaces (Bosley). Graphics have several advantages for communicating with international readers:

- Graphics can "fit into space too small for text" (Bosley 5) and can "reduce the size and number of editions of documents" (Horton 682–683).
- Graphics can help a reader learn because they are less ambiguous. Readers find it "easier to see and understand than to see, translate, and then understand" (Horton 683).
- Graphics can improve reader comprehension (Horton 683).
- Graphics can replace some technical terms that writers can't easily translate (Bosley).

William Horton and Deborah Bosley suggest some guidelines for creating graphics for international readers:

- **Give graphics a neutral look** (Horton). For example, use a simple line drawing of a hand; the hand shouldn't appear to be masculine or feminine. Use outlines or neutral drawings such as stick figures to represent people (Bosley).

- **Use simple graphics.** Eliminate any unnecessary details (Bosley; Horton).

- **Use color only where the chosen color doesn't cause readers to interpret the graphic incorrectly.** The symbolic meaning of color varies among cultures. For example, in Japan, blue symbolizes "villainy," whereas in Arabic countries blue symbolizes virtue, faith, and truth. Bosley suggests using black and white or gray and white for international graphics, but Horton suggests that "color can prove especially valuable" if the writer carefully considers symbolic meanings (687).

- **Use graphics that don't have religious or English/North American connotations** (Bosley; Horton). For example, avoid light bulbs to indicate ideas or red, octagonal shapes to indicate "stop" (Bosley).

- **Consider the reading direction of the readers** (Horton). North American readers usually read graphics from left to right and clockwise; however, Middle Eastern readers read graphics from right-to-left in a counterclockwise direction (Bosley). Horton suggests designing international graphics that readers can read from top to bottom; the graphic might also include an arrow to direct the reader.

A large-scale map of the Bobwhite Quail habitat in Texas appears in Figure 26 in Appendix C (see page 51).

If you want readers to take another look at a visual aid that you discussed earlier in your document, you might write the following:

The nonspinning portion of the Galileo orbiter, discussed earlier, provides a stable base for four remote sensing instruments (see Figure 3.2, page 120, for a diagram of the orbiter).

PRINCIPLE 5: USE COMPUTER SOFTWARE TO CREATE PROFESSIONAL-LOOKING VISUAL AIDS

Several types of computer software let you create professional-looking visual aids: spreadsheets, graphics, and drawing software. With spreadsheet software, you can input data to a spreadsheet and then use the spreadsheet to create various tables and graphs. You then can import these tables and graphs into current word-processing software. With graphics software you can create visual aids such as bar graphs, line graphs, flow charts, organizational charts, and pie charts. These software programs make your job easy and your visual aids as professional-looking as those created by a graphic artist. You can easily import visual aids created with most graphics software into documents created with word-processing software. With drawing software you can create pictograms and drawings. This type of software tends to be more difficult and time-consuming to use and learn than are spreadsheet and graphics packages, but it allows you to create drawings and pictograms much like those done by a graphic artist or draftsperson.

You can use scanners to reproduce both photographs and text. Scanners take photographs and text and save these images onto a floppy or hard disk. Then with appropriate software you can manipulate these images. For example, you can make scanned photographs or other images larger or smaller, and you can delete background objects from a photograph. You also can take two different photographs and combine them to create a new image.

Computer software allows you to try out several versions of a visual aid before you decide on the final version. When you select the final version and pull it into your word-processed document, you can move the visual aid around on a page or within the document until you find the most appropriate location for it. Some word-processing software even lets you wrap the text around the visual aid to gracefully integrate the visual aid with the words on the page.

Although graphics software and scanners can help you to create professional-looking visual aids, they raise some practical issues for you to consider. Because graphics software and scanners are becoming increasingly easy to use, you may be tempted to create more visual aids than your readers need. Resist the temptation: unnecessary visual aids will clutter the document and take up valuable space. Many writers create "busy" visual aids that actually confuse readers or deemphasize important information; many writers inappropriately use the preset templates for visual aids such as pie charts, bar graphs, and line graphs. These preset templates are not effective for some data—for example, they may distort some trends in a line graph or bar graph by using an inappropriate scale.

CONCLUSION: ETHICS AND VISUAL AIDS

Current graphics software and scanners allow writers to manipulate data, pictures, and images in ways that were not easily possible before this technology became available. Writers often have to make ethical choices when using this technology. Your readers will expect your visual aids to be ethical, accurate, and honest.

One type of manipulation results from airbrushing—deleting images or objects from a photograph. A common use of airbrushing is to eliminate blemishes and wrinkles from close-up photographs of people's faces. Airbrushing is ethical and legitimate when used to highlight essential or important information in a picture; airbrushing becomes unethical when it removes information from a photograph to deceive or mislead the viewers.

Bar graphs, line graphs, and pictograms require you to create a scale on the horizontal or vertical axis. The scale you select will affect how your readers perceive your data. Be sure that the scales you create present data honestly. If you use inappropriate scales, you will exaggerate the differences in data when differences are minor, or you will make differences in data look small even though they really are great. Let's look at an example.

Figure 11.37 shows the most recommended home builders. The difference between Burgert, the most recommended, and Raign, is only 1.34 percent. The bar graph, however, makes the difference between Burgert and Raign look quite dramatic—certainly more than 1.34 percent. The scale that determines the length of the bars could mislead readers to believe that the percentage of people recommending Burgert over Raign is much greater than it really is. The graph needs a smaller scale and size to more accurately represent the difference between Burgert and the other builders (see Figure 11.38).

As you create visual aids requiring scales, make sure that the visual aid accurately and honestly presents the data and the differences among the data.

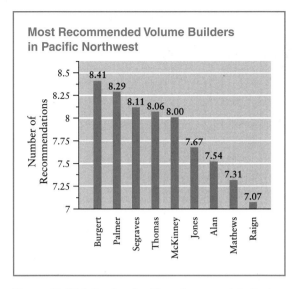

Figure 11.37 A Bar Graph with an Inappropriate Scale

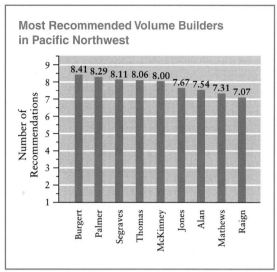

Figure 11.38 A Bar Graph with an Appropriate Scale

WORKSHEET for Creating and Using Effective Visual Aids

Principle 1: Look for Areas Where Visual Aids Will Help You Communicate

- Can you use visual aids to show readers how to follow instructions or explain a process?
- Can you use visual aids to show readers what something looks like?
- Can you use visual aids to show and summarize relationships among data?
- Can you use visual aids to emphasize or reinforce information?
- Can you use visual aids to show how something is organized?
- Can you use visual aids to simplify complicated concepts, discussions, processes, or data?
- Can you use visual aids to add interest to your document?

Principle 2: Design Visual Aids That Are Clear

- Are the visual aids simple and uncluttered? Do they emphasize or show the information that you intend?
- Does each visual aid have a number and a descriptive title?

- Are the titles of the visual aids positioned consistently throughout the document?
- If international readers will read your document, can they read and understand the visual aids?

Principle 3: Select the Appropriate Visual Aid

- When you want to show what something looks like, have you used drawings or photographs?
- When you want to show how to follow instructions, have you used drawings or photographs?
- When you want to explain a process, have you used flow charts or diagrams?
- When you want to show or summarize relationships among data, have you used tables, bar graphs, line graphs, pie charts, or pictographs?
- When you want to show how something is organized, have you used organizational charts?

Principle 4: Integrate Visual Aids into the Text

- Have you introduced each visual aid appropriately?
- Have you referred to each visual aid?
- Have you placed each visual aid as close as possible to its text discussion?
- Have you explained the purpose of the visual aid?
- Have you told the readers what to notice in the visual aid?

Principle 5: Use Computer Software to Create Professional-Looking Visual Aids

- When possible and appropriate, have you used computer software or scanners to create visual aids?
- Have you excluded unnecessary or ineffective visual aids?
- Have you manipulated data, pictures, or images appropriately?

EXERCISES

1. Visit the computer labs available to you on campus. Find out the following:

   a. What graphics software is available to students, and what types of visual aids can you create using the software?

   b. What drawing software is available to students, and what visual aids can you create using the software?

   If your campus doesn't have labs or graphics and drawing software, visit a computer software store to gather information. Create a table summarizing the information that you gathered. Then write a memo to your instructor reporting what you found out about available graphics and drawing software. With your memo, include the table that you created. Be sure to number and label it and integrate it with the text of your memo.

2. Figure 11.39 indicates the number of tax returns filed electronically to the ten IRS service centers from 1986 to 1990. Use the information in this figure to create the following visual aids. For each visual aid, include a number and a descriptive title. When possible, use computer software to prepare the visual aids.

   a. A line graph showing trends in filing individual tax returns electronically to the following service centers from 1986 to 1990: Memphis, Ogden, Kansas City, and Philadelphia.

   b. Two pie charts showing the proportions of total returns filed electronically to the cities serviced by the Memphis service center in 1986 and 1990. You will need to determine the percentage of the total number of individual returns filed electronically for each city.

   c. A bar graph comparing the total number of individual returns filed electronically to the Austin, Ogden, and Philadelphia service centers from 1986 to 1990. Remember that time is an independent variable.

   d. A pictograph showing the number of individual tax returns filed electronically from 1986 to 1990 in the United States.

3. Examine several technical publications or journals in your field. Select examples of effective and ineffective photographs, diagrams, and drawings. Write a memo to your instructor analyzing the photographs, diagrams, and drawings that you selected. Include a copy of the visual aids at the appropriate place in the memo. Number the visual aids and give them titles.

4. Create a drawing that you might use in a set of instructions or operating manual for a piece of equipment. You might select a household appliance, equipment used in your field, or equipment for which you are writing instructions in your technical writing class. Label the appropriate parts of the equipment, and give your drawing a number and a descriptive title. You can create the drawing by freehand, with drawing software, or with a scanner. If you scan a drawing, then use appropriate computer software to create labels for each part.

5. Create an organizational chart for an organization that has at least four levels of managers or departments. Use one of these organizations:

   • A civic organization such as the local Boy Scouts or Girl Scouts
   • The company you work for
   • A campus or student organization such as a fraternity or sorority or a service organization
   • A city department such as the fire or police department

6. Prepare a flow chart illustrating one of these processes. Include readable labels, a descriptive title, and a number.

   • Logging onto the World Wide Web
   • Applying for a passport
   • Applying for financial aid at your college or university

- Explaining a process or procedure common in your field or at your place of employment
- Applying for graduation at your college or university

7. Create a table using this information:

From 1964–1992, persons 25 to 44 years old were surveyed about their education and about their voting in presidential elections. The educational levels were divided into 1–3 years of high school, a high school diploma, 1–3 years of college, or a bachelor's or advanced college degree. The participants in the survey also indicated whether or not they had voted in the presidential elections in 1964, 1976, 1984, 1988, and 1992. In 1964, 60% of the people with 1–3 years of high school voted in the election, 78% of those with a high school diploma voted, 82% of those with 1–3 years of college voted, and 84% of those with a bachelor's or advanced degree voted. In 1976, 39% of those with 1–3 years of high school voted, 59% of those with a high school diploma voted, 63% of those with 1–3 years of college voted, and 79% of those with bachelor's or advanced degrees voted. In 1984, 30% of those with 1–3 years of high school, 49% of those with a high school diploma, 62% of those with 1–3 years of college, and 75% of those with a bachelor's or advanced degree voted. In 1988, 23% of those with 1–3 years of high school, 48% of those with a high school diploma, 62% of those with 1–3 years of college, and 75% of those with a bachelor's or advanced degree voted. In 1992,

28% of those with 1–3 years of high school, 51% of those with a high school diploma, 68% of those with 1–3 years of college, and 79% of those with bachelor's or advanced degrees voted.

The same group of 25- to 44-year-olds were surveyed about their voting in congressional elections in 1974, 1982, and 1990. In 1974, 25% of those with 1–3 years of high school, 43% of those with a high school diploma, 50% of those with 1–3 years of college, and 60% of those with bachelor's or advanced degrees voted. In 1982, 20% of those with 1–3 years of high school, 38% of those with a high school diploma, 47% of those with 1–3 years of college, and 58% of those with bachelor's or advanced degrees voted. In 1990, 18% of those with 1–3 years of high school, 37% of those with a high school diploma, 49% of those with 1–3 years of college, and 59% of those with bachelor's or advanced degrees voted. [Source: Dept. of Education, Office of Educational Research and Improvement, *The Condition of Education 1994*, NCES 94-149. (Washington: GPO, 1994).]

8. Create two bar graphs for the information presented in Exercise 7.

9. Decide when you would use the bar graphs and when you would use the table that you created in Exercises 7 and 8. Write a memo to your instructor explaining when you would use the tables and bar graphs. Include the bar graphs and tables with the memo.

Figure 11.39 The Table for Exercise 2

Number of Returns Filed Electronically					
Individual Returns					
Service centers & districts	1986	1987	1988	1989	1990
United States	**24,814**	**77,612**	**683,462**	**4,160,516**	**4,193,242**
Andover	**0**	**172**	**16,631**	**74,672**	**291,168**
Albany	—	172	6,327	10,692	34,677
Augusta	—	—	—	2,448	16,660
Boston	—	—	—	11,151	55,334
Buffalo	—	—	13,304	66,016	95,491
Burlington	—	—	—	1,546	6,583
Hartford	—	—	—	5,446	47,764
Portsmouth	—	—	—	2,744	23,550
Providence	—	—	—	4,629	12,109
Brookhaven	**0**	**0**	**0**	**14,404**	**186,433**
Brooklyn	—	—	—	11,193	58,864
Manhattan	—	—	—	3,211	42,670
Newark	—	—	—	—	84,899
Philadelphia	**0**	**8,913**	**58,508**	**69,198**	**319,449**
Baltimore	—	—	—	8,559	61,903
Philadelphia	—	—	—	—	85,103
Pittsburgh	—	—	—	—	42,603
Richmond	—	8,913	58,508	60,639	120,166
Wilmington	—	—	—	—	9,674
A/C International	—	—	—	—	—
Atlanta	**0**	**0**	**0**	**92,897**	**520,871**
Altanta	—	—	—	—	187,501
Columbia	—	—	—	35,081	106,655
Fort Lauderdale	—	—	—	9,096	69,092
Jacksonville	—	—	—	48,720	157,623
Memphis	**1,953**	**16,376**	**152,199**	**238,122**	**699,407**
Birmingham	—	—	28,813	47,150	110,585
Greensboro	1,953	16,376	123,386	142,943	251,058
Jackson	—	—	—	—	45,758
Little Rock	—	—	—	—	67,352
Nashville	—	—	—	48,029	143,207
New Orleans	—	—	—	—	81,447
Cincinnati	**9,157**	**25,976**	**153,492**	**267,458**	**612,306**
Cincinnati	9,157	25,976	60,558	61,288	105,062
Cleveland	—	—	—	20,882	82,192
Detroit	—	—	—	51,582	136,678
Indianapolis	—	—	62,036	82,482	161,324
Louisville	—	—	30,898	43,902	91,466
Parkersburg	—	—	—	7,322	35,584
Kansas City	**0**	**440**	**5,450**	**42,776**	**474,214**
Chicago	—	—	—	12,471	166,019
Des Moines	—	—	—	—	35,181
Milwaukee	—	440	5,450	14,001	64,880

Figure 11.39 (cont.)

Springfield	—	—	—	16,304	67,840
St. Louis	—	—	—	—	96,540
St. Paul	—	—	—	—	43,754
Austin	**0**	**0**	**70,832**	**141,766**	**474,204**
Albuquerque	—	—	—	—	35,424
Austin	—	—	—	26,623	88,593
Dallas	—	—	70,832	97,565	203,411
Houston	—	—	—	47,578	61,496
Oklahoma City	—	—	—	—	60,128
Wichita	—	—	—	—	45,152
Fresno	**0**	**0**	**10,592**	**43,342**	**225,048**
Honolulu	—	—	—	—	10,926
Laguna Niguel	—	—	—	10,536	120,148
Los Angeles	—	—	—	5,462	38,816
San Francisco	—	—	—	9,460	17,110
San Jose	—	—	10,592	17,884	38,048
Ogden	**13,704**	**25,735**	**96,880**	**175,777**	**390,142**
Aberdeen	—	—	—	1,404	8,873
Anchorage	—	—	—	883	6,222
Boise	—	—	—	7,296	14,336
Cheyenne	—	—	—	4,721	10,365
Denver	—	—	—	22,018	52,863
Fargo	—	—	—	408	6,647
Helena	—	—	—	3,192	11,162
Las Vegas	—	—	—	3,618	14,885
Omaha	—	—	2,343	12,491	30,447
Phoenix	13,704	19,142	47,998	45,702	66,509
Portland	—	—	—	19,087	31,311
Sacramento	—	6,593	12,312	14,759	30,062
Salt Lake City	—	—	16,657	12,391	33,582
Seattle	—	—	17,570	27,807	72,878

Source: Dept. of the Treasury, Internal Revenue Service, *1990 Annual Report from the Commissioner of Internal Revenue,* Publ. 55 (Washington: GPO, 1990) 27.

Chapter 12

Preparing Front and End Matter

While at work, you will write many different documents. These documents might include a progress report for your manager, a proposal for revising the plant design, or a feasibility report recommending new hardware for the manufacturing division. For many of these documents, you'll want to include reference aids, often called front and end matter. Front matter consists of the reference aids that come before the body of the document. End matter consists of reference aids that come after the body of the document. Front and end matter have various purposes such as

- **To help readers locate information in the document.** The table of contents, list of illustrations, and index help readers to find the information.

- **To help readers decide whether they want to read the document.** The abstract, executive summary, and the table of contents give readers the information they need to decide whether they will read the document.

- **To replace the document when readers may not have time to read the entire document.** The executive summary may replace the document for executives and managers.

- **To help readers to understand the document.** The glossary, list of symbols, and the appendix may help readers to understand or may support information in the document.

Few documents have all varieties of front and end matter discussed in this chapter. As the writer of a document, you'll determine the type of front and end matter that best meets your purpose and your readers' needs. You might decide to sequence the front and end matter differently in some documents; or your company may have standard formats and style guidelines, or even printed forms, for some front and end matter. Before writing a document, check to see whether your company has such guidelines for the type of document that you are writing. If it does, follow them. If it doesn't, find copies of successful documents written by others in the company. These documents will show you how other employees formatted the front and end matter of similar documents and perhaps reveal some of your company's unwritten preferences for front and end matter. If your company doesn't have guidelines for front and end matter, you will have to decide what format to use. This chapter presents three principles to help you prepare effective front and end matter.

PRINCIPLE 1: PREPARE THE FRONT MATTER

Many documents contain one or more of these items of front matter before the body of the document:

- Letter of transmittal
- Cover
- Title page
- Table of contents
- List of illustrations
- Abstract or executive summary

These elements identify or give an overview of a document and help readers to locate information and illustrations. We will examine each one in the rest of this section.

Letter of Transmittal

The letter of transmittal, or cover letter, has the following objectives:

- To summarize the subject and purpose of the document
- To identify the occasion—the reason for preparing the document
- To emphasize any information in the document that is likely to particularly interest the readers—information such as methods, conclusions, recommendations, or changes from the proposal or original plan for the document

You might include the following information in a letter of transmittal:

In the First Paragraph . . .
- State the title or subject of the document.
- State the occasion of the document—the reason for preparing it, such as to complete a class assignment, to complete a request from a manager or client, or to respond to a request for proposal.

In the Middle Paragraph(s) . . .
- State the purpose of the document. (Some writers include the purpose in the first paragraph.)
- Mention any specific information from the document that may especially interest readers.
- Summarize your conclusions and recommendations (unnecessary for instructions and manuals).
- *Optional*: Mention and possibly explain any changes to your work since the proposal or to the document since you last corresponded with the readers.

In the Final Paragraph . . .
- *Optional*: Offer to answer any questions that readers may have about the document or its contents.
- Mention and possibly thank any person, group, or organization that helped you prepare the document.

You can either attach the letter of transmittal to the cover of the document, place it inside the cover before the title page, or send it separately. If you decide to send the letter separately, be sure that it tells readers when you or your company plans to send the document itself.

The letter of transmittal is the first part of your document that readers will see. Therefore, it should give a good impression of you and your company. Figure 12.1 shows a letter of transmittal written by a technical writing student. She prepared the report mentioned in the letter for the Louisiana Parks and Wildlife Department.

Figure 12.1 A Letter of Transmittal

Louisiana State University
Department of Environmental Studies
Baton Rouge, Louisiana 85004

April 23, 1998

Dr. Sam Woods
Director
Department of Parks and Wildlife
P. O. Box 13726
New Orleans, LA 85007

Dear Dr. Woods:

We are pleased to submit the accompanying report, "Black-Bellied Plover Habitat in Louisiana," in response to your request. The report examines Black-Bellied Plover habitat in Louisiana as part of a program to save this species from becoming endangered.

For this report, we examined the literature about previous sightings of Black-Bellied Plover in Louisiana and analyzed satellite images of those sighting locations. Based on this information, we concluded that Black-Bellied Plover prefer pasture/shrub land. To protect any remaining Black-Bellied Plovers, we must conserve and monitor the locations where the bird has been most frequently sighted.

If you have any questions, please call me at (504) 555-2161.

Sincerely,

Danielle Brown
Research Assistant

Annotations:
- Title of document
- Occasion of document
- Purpose of document
- Conclusion
- Recommendation
- Offer to answer questions

THE READER'S CORNER

The First "Covers"

The history of writing formats is logically inseparable from the history of writing systems themselves. Historians believe that two written systems, developed independently of one another, are the source of all the major writing systems. The Chinese developed a writing system that influenced all Eastern writing; the Sumerians developed a system that influenced all Western writing. The Sumerian script, eventually known as cuneiform, first appeared on small tokens for simple bookkeeping purposes. As the Sumerian civilization developed from a hunter-gatherer to an agricultural society (around 8000 B.C.), the number of tokens in use increased. Markings on distinctively shaped tokens, some in the form of animals, stood for the real thing. By 3500 B.C., the Sumerians were building cities, and their lives were increasingly dedicated to commercial growth. To conduct commercial transactions, they constantly needed more tokens. Perhaps that is the reason the Sumerians developed clay envelopes, in which archaeologists have found tokens stored: to protect the tokens during transactions. The Sumerians duplicated the markings on the tokens on the envelopes, and eventually the Sumerians realized that the tokens themselves were no longer necessary: all the information they needed was on the envelopes. Some historians argue that this moment—when written characters were finally detached from their small clay embodiments—marks the beginning of abstract, alphabet-based writing.

Cover

The cover of a formal report serves two basic purposes:

- To protect the pages
- To identify the document

Before you design a cover, check to see whether your company has a standard cover design to appear on all documents. If it does, use that design. If it does not, and if you are responsible for designing covers, keep in mind that the cover may help to spark readers' interest or establish a certain tone. For example, if you're preparing a cover for a proposal to customize certain telecommunications functions for a corporation, you might customize the cover by using the client corporation's colors or displaying a picture of the client's headquarters.

For the cover of most documents, use heavy yet flexible paper or card stock. Most photocopy shops carry heavy paper and card stock in various weights and colors. Some shops will be able to laminate your cover.

Use any of these methods to print the cover and attach it to the document:

- **Use a laser printer to print the cover on ordinary paper; then photocopy the cover onto heavier paper such as card stock.** Heavy paper can damage laser printers. Therefore, you need to print the cover on printer paper and then copy it onto heavier stock. Laminate the cover for durability and a more professional-looking appearance.
- **Bind the document with spiral binding or three-ring binding.**
- **Use a binder that has a clear pocket on the front to hold the cover that you have printed.**

These printing and binding options are inexpensive and give reports a professional appearance. Spiral or three-ring binding secures the pages of the document much better than a paper clip or a file folder. Most photocopy shops have the machinery to bind documents.

Most covers include some or all of this information:

- Document title
- Your name
- Name of the organization that is issuing the document
- Name of the organization or group for whom you prepared the document—unless the document is for the general public

Figure 12.2 shows the cover of a proposal issued by a telecommunications company. The cover mentions the title of the report, the name of the issuing company (TWIN, Inc.), and the identity of the intended readers (officials in Courtney County); but it does not give the writers' names. Figure 12.3, in contrast, shows the cover of a document prepared for the general public. This cover identifies the issuing organization (National Petroleum Producers) but does not mention its intended readers.

Title Page

Some title pages look exactly like the cover; some repeat only certain parts of the cover; and some are completely different from the cover, having few if any graphics and no color. Title pages contain some or all of this information:

- Document title
- Name of the organization or group for whom you prepared the document
- Your name
- Name of the organization that is issuing the document
- Date that you submit the document to its intended readers

Figure 12.4 shows the title page of the document whose cover appears in Figure 12.3. This title page, unlike the cover, identifies the writer. Figure 12.5 presents the title page from a student document.

Many companies have a specific format for title pages. Some standardized formats call for much more information than generally appears on a title page (see Figure 12.6).

Figure 12.2 A Cover That Identifies the Intended Readers and the Issuing Organization

How the
Best Is Done

Proposal for Courtney County
Request for Proposal Number 96-025

offering a rugged, reliable solution for
an inmate telephone system

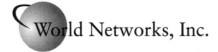

World Networks, Inc.

Source: Courtesy of Tonya McKinney.

Figure 12.3 A Cover for a Document Written for the General Public

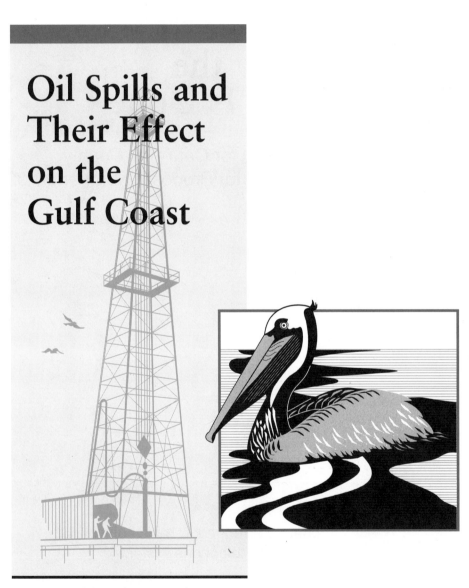

Oil Spills and
Their Effect
on the
Gulf Coast

National Petroleum Producers
BioServices Research Center
New Orleans, Louisiana

Figure 12.4 A Title Page

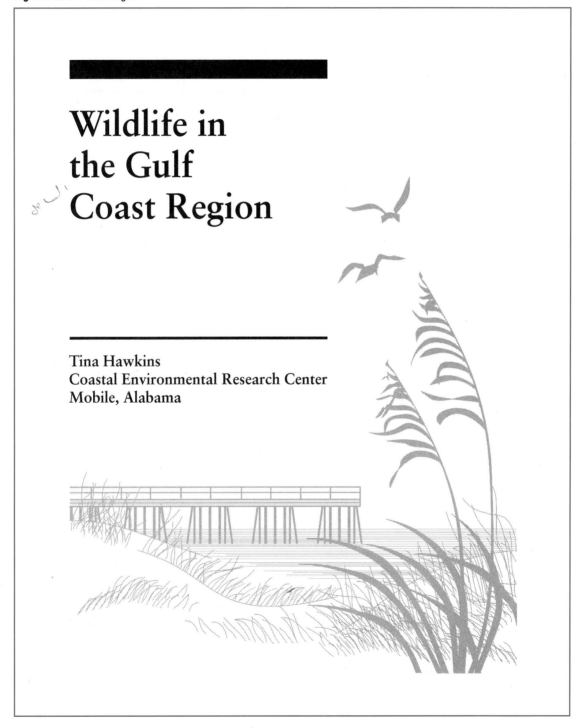

Figure 12.5 A Title Page from a Student's Report

Black-Bellied Plover Habitat in Louisiana

Prepared for
Louisiana Department of Parks and Wildlife

By Danielle Brown
Louisiana State University
April 1998

Figure 12.6 A Standardized Title Page for an Internal Technical Document

Zych and Powers Cover Sheet
Engineering and Construction/Fossil

Sheet _____ of _____
File No. _____ - _____

Division/Plant _____

Subject _____

Project Title _____

■ ■ ■ ■ ■

Prepared by _____ Date _____

Checked by _____ Date _____

Approved by _____ Date _____

■ ■ ■ ■ ■

Comments by _____ Date _____

_____

_____

_____

_____

_____

_____

Associated Zych and Powers Drawing Numbers

_____

_____

_____

Table of Contents

The table of contents is a sort of road map. It indicates what a document is about and helps readers to locate specific sections or to read selectively. The most effective tables of contents list more than just the first-level headings in a document. (If your document has only one level of heading, consider subdividing some sections to help readers locate information. Be sure to follow the guidelines for outlining presented in Chapter 7.) Figure 12.7 shows a table of contents that contains only first-level headings that convey no information about the subject of the document. Readers curious about the "Discussion" section, for example, would have to search more than fifteen pages to find a particular subsection or topic.

To prepare an effective table of contents, follow these tips:

- **Use the exact wording that appears in the headings and subheadings in the body of the document.** If the heading in the body of the text is "Habitat of Black-Bellied Plover," the wording in the table of contents should be the same, not a shortened version such as "Habitat."

- **Use indentation and varying typeface to indicate the various levels of headings in the document** (see Figure 12.8).

- **List only the first three levels of headings if your document has more than three levels.** Including four or more levels will make the table of contents hard to read.

- **If possible, use for each heading level the typeface that you used in the body of the document.**

- **Use guide dots (. . . . .) to connect the headings and the page numbers** (see Figure 12.8).

Figure 12.7 A Vague, Uninformative Table of Contents

Figure 12.8 An Effective Table of Contents

Contents

Abstract ii
List of Illustrations iv
Introduction 1
Black-Bellied Plover and Its Habitat 2
    Description of Black-Bellied Plover 2
    Habitat of Black-Bellied Plover 5
    Migration of Black-Bellied Plover 7
    Status of Black-Bellied Plover 11
Methods for Identifying Black-Bellied Plover Habitat 13
    Historical Sightings of Black-Bellied Plover 14
    Satellite Imagery of the Habitat 20
        Rectifying the Images 23
        Classifying the Landuse 27
    Remote Sensing of the Habitat 28
Results from the Sightings Information, Satellite Imagery, and Remote Sensing 29
    List of Historical Sightings of Black-Bellied Plover in Louisiana . . 30
    Landuse Classes in the Satellite Imagery 32
    Landuse Class of Black-Bellied Plover Habitat 35
Recommendation for Protecting Black-Bellied Plover in Louisiana . . 37
    Landuse in the Black-Bellied Plover Habitat 38
    Habitat Areas in Louisiana 39
Works Cited 41
Appendixes 42
    A. Satellite Imagery of Similar Habitats along the Gulf Coast 43
    B. Remote Sensing of Similar Habitats along the Gulf Coast 49

Show heading levels by indenting.

Line up all numbers, Arabic and Roman, on right-hand digits.

Guide dots

Contents

◄ Figure 12.9
A Decimal-Style Table
of Contents

• **Include the list of illustrations, abstract or executive summary, and any other front matter except the cover, title page, and letter of transmittal.** Use lowercase Roman numerals (i, ii, iii, etc.) for the page numbers of list of illustrations, abstract, executive summary, and any other front matter (see Principle 3 on page numbering later in this chapter).

Some word-processing software has functions for generating a table of contents after you have typed your document. These functions can save you time and help you to use in the table of contents the exact wording that appears in the body of the document. Check the user's manual or online help of your word-processing software to see whether it has a function for generating a table of contents. You can use this same function to generate the list of illustrations, discussed in the next section.

The most commonly used style for the table of contents appears in Figure 12.8. Many writers and companies, especially in the sciences, prefer a decimal system, which adds decimal numbers to the headings and subheadings in the table of contents (see Figure 12.9). Neither of these styles is better than another, so select the style that your readers or company expects. If your readers and your company have no expectations, look at similar documents to see how others in your company or field have prepared tables of contents; then pattern your table of contents accordingly.

List of Illustrations

If you use any visual aids in your document, list the numbers and titles of these visual aids in a list of illustrations (see Figure 12.10). The list of illustrations appears on a separate page after the table of contents. The list of illustrations is sometimes titled "List of Tables and Figures." To prepare a list of illustrations, follow these guidelines:

• If your document contains only tables, title the list "List of Tables" or simply "Tables." If your document contains only figures, title the list "List of Figures" or simply "Figures."

Figure 12.10
A List of Illustrations

- If your document contains both tables and figures, separate the tables from the figures in the list of illustrations.
- Use Arabic numerals (1, 2, 3, etc.) for the figures and uppercase Roman numerals (I, II, III, etc.) for the tables.

Abstract and Executive Summary

The abstract and executive summary give an overview of the facts, results, conclusions, and recommendations of a document. They present the information that readers need to act or make a decision without reading the entire document or to decide whether they want to read the entire document or just parts of it.

The abstract and executive summary generally appear near the beginning of a document. In this section, you will learn how to write informative abstracts, descriptive abstracts, and executive summaries.

Writing Informative Abstracts

Informative abstracts are generally for readers knowledgeable about the topic of the document. These abstracts must be able to stand independently from the document. When writing an informative abstract, follow these guidelines:

- **Identify the document.** Because an informative abstract may stand independently from the document, just writing "Abstract" above the text of the abstract will not give potential readers enough information. Instead, also include the document title, your name, and perhaps the name of your company or department.

- **State the objectives or problem addressed in the document.** Don't assume that readers know the objectives or the problem that your document addresses. Instead, mention the objectives or the problem in a few sentences. With this information, readers can decide whether your document contains information that they need or want to read.

- **Conclude with the key results, conclusions, or recommendations.** Because an informative abstract must be able to stand alone, mention the key results, conclusions, or recommendations of your research or document, excluding all examples and details. This information will be the largest part of the abstract. If the methods used to conduct the research are new, unique, or vital to understanding your results, conclusions, or recommendations, mention them too.

Generally, abstracts are one paragraph long. Figure 12.11 presents an informative abstract of a report on the habitat of the Black-Bellied Plover. The abstract identifies the report's title and writer. The writer also states the objective of her report in the first two sentences and then concludes with the key

Abstract
Black-Bellied Plover Habitat in Louisiana

By Danielle Brown

The Black-Bellied Plover (*Pluvialis squatarola*) is a shorebird species threatened with becoming endangered because of the loss of habitat through twentieth-century urbanization. As a step toward preventing this species from becoming endangered, this report identifies the Black-Bellied Plover habitat in Louisiana. To identify the habitat, I examined information about Black-Bellied Plover sightings in Louisiana over the last 50 years and the landuse categories derived from satellite imagery of the sighting locations. These examinations indicate that Black-Bellied Plover habitat in Louisiana is generally pasture and shrubland. To protect this species, I recommend that the Louisiana Department of Parks and Wildlife or the private sector conserve and monitor this habitat, especially in the areas where the most frequent sightings have occurred on Grand Isle and around Calliou Bay.

— Title of the document

— Problem addressed in document

— Conclusion
— Recommendation

Figure 12.11 An Informative Abstract

results of her research and a recommendation. You can also find good examples of informative abstracts in professional journals. Many journals limit abstracts to 200 words.

Writing Descriptive Abstracts

A descriptive abstract, unlike an informative abstract, is not a substitute for the document itself. Instead of reporting key results, conclusions, and recommendations, a descriptive abstract mentions the major topics of the document. Its purpose is to help readers decide whether they want to read the document. Figure 12.12 presents a descriptive abstract of a report on the habitat of the Black-Bellied Plover.

Figure 12.12
A Descriptive Abstract

Abstract
Black-Bellied Plover Habitat in Louisiana

By Danielle Brown

The Black-Bellied Plover *(Pluvialis squatarola)* is a shorebird species threatened with becoming endangered because of the loss of habitat through twentieth-century urbanization. This report identifies Black-Bellied Plover habitat in Louisiana based on previous sightings over the last 50 years and on landuse categories derived from satellite imagery of some of these sighting locations. The report also recommends conservation techniques to protect this species.

Writing Executive Summaries

Executive summaries present the conclusions and recommendations of a document (see Figure 12.13). An executive summary provides the information that its readers need to act or to make a decision. The readers of an executive summary are not necessarily the primary readers of the document itself. Let's consider an example in which the primary readers of the executive summary and of the body of the document are different people.

Engineers write a report on pipe stress problems at an electricity-generating plant. The primary readers of the report are other engineers and the plant operations manager—all experts in engineering and electricity-generating plants. In the report, the writers mention the methods they used to examine the problem, the specifications of the testing of the pipes, and the detailed results of those tests. They use technical language, knowing that their professional colleagues will understand it. However, many of the people who will decide whether to fund the solution that the engineers propose aren't engineers. For these readers, the engineers write an executive summary in which they use nontechnical language and include only the information that these individuals will likely need to knowledgeably decide about the proposed solution.

In your executive summaries, use nontechnical language, and give readers only the information they will need to determine whether they should read your document. Readers of executive summaries don't want or need detailed information about the methods; in fact, for many of these readers, detailed information about your methods or about the theories behind your project may be confusing or frustrating. Instead, these readers want the following:

- **A general overview of the topic of the document or research.** In this overview, succinctly state the topic of your document—as the problem addressed, the procedure or situation analyzed, and so on. Also briefly state the objective of your document or research. In some instances, you may need to provide some background information to help readers understand the topic.

- **A concise statement of the key results, conclusions, and recommendations without excessive detail.** Readers want to know the "bottom line."

Put yourself in the readers' shoes and try to anticipate the questions that they may ask as they read the summary:

- **What problem or situation does the document address?** Specifically identify the problem or situation that your document addresses. Readers will be especially interested in how the problem or situation directly affects them, their employees, their department, or their company. They also will be interested in the cost of the problem or situation to their department or company.

- **How will the results, conclusions, and recommendations affect the department, employees, company, and others?** Again, readers will be especially

Recommendations for Improving the Technical Writing Computer Lab

Overview

The Technical Writing Computer Lab has outdated equipment. Specifically, the lab has sixty 486 personal computers with dual floppy disk drives. Both the personal computers and the Macintosh computers have 14", low-resolution monitors. These computers cannot support the latest *Windows* software applications or desktop publishing. Although the lab does have twelve Pentium-class personal computers with 3½" and CD-ROM drives, faculty members cannot conduct classroom activities with only twelve computers. Also, with only twelve up-to-date computers, many students get little if any experience on the type of computer technology they will use in the workplace. Because of our outdated computer equipment, many faculty members are not requiring their students to use computers to create their technical writing documents and are, therefore, not adequately preparing their students for the workplace.

We have considered three ways to deal with this problem:

- Close the lab and force students to use their own personal computers and the open-access labs in the library.
- Request that the College of Arts and Sciences provide $400,000 dollars during the next fiscal year to upgrade all the personal computers and to buy current versions of *Windows* and desktop publishing software. With this request, the student fees would remain at the current level of $70 per student per technical writing class.
- Raise the student fees to $98 per student in the next three fiscal years. With this fee, we can update twenty computers and buy *Windows* and desktop publishing software for these computers the first year, and do the same for the remaining twenty computers the second year, and the final twenty computers the third year.

Conclusions/ Recommendations

After careful study, we recommend the second solution. However, if the College of Arts and Sciences will not provide the $400,000, then we recommend the third solution. We do not recommend the first solution because the technical writing faculty and students need a lab where they can hold class—the open-access labs are not set up for faculty members to conduct class sessions. The second and third solutions would provide faculty with a place to conduct classroom sessions and students with up-to-date computers and software that they will encounter in the workplace.

Figure 12.13 An Executive Summary

interested in costs and savings. Readers of executive summaries are less interested in details and evidence that supports the findings and more interested in information that will help them to make a decision or implement recommendations.

- **What are the key results, conclusions, or recommendations?** If you know that readers will understand the subject of your document, mention your key results. Such readers may expect you to summarize the significant data concerning the results. Briefly summarize your results and significant data, keeping in mind that these readers will use this data to make decisions, not to conduct further studies. Some readers, in contrast, may not understand your subject or may not want to read about your results. For these readers, leave out the results and present only conclusions and recommendations. Such readers are interested in what action you recommend based on your analysis or research—even if your recommendation is simply to study a situation or problem further or to "wait and see."

For most documents, place the executive summary at the front of the report. In some organizations, the executive summary circulates separately—it is not bound with the document. In other organizations, the executive summary is bound with the document and appears prominently, before the document. The executive summary presented in Figure 12.13 focuses effectively on the conclusions and recommendations.

PRINCIPLE 2: PREPARE THE END MATTER

End matter appears after the body of a document. However, some traditional end-matter elements, such as the glossary and list of symbols, may appear before the body, in which case they are part of the front matter. Some of the most common types of end matter in technical documents include the following:

- Works cited list or list of references
- Glossary
- List of abbreviations or symbols
- Appendix

Works Cited List or List of References

If you cite the works of others in your document, include a works cited list or a list of references after the body of your document. You might use MLA, APA, or a company-approved style of documentation. For specific information about documenting sources, see Chapter 6, "Gathering Information for Your Readers."

Glossary

A glossary is an alphabetical list of specialized words and their definitions (see Figure 12.14). A glossary provides definitions of terms unfamiliar to some readers, without slowing the flow of the document. Effective glossaries allow you to meet the needs of readers with different levels of technological expertise (see Chapter 3). To write an effective glossary, follow these tips:

- **In the body of the document, identify all words that appear in the glossary.** Put these terms in italic or boldface type, or place an asterisk next to each one. Use the same system of marking throughout the document, and be sure

Figure 12.14
A Partial Glossary

Glossary

American Standard Code for Information Interchange (ASCII)
A seven-bit code intended as a U.S. standard for interchanging information among communication devices.

asynchronous
A method for transmitting data in which each character is sent one bit at a time. Each character has a start and stop bit to synchronize signals between the sending device and the receiving device. See **bit**.

bit
A binary digit, either 0 or 1.

byte
The amount of space in computer memory or on disk occupied by a single character. A byte can be 6, 8, or 9 bits. See **bit**.

gateway
A hardware/software package that allows incompatible protocols to communicate. Usually connects personal computers to a host machine. See **host**.

host
A computer attached to a network that provides services to another computer beyond simply storing and forwarding information. See **network**.

local area network (LAN)
A system that links computers to form a network, usually with a wiring-based cabling scheme. LANs connect personal computers to allow users to communicate, share resources, and gain access to remote hosts or other networks. See **host**.

network
A system that sends and receives data and messages, typically via a cable. A network allows a group of computers to communicate, share peripherals (such as printers), and gain access to remote hosts and other networks.

---

to explain to readers what you are doing—perhaps in the letter of transmittal or in a footnote accompanying the first glossary word in the text. This footnote will explain that terms defined in the glossary appear in the body of the text in, for example, boldface italic type: "This and all other terms appearing in boldface italic type are defined in the Glossary, which begins on page 77."

- **Carefully define all terms that readers may not understand.** In the definition, use words that readers are likely to understand, and include cross-references to other closely related terms defined in the glossary (see Figure 12.14).

- **List the words in alphabetical order.**

- **Use sentence fragments, not complete sentences, for the primary definitions.**

- **Include the glossary and its first page number in the table of contents.**

Figure 12.14 shows part of a glossary from a document on computer networking products.

List of Abbreviations or Symbols

If your document contains many abbreviations or symbols, include a list explaining what they mean (see Figure 12.15). This list usually appears at the end of a document before the appendix, although some writers put it in the front matter after the table of contents and list of illustrations. List the abbreviations in alphabetical order, and use phrases for the definitions.

Appendixes

Appendixes generally contain information that is *not essential* for readers to understand the main points, conclusions, and recommendations. Appendixes contain information that may interest only a few readers or that would interrupt the flow of the document. An appendix might include maps, details of a survey or experiment, a sample questionnaire, an interview, large diagrams or charts, computer printouts, or supporting documents. Any of these items should supplement the body of the document. Material in appendixes supports information in the body of the document, offering further reading or sources where readers can learn more.

To prepare an effective appendix, follow these tips:

- **At the appropriate place in the body of the document, mention each appendix.** For instance, if you summarize survey results in the body of the document and include the survey instrument and tabulated results in an appendix, tell readers: "Sixty-five percent of the respondents reported that they used electronic mail more frequently than voice mail (see Appendix B for the tabulated results)."

- **Put each major item into a separate appendix.** Identify each appendix with a letter or a title: Appendix A, Appendix B, and so on.

- **List each appendix in the table of contents.**

Figure 12.15
A Partial List of
Abbreviations

Abbreviations	
ESS	Electronic Still Store. The graphics box over the anchor's shoulder.
NC	News Conference.
PREPS	Preparations. Used in story descriptions.
REAX	Reactions. Used in story descriptions.
SOT	Sound On Tape. Used in a script to tell the editor where to place the sound on tape.
VO	Video Only.

ISSUES IN CONTEXT

What Will Front and End Matter Look Like in the Coming Century?

The Internet and the World Wide Web are redefining traditional notions of what makes up front and end matter and what constitutes the appropriate format for documents. Online documents aren't mirror images of their paper counterparts. Gary Beason explains that when a certain computer company put its documents on the Web, the "boundaries between individual books [documents] began to disappear"; the books became more of a searchable database than a traditional book with chapters, a title page, and an index (339). Unlike traditional paper documents, documents on the Web are dynamic. Beason reports that these Web documents multiply into a set of documents in part because a series of files makes up the documents—files that are often in flux (Beason). Traditional paper documents, on the other hand, are static—once they appear in print. However, does this dynamic, flexible nature of online documents suggest that we should put all documents online or that readers prefer online documents?

Online and paper documents each have distinct advantages. Online documents cost less than paper documents and provide instant access to information, especially with computer software and hardware. Paper documents, on the other hand, are easier to read; if a document is "more than a few sentences, print is easier to read than a monitor" (Bellis 21). How, then, do you decide what to put online and what to put on paper? Jack Bellis suggests a combination of both online and paper documents to take advantage of the strengths of each. As you seek this balance between online and paper, consider that the written product will change as technology changes; but the change should not be arbitrary (Beason 348). Thus, will documents in the future have the front and end matter of today's documents? That decision may just be up to you and your coworkers.

- Put *essential* items into an appendix only when these items are so long or so large that putting them in the body of the document would severely interrupt the flow of information.

PRINCIPLE 3: NUMBER THE PAGES

Follow standard practice when numbering the pages of your document (see Figure 12.16):

- Use lowercase Roman numerals (i, ii, iii, etc.) for the front matter.
- Use Arabic numerals (1, 2, 3, etc.) for the body and end matter.

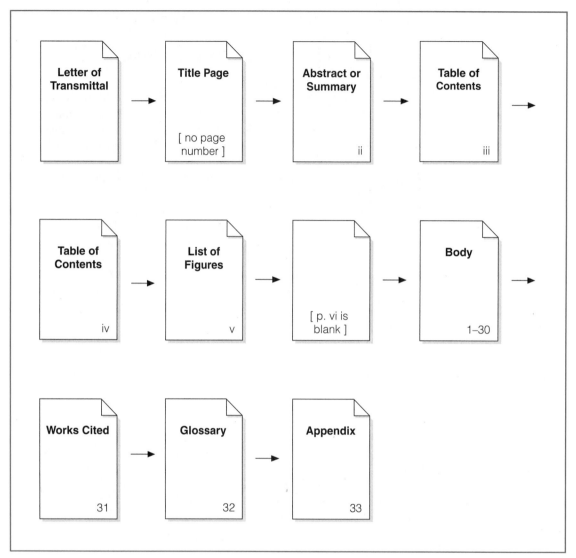

Figure 12.16 Sample Page Numbering of a Formal Document

- Put the odd numbers on right-hand pages and the even numbers on left-hand pages.
- Begin the body of the document on a right-hand page even if doing so means that the facing left-hand page will be blank.
- Leave the title page and any blank pages unnumbered even though you will include them in your page count.

Figure 12.16 shows the page numbering of a formal document. The writer leaves the title page, page i, unnumbered. The writer uses lowercase Roman numerals for all the front-matter elements. The first page of the body is a right-hand page. Page vi, the left-hand page that faces the first page of the body, is blank because the list of figures fits on page v.

You can put page numbers in two effective places on a page: the top or bottom outside corners (see Figure 12.17).

- On left-hand pages, place the page number in the top or bottom left-hand corner.
- On right-hand pages, place the page number in the top or bottom right-hand corner.

Figure 12.17 The Position of Page Numbers and Headers or Footers on Facing Pages

Page numbers in the outside corners are easier for readers to see as they flip through a document than are page numbers in the center of the top or bottom margins or in the inside corners. You also can help readers locate information by including a header or a footer with the page numbers. For more information on page numbers and headers and footers, see the discussion of page layout in Chapter 10, "Designing Documents for Your Readers."

CONCLUSION

When you know the readers and purpose of your document, you can select the appropriate front and end matter. Front and end matter help readers to locate information, to understand the information, and to decide whether they will read a document. Front matter can even substitute for a document when readers don't have time to read the entire document. From the front and end matter, readers often draw their first impressions of a document. If, for example, the cover has an unprofessional or uninteresting appearance, readers may decide to ignore the document. If the table of contents doesn't help readers to locate information, readers may not find the information they need and may use another company's product. If a manual lacks an effective index, readers may ignore the manual and instead call you or your company for help; such help can be time consuming and unnecessarily expensive.

The principles you've learned in this chapter will help you to prepare effective front and end matter. In the workplace, remember to look at documents prepared by your coworkers or at company style manuals to determine company preferences and guidelines for preparing front and end matter.

WORKSHEET for Preparing Front and End Matter

Principle 1: Prepare the Front Matter

- Does the letter of transmittal summarize the subject and purpose, identify the occasion, and emphasize particularly important information from the document?
- Does the cover create a positive impression of you and the document itself?
- Does the title page include the title and, when necessary, your name, the company's name, and the date?
- Have you included all first-, second-, and third-level headings in the table of contents?
- Does the table of contents create an effective road map of the document?

- Have you included all visual aids in the list of illustrations?
- Does your document need an abstract? If you include an informative abstract, is the title informative? Have you stated the objectives, key results, conclusions, and recommendations as needed? If you include a descriptive abstract, have you excluded key results, conclusions, and recommendations?
- Does your document need an executive summary? Does the summary give an overview of the document and concisely state key results, conclusions, and recommendations?

Principle 2: Prepare the End Matter

- Have you included the end-matter elements that readers need and expect?

Principle 3: Number the Pages

- Have you numbered the pages correctly?
- Have you placed the page numbers in the outer corners of the pages?

1. Write a letter of transmittal for a document that you are writing. Follow the paragraph-by-paragraph outline on page 281.

2. Prepare a tentative table of contents for a document that you are writing. Include all first-, second-, and third-level headings that you intend to use.

3. Design a cover and title page for a document. Use word-processing, graphics, or desktop publishing software. As you design the cover, decide what materials and binding style you will use. When you complete the cover and title page, turn in the following to your instructor:

   • A memo explaining the material you will use for the cover and justifying your design of the cover and title page—that is, why you selected the graphical elements, what the graphical elements represent, whether the design is the company's standard design, and so on
   • The cover printed on plain paper (indicate in the memo how you will present the final version of the cover: type of paper, type of binding, etc.)
   • The title page

4. Decide whether any material for a document that you are writing should appear in an appendix. Then write a memo to your instructor explaining your decision. If you decide to include material in an appendix, answer these questions in your memo:

   • Why is the material better placed in an appendix rather than in the body of the document?
   • If the material won't go into the body of the text, why should the material appear in an appendix rather than the body of the document?
   • What readers are likely to be interested or to need the information presented in the appendix?
   • What is the purpose of the material that will appear in the appendix?

5. Decide whether a document that you are writing should have an informative abstract or an executive summary. Then write the abstract or the executive summary for your document.

6. Write a memo to your instructor evaluating the letters of transmittal that appear in Figures 12.18 and 12.19. In your memo, comment on whether the letters are clear and contain all the elements listed on page 281.

7. Write a memo to your instructor evaluating the tables of contents in Figures 12.20 and 12.21. As you evaluate, consider whether they provide an effective road map to the document and give readers information about the subsections of the report.

8. Write a memo to your instructor evaluating the executive summary shown in Figure 12.22. Comment on how well it gives a general overview of the document and concisely states key results, conclusions, and recommendations. Also consider whether the writer has answered the questions that readers might ask.

9. Figure 12.23 presents the body of the report "Prescribed Range Burning in Texas." Readers of this report know little about prescribed range burning. Using the information presented in this report, prepare the following elements:

   • Letter of transmittal addressed to the readers
   • Title page
   • Table of contents
   • Executive summary
   • Informative abstract

10. Figure 12.23 contains style, design, and visual aid problems. Write a memo to your instructor identifying the types of style and design problems. Include examples of the problems from Figure 12.23. Be prepared to discuss your memo in class.

11. Rewrite a passage from Figure 12.23. The passage must have some of the style problems that you identified in Exercise 10. The passage must be at least three paragraphs.

Figure 12.18
Letter of Transmittal
for Exercise 6

Dear Dr. Raign:

I submit the accompanying report entitled "Dentistry in the North Carrollton Area" as the final project for ENGL 301, Technical Writing.

The report presents information from a demographic study of the north Carrollton area and from interviews with area dentists. This information will help dentists in this area better understand their market and its opportunities. My study indicates that the north Carrollton market is quickly being saturated with dentists. For new and established dentists in the area to be competitive, I recommend that they create a positive, innovative environment, establish good relationships with patients and other dentists, establish and justify reasonable and competitive fees, add a personal touch to their practice, and develop a marketing plan.

I especially want to thank all the area dentists who have willingly assisted and encouraged me during this study. If you have questions about the accompanying report, please call me at 696-4122.

Sincerely,

Jennifer T. Valentine
Attachment

Figure 12.19
Letter of Transmittal
for Exercise 6

Dear Michael,

Attached is the project report for the last six months for engineering and design activities for the Oakmont Station. To date, we have spent a total of 466,726 hours on these activities. The attached report is self-explanatory and provides information on the project schedule, project cost, specific engineering and design activities, and our recommendations for the remainder of the project.

If you have questions about the report, you may contact me at my office.

Sincerely,

Jim Anderson
Project Manager

Enclosure

Figure 12.20 Table of Contents for Exercise 7

Contents

Figure 12.21 Table of Contents for Exercise 7

Contents

Figure 12.22

The Executive
Summary for
Exercise 8

Executive Summary

In the first part of this report, I define typical technical writing jobs such as those in the public and private sectors. I then use these categories to organize the types of jobs uncovered in a seven-week survey. The remainder of the paper offers possibilities for students to enhance their degrees by gaining knowledge about software which employers required in the advertisements found in the survey.

According to the survey, most job openings for technical writers require the following:

- at least two years of related work experience
- working knowledge of a broad range of computer software
- specialization in technical fields

According to the survey, most of the job opportunities were in the area of user documentation. Of the employers requiring academic degrees, 30.3% specified a technical writing degree along with the two years of related work experience.

Based on the survey, the employers most frequently requested knowledge of one or more of the following software:

- Word
- Ventura
- Framemaker
- Windows

Based on the survey, the employers most frequently requested a specialization or background knowledge in the following areas:

- telecommunications
- public relations
- on-line documentation
- project management
- technical editing
- Web page design

Source: Courtesy of John P. Ramsey.

Figure 12.23 The Report for Exercises 9, 10, and 11

Prescribed Range Burning in Texas

Larry D. White and C. Wayne Hanselka

Introduction

Fire was a natural ecological factor on most Texas rangelands before European settlement; therefore, native vegetation is well adapted to burning. Fire effectively suppresses most woody plants while encouraging grass and forb growth. However, sound range, livestock and wildlife management must accompany the use of fire if benefits are to be realized.

Prescribed range burning follows guidelines that establish the conditions and manner under which fire will be applied on a specific area to accomplish specific management and ecological objectives. This contrasts with wildfires that can occur any time fuels will burn, often under extremely hazardous conditions. The conditions selected for a prescribed burn (season, vegetational growth stage and weather factors) must be conducive to *safe* and *effective* burning. Management objectives determine the fire characteristics needed to maximize benefits, minimize damage and conduct a safe burn.

The most commonly recognized management objectives that can be accomplished by using prescribed fire include:

- Improved pasture accessibility
- Increased production of forage and browse
- Suppression of most brush and cacti species
- Control of selected forbs and/or grass species
- Improved herbaceous composition
- Improved grazing distribution of livestock and wildlife

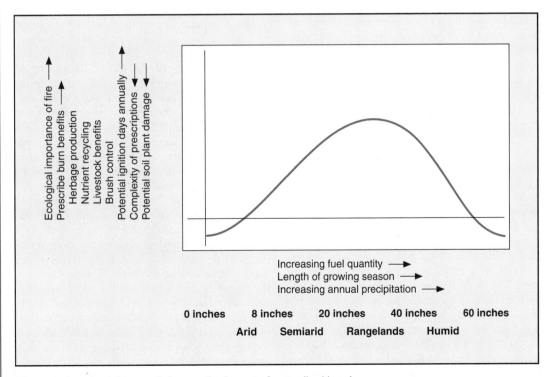

Figure 1. A variety of factors influence the impact of prescribed burning.

Figure 12.23 (cont.)

- Increased available forage and browse
- Improved forage quality and/or palatability
- Increased animal production
- Removal of excessive mulch and debris
- Control of certain parasites and pests
- Improved nutrient cycling

Each management objective requires a particular set of conditions for burning and a specific type of fire to achieve the desired response. Therefore, carefully evaluate objectives before a fire plan is developed.

Different Fires—Different Responses

Plant response after a fire is influenced by the intensity of the fire, condition of plants at the time of the burn and weather conditions and grazing management decisions following the fire. However, fire effects differ depending on rainfall, fuel quantity and length of growing season (figure 1).

Several factors that determine a fire's intensity are fuel quantity and continuity, air temperature, humidity, wind speed, soil moisture and direction of the flame front movement relative to the wind. Generally, the intensity of a fire increases with greater quantity and continuity of fuel, higher temperature and wind speed and lower humidity and soil moisture. A fire set to move in the same direction as the wind (headfire) tends to be more intense than a flame moving against the wind (backfire). Controlling the fire's intensity through correct firing techniques under appropriate conditions is a key factor in achieving the desired responses from a prescribed burn.

An equally important factor to consider when planning a burn to accomplish specific objectives is the stage and type of growth of desirable and target species. For example, the growth stage of forbs at the time of the burn greatly affects the current and following year's production. Forbs are prolific seed producers, but an untimely fire can destroy forb reproduction and wildlife food. Forb seedlings are highly susceptible to fire; therefore, a late winter burn after many annuals have germinated reduces their population. Burns conducted during early to mid-winter with good soil moisture result in late winter annuals and allow rapid recovery of perennials.

Non-sprouting shrubs are easily killed by fires even though the foliage is not consumed (for example, Ashe juniper). Most shrubs sprout from a bud zone at or below the soil surface. These plants are difficult to kill after the seedling stage. However, top kill is often achievable and greatly reduces competition with perennial grasses and forbs for several years. Because of the extensive root system on mature brush plants, sprouts often grow rapidly and produce canopies similar to pre-burn conditions in 3 to 5 years depending on species.

Perennial grasses are better adapted to burning than woody plants and forbs because of differences in location of growing points. For most grasses (during dormancy), the growing points are located near or below the soil surface. Annual grasses may be killed by fire after they germinate but may be promoted if burning occurs before germination. Fires that consume annual grasses before seed drop greatly reduce next year's seedling production and affect food supplies for some wildlife, such as quail.

The differences in growth cycles between warm and cool season grasses allow timing a burn to enhance one class over the other. Early greenup grasses, such as threeawn, can be harmed by an early spring burn with little damage to deep-routed perennial grasses. However, cool and wet soil conditions can reduce heat penetration to the sprout zone of shrubs resulting in less damage. Usually, late winter burns improve forage quality, provide rapid grass recovery for earlier grazing, control winter annuals and reduce shrub competition by top removal and seedling kill.

Winter dormant plants recover faster than drought-stressed plants burned during the spring, summer or fall. Also, summer fires are extremely hot and more damaging to vegetation than winter burns. The vegetation is drought stressed and highly flammable at this time of year. High soil temperatures and low humidity combined with flammable fuels contribute to summer burn intensity. Use summer burns only after careful evaluation and planning. If the burned area remains bare for long periods, the potential for soil erosion is greatly increased.

In summary, much of the prescribed range burning involves the correct combination of firing tech-

Figure 12.23 (cont.)

niques, seasonal timing and appropriate weather and range conditions on the day of the burn.

However, these are not the only factors that influence plant response after a burn. Precipitation amounts and season received have a significant effect on range recovery following a burn. Grazing management practices are also important in affecting the recovery rate and level of recovery.

Principles for Using Prescribed Fire

A successful burning program involves three basic steps: (1) thorough planning which includes total range evaluation, pasture selection, management goals, training for conducting a safe burn and preparations for the burn; (2) safe and effective execution of the burn on the specified area(s); and (3) sound range, livestock and wildlife management before, during and after the burn(s).

The Fire Plan

The fire plan identifies the recommended guidelines, procedures, preparations and resources needed for conducting a burn. The plan should describe ignition procedures, location of control crews and location of firelines. Have a contingency plan for control if the fire should escape. Discuss this with your volunteer fire chief in advance of the burn. Volunteer fire departments should be notified of the burn date(s) and burn plan. Regulations for prescribed burning are controlled by the Texas Air Control Board. Obtain and follow current regulations.

Several points to remember in planning a burn are:

- Preburn grazing management (including wildlife population control) is necessary to allow adequate fuel build-up and improved desirable plant vigor.
- Prescribed burns require adequate preparation, equipment and experienced personnel.
- Fire plans and prescriptions are only guidelines.
- Fire behavior must be predictable for effective containment.
- Fire intensity is determined by weather, fuel conditions and type of fire.

- The greater the intensity of the fire, the greater the risk of escape.
- Fire primarily topkills perennial plants.
- Vegetation recovery rate is dependent on species, their vigor, fire temperature, weather conditions and management before and after the burn.
- Postburn management of livestock and wildlife is critical to recovery and improvement of desirable plant species.
- Repeated fires are usually necessary to meet objectives.

Prescribed fire can be used alone or in combination with other range improvement practices (table 1). If sufficient grass fuel cannot be produced, use more intensive practices combined with proper grazing management to promote range improvement. Using fire in combination with other practices often extends longevity and improves the economic rate of return.

Executing the Burn

Consider the day of the burn as judgment day. The first priority is to insure that preparations are complete and check local weather forecasts. The National Weather Service can provide an estimate of conditions during and following the burn. Also measurements of on-site wind speed, wind direction, air temperature and relative humidity are recommended before and during the burn for timely adjustments in procedures.

Only one person (the fire boss) should be in charge of the burn. Identify who the fire boss is to prevent false alarms and unnecessary expense to the fire departments. This person must decide whether to burn and constantly re-evaluate fire behavior, ignition and control during the fire. Even after years of experience, there is always a need for concern and constant alertness. No prescription can be followed to the letter but must be adapted each moment before and during the burning. Before beginning the burn give final notification to volunteer fire departments, sheriff's departments and neighbors. This cannot be overemphasized.

Use small test fires to evaluate fire behavior each time conditions change and adjust the plan as

Figure 12.23 (cont.)

Range Condition	Percent of potential	Brush management practice
Excellent	100 to 75	Prescribed burn Individual plant treatment Biological control
Good	74 to 50	Roller chop Individual plant treatment Prescribed burn Biological control
Fair	49 to 25	Roller chop and burn Shred and burn Chain and burn Broadcast herbicide Broadcast herbicide and burn Biological control
Poor	24 to 0	Root plow and seed Disk and seed Tandem roller chop, seed and burn

Table 1. Relationship between range condition and optimum use of brush management practices.

needed. The test fire allows better evaluation of existing conditions and potential outcome of the larger burn before a commitment is made. Changes may be necessary to maintain control or to alter intensity of the fire to accomplish specific management objectives. Once the fuel is burned, the opportunity for that season is gone.

Ignition crews must be constantly aware of fire behavior. The potential for escape is greatest during ignition if current factors are not fully appreciated. Make adjustments immediately for any changes in wind direction, velocity, fuel flammability and relative humidity.

The person igniting the fire must be careful never to allow a heat build-up that can escape. Do not get in a hurry; allow the fire to do its job. Flame heights become dangerous when they reach more than halfway across the fireline. Avoid conditions that carry ignited leaves and ash outside the burn area.

Maintain two-way communication between all personnel. Accurate and rapid communication allows proper decisions and immediate action.

Keep sprayers, along with an accessible water source, readily available for controlling small fires.

The need for other equipment such as a dozer, chain saws, handtools and graders will depend on conditions. Everyone on the fire should understand their responsibilities and the burn plan. Only the fire boss should direct the actions on the burn, including control of any escaped fires.

Predicting Fire Behavior

Weather conditions and firing techniques significantly influence fire behavior. The variables most affecting fire behavior are topography, fuels, weather and firing techniques. These factors may be counteractive, additive or dominant.

Topography

Topography affects wind behavior and heat build-up which in turn affects flame front movement over the area. Prediction of wind patterns is necessary so that prefire control measures are taken and appropriate firing procedures are used. A fire moves faster upslope and slower downslope when compared to level terrain. Wind is channeled up canyons with increasing speed. In addition, wind in valleys and on slopes moves upward during the day because of surface heating and downward at night

Figure 12.23 (cont.)

because of surface cooling unless prevailing winds are strong enough to overcome local conditions. Eddy currents over the crest of a hill and around objects create different fire intensities, rates of spread and direction of fire front movement. Sometimes these conditions create fire whirlwinds that can carry sparks, burning debris or flames across a normally safe fireline. Firewhirls are small, tornadic winds, like a dust-devil, created from intense hot spots and rapid rising air at a concentration point.

Fuel

Fuel moisture content directly affects ignition and flammability. Green, living tissue is more difficult to ignite than dead material, which ordinarily promotes the spread of fire. Temperature, humidity, wind, precipitation and dew, season, time of day, topographic location and microclimate determine fuel moisture. Completely dried grass crackles and breaks easily into pieces when crushed in the hand, while dry twigs snap. In general, grass fuels are relatively safe to burn, whereas plants with high oil content are explosive and can create serious firebrand problems. Moisture content of dead grass, leaves and small branches changes quickly with atmospheric moisture; hence they are considered fast burning fuels. Logs, stumps and large branches, by contrast, take up moisture more slowly. Longer periods of atmospheric drying (several days) are required for prescribed burns to consume logs. Once these fuels have been ignited they may burn for several days. Do not concentrate these fuels near firelines.

The quantity of fuel that burns determines the amount of heat developed during a fire. Generally, 1,500 to 2,000 pounds of grass per acre are required for an effective broadcast burn. The heat generated affects fire characteristics and results. A good grazing management program allows for development of necessary fuel, especially in above-average rainfall years.

Weather

Weather conditions before, during and after the burn have a major influence on fuels, conditions, procedures and recovery. Predicting wind speed and direction is necessary so that the fire burns in a

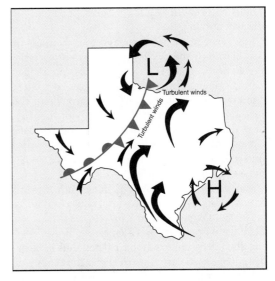

Figure 2. Prevailing wind direction depends on the location of fronts and high and low pressure cells.

predetermined manner. Wind movement can be predicted if burning is conducted with a knowledge of weather systems and the effect of high and low pressure cells. Winds associated with frontal weather systems will shift in a clockwise direction as the front approaches and passes over (figure 2). Wind direction changes quickly as a front moves through an area. The wind in South Texas will be from the southeast shifting to the southwest as a front approaches. In North and West Texas, winds are usually from the southwest shifting to the west. Wind speed increases and is often gusty and turbulent just before the front passes. After passage of the front, the wind direction is usually from the north and may be unstable for some time. After a day or two, the winds will be from the northeast or east. The shape of the front and rate of movement are important. Generally, movement of fronts during the winter causes constantly changing conditions in Texas.

Wind speed greatly affects the flame height, rate of spread and uplift of embers and burning material. Speed must be sufficient to carry fire easily through the fuels but not high enough to cause the fire to jump the downwind firelines. Wind speed

Figure 12.23 (cont.)

should be between 5 and 15 miles per hour for effective burning.

Low wind movement is dangerous because of possible whirlwind development and unpredictable direction of spread. High wind speeds may reduce fuel consumption and increase chances of escape. Wind direction must be consistent throughout the burn to avoid unpredicted fire behavior. Usually, large fires create their own wind around the convection column of smoke, heat and flame front. Two fires moving toward each other can create an intense hot spot or firewhirl.

The height and density of plants affect wind velocity. Unless sufficient fuel occurs within a brush stand, wind velocities may be insufficient to move flames properly and damage the brush. Also fuel should be uniformly distributed and in sufficient quantity to carry the fire under the canopy of a shrub or tree to generate the necessary heat to kill plant tissue. Mechanically cleared firelines and roads in brush or trees create openings that produce unusual wind movements.

Relative humidity affects fuel moisture, fire intensity and rate of spread. The lower the relative humidity, the hotter the fire and the greater the risk. Fine fuels such as grass burn with the same intensity when relative humidity is between 25 to 45 percent. Cooler fires result when the relative humidity is 45 to 60 percent. Less uniform and intense fires occur when relative humidities are above 60 percent. Do not attempt to burn when relative humidities are below 20 percent.

Day to night changes in air temperature and relative humidity create different fire behavior potentials. Fires of different intensities can be executed by selecting different times of day or night and different weather conditions. The density of a brush stand and the amount of shade created by the vegetation affect the relative humidity near the soil surface. Except under extremely dry conditions, brush stands burn slower and less intensely than open grassland areas.

Firing Techniques

Proper ignition procedures are needed to effectively contain a fire and accomplish management objectives. Ignition procedures greatly influence fire behavior and spread. Fires either move in the same direction as wind (headfire), in an opposite direction of wind (backfire) or at a right angle to the wind (flankfire)(figure 3). The headfire is the most intense because of its faster rate of spread, wider burning zone and greater flame heights. The flankfire is of intermediate intensity.

Backfires require higher fuel quantities and a more continuous fuel distribution than headfires. Since backfires move slower and have a less intense flame front, they are easier to control. Also, in heavy fuels, a backfire may consume more fuel and provide greater plant basal damage to brush than fast moving headfires by keeping heat closer to the soil surface. Set backfires as close to the fireline as possible to prevent high flames and embers from crossing the fireline.

Headfires are effective at top killing shrubs and trees with intense heat several feet above the soil surface. Headfires burn under a wider range of weather and fuel conditions than backfires but are more dangerous. Headfires may be required to burn large acreages in a reasonable amount of time. However, a series of firelines across a pasture can be used to set a number of backfires in a short period. Costs of fireline construction are higher.

A combination of the head and backfiring technique is the stripfire. This is simply a line of fire set within the pasture at right angles to the wind direction. The result is a headfire across the strip and backing fire into the wind. This technique is used to speed up the widening of firelines. The ignition crew should regulate the width of the strip so that the flame front does not leap the fireline or burned-out area. Changes in fuel quantity and continuity require appropriate changes in width of the strip-fired area.

Once a headfire moves 50 to 100 feet, its major flame front characteristics have developed. A 50- to 100-foot wide stripfire can be set to confirm the necessary width of the fireline before setting the major headfire. Properly station all control crews for this test burn. Do not set a second stripfire or the headfire until the flame-front from the strip has calmed.

Backfiring from a fireline, followed by headfiring, has been successfully used throughout Texas (figures 4 and 5). The backfire plus stripfiring is used to sufficiently widen the downwind fireline

Figure 12.23 (cont.)

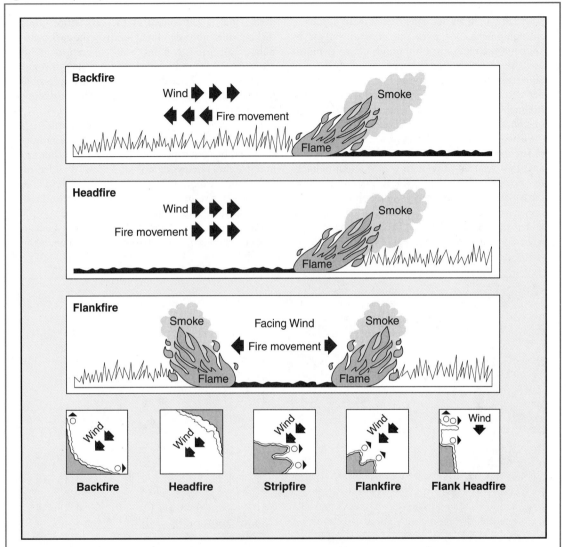

Figure 3. Firing techniques commonly used for prescribed burning.

before the headfire is ignited. This allows flexibility in wind direction and potentially more suitable burn days during a season than when a plan requires a specific wind direction. Also, adjustments in firing can compensate for shifts in wind direction. Observing backfires and stripfires improves judgment on fireline width, potential escape conditions and flammability before setting the headfire.

Fire Containment Practices

Containing a fire to the specified area requires use of natural or man-made breaks in fuel continuity and burning under conditions that minimize chances of escape. Improperly set fires could escape across any fireline. Exercise constant vigilance by personnel throughout all burns. The key to containment is immediate response to any potential escape.

Figure 12.23 (cont.)

Usually, firelines are constructed using mechanical equipment to expose the mineral soil or by applying fire retardant compounds or water on the fuel. Always plow firelines away from the area to be burned to prevent burying fuel that can smoulder and create sparks for long periods. Usually a fireline 1 or 2 blades wide is adequate, depending on conditions and firing techniques.

Generally, adapt the firing procedure to the kind of firelines and natural barriers available. Use a 1- or 2-foot retardant fireline if care is taken to backfire precisely along the chemical line and not promote flames that can reach flammable fuels. Thus, fire is used under carefully controlled conditions to widen and create a sufficient fireline. Disking is satisfactory if mineral soil is well exposed and flammable fuel is eliminated in the disk strip. Often disking does not adequately destroy the fuel continuity, and use of hand tools or retardants is required to prevent fire from skipping through patches of fuel. Also, disking may reduce accessibility for trucks and sprayers to move quickly along the fireline.

Drip torches (using a diesel-gasoline mixture) are recommended to set uniform, narrow fires without considerable resetting. Burning tires, pear burners and matches are less reliable and create a wider initial flame front. Erratically set fires result in stringers of fire proceeding at different rates drawing each other and creating erratic behavior.

Use special care when burning volatile fuels to prevent embers from crossing firelines. For exam-

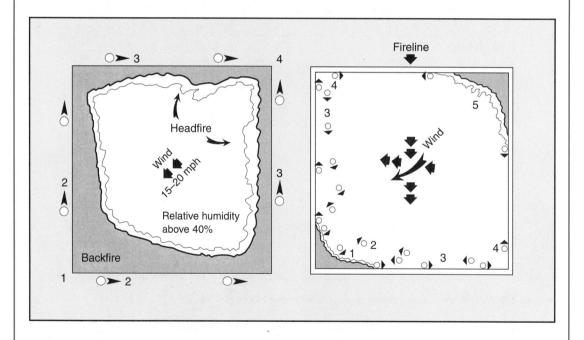

Figure 4. Using combinations of backfiring, stripfiring, flank headfiring and headfiring allows the fire boss and ignition crews to conduct successful burns with fire to help contain the burn. One procedure (left) utilizes a backfire (1) lit simultaneously in each direction. (2) After the backfire has burned 50 to 100 feet on the downwind sides, ignite the remainder of the area (3) and burn as a headfire (4). (From publications by Dr. Henry Wright, Texas Tech Univ.) By using all combinations of firing techniques (right), more difficult burns can be accomplished. The backfire plus narrow stripfires (1) are used to widen the firelines on downwind sides. A wider stripfire is used to increase fireline width and test burnout for containment of the headfire (2 and 3). A flank headfire is used to widen burnout of corners (4). The headfire is set using two torches to the burnout corners (5).

Figure 12.23 (cont.)

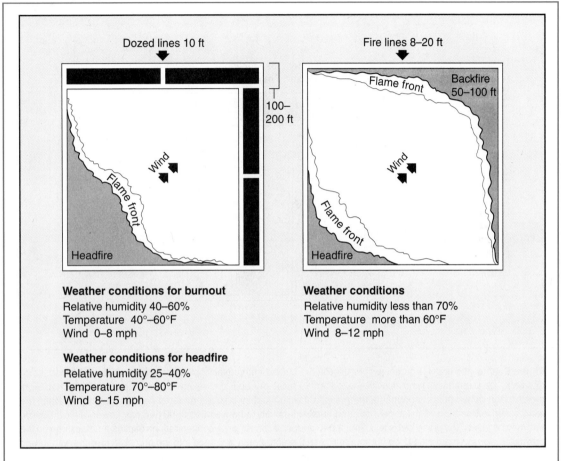

Dozed lines 10 ft

Fire lines 8–20 ft

100–200 ft

Flame front

Backfire 50–100 ft

Wind

Wind

Flame front

Flame front

Headfire

Headfire

Weather conditions for burnout
Relative humidity 40–60%
Temperature 40°–60°F
Wind 0–8 mph

Weather conditions for headfire
Relative humidity 25–40%
Temperature 70°–80°F
Wind 8–15 mph

Weather conditions
Relative humidity less than 70%
Temperature more than 60°F
Wind 8–12 mph

Figure 5. Fire plans and prescriptions differ with objectives, vegetation, personnel training, etc. Fixed wind direction (left) requires burnout of upwind firelines in January and February and ignition of the headfire in February or March. A fire plan using "simultaneous" backfiring and headfiring (right) requires greater coordination and on-the-ground judgment but does not require a fixed wind direction in the prescription. (From publications by Dr. Henry Wright, Texas Tech Univ.)

ple, burn juniper piles within 500 feet of the perimeter during the growing season or under high moisture conditions when the surrounding grass is not flammable (figure 6). Use this same practice for any brush pile or concentration of dead fuel that poses a threat to containment. Hot fires under piles will destroy existing vegetation, especially if burned during the growing season. Hand seeding in the ash may be a valuable practice for more rapid recovery.

Safety is the Key

If it cannot be done safely, do not burn. Escaped fires can damage property, life, equipment, animals and vegetation that negate the beneficial effects achieved with the planned burn.

The fire boss is responsible for executing the burn safely and effectively. Burn plans provide realistic guidelines for when, where and how to conduct the burn. However, actual burn conditions seldom per-

Figure 12.23 (cont.)

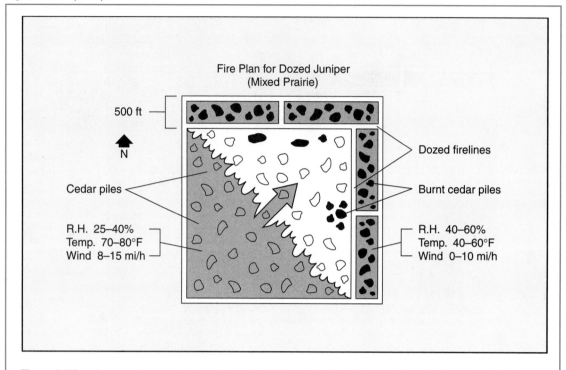

Figure 6. When the grass is green, juniper piles in the 500-foot strip (black splotches) on the downwind sides (north and east) are burned with wind velocities less than 10 miles per hour and relative humidity above 45 percent. Eight months later (when grass is dormant), the grass in the 500-foot strip is burned (strip-headfire technique) when the wind speed is less than 10 miles per hour and relative humidity is between 40 to 60 percent. Lower relative humidities may be used if the grass fuel is less than 2,000 pounds/acre. All large concentrations of piles are backfired on the downwind sides of main area to be burned, and then the entire area is burned into the prepared firelines with a wind speed of 8 to 15 miles per hour and a relative humidity of 25 to 40 percent. (From publications by Dr. Henry Wright, Texas Tech Univ.)

fectly match the desired guidelines. Apply techniques that best match the current and expected conditions and use experienced personnel to provide leadership. Do not wear clothing that is highly flammable or melts easily; cotton is recommended.

The landowner using prescribed fire is legally responsible. Arrange for liability insurance and involve neighbors in planning and executing the burn(s). Inform fire and sheriff's departments. Proof of planning and use of accepted burning practices may be invaluable in negating charges of negligence if a fire escapes, resulting in a lawsuit. The Texas Air Control Board in Austin has specific regulations on when and under what weather con-

ditions prescribed burns can be legally conducted. Obtain a copy of the regulations. It is the manager's responsibility to have flagmen on highways to slow traffic if smoke obscures visibility. Generally, fires should move away from highways or houses with a good uplift of smoke. Do not burn when temperature inversions can occur. Ask your weather service if such conditions are likely during the burn and following night.

The bottom line in safety is to have a good plan, executed under appropriate conditions with adequate equipment, personnel and preparations. This includes a plan for containing any fire that escapes from the specified area.

Figure 12.23 (cont.)

Burn Prescriptions

Generally, the prescription for a successful burn includes wind speeds of 5 to 15 miles per hour, steady wind direction, air temperature 40° to 80°F., relative humidity 25 to 60 percent and uniform fuel continuity of 1,500 pounds per acre or more. Generally, fire intensity and rate of spread increase with drier fuel, lower RH and higher air temperature, wind speed and fuel quantity.

Costs of Prescribed Burns

The cost of a prescribed burn differs for each ranch, pasture and time of year. Each ranch must develop a budget and keep records of actual expenditures for future analysis. In some counties cost-share assistance is available for fireline construction, labor and equipment rental. Costs range from 50 cents per acre to $8 to $10 per acre or more depending on fireline construction and manner of calculation. Costs of follow-up burns should be lower, however.

Summary

Prescribed burning is a viable improvement practice for most Texas rangelands. When integrated with other practices, fire can be used to maintain desired vegetation composition and structure. Many managers are not able to effectively use fire until they achieve better range conditions. Good grazing management programs complement prescribed burning.

The basic principles affecting fire behavior are considered by the manager for developing a realistic fire plan. The fire plan identifies the overall objectives for the ranch as well as for each pasture and range site to be burned. Ideally, burn entire management units to avoid overconcentration of livestock and wildlife. Base the stocking rate on actual acreage burned and adjust for recovery rate. Control white-tailed deer and exotic game populations to prevent overuse of key browse and forb species.

Burning when brush regrowth is young and when fine fuel loads are near maximum can more effectively maintain high production ranges. Brush stands require two to three burns before most objectives are realized. Select the better sites for burning; hence, the net return per dollar invested should be higher.

Described techniques, prescriptions and guidelines provide a basis for using prescribed fire. Consider local experience when adapting prescriptions and plans. Emphasize safety [and] avoid overoptimism. Use fire where benefits can realistically be achieved and integrated with the ranch operation. Take advantage of high forage production years, using excess forage as fuel for a burn. Careful grazing management is an important part of any prescribed burning program.

Assistance and training are available for developing your prescribed burn program. Agencies currently involved are the Texas Agricultural Extension Service, Soil Conservation Service, Texas Forest Service and Texas Parks and Wildlife.

Acknowledgments

Cover photos supplied by J.F. Cadenhead, W.A. McGinty, R.Q. Landers and L.D. White. The authors wish to thank Tommy Welch, R.Q. Landers and Calvin Richardson for their in-depth review of the manuscript.

Source: Larry D. White and C. Wayne Hanselka, *Prescribed Range Burning in Texas*, 5M-8-91 (College Station: Texas Agricultural Extension Service, 1991). Reprinted by permission of the authors.

PART III

PRODUCING EFFECTIVE DOCUMENTS FOR YOUR READERS

Chapter 13

Planning and Writing Reader-Oriented Proposals

Proposals are documents designed to persuade someone to follow or accept a specific course of action. Proposals usually offer to solve a problem or to provide a service or product, and then they suggest a specific plan for solving the problem or for providing the service or product. Some proposals also lay out a specific timetable and budget. An effective proposal is persuasive; it convinces readers to accept and possibly to pay for the work that it proposes. If you propose a project for a fee, you will want to persuade your readers that you can carry out the project within a reasonable time and at a reasonable cost. A proposal, then, is a "sales" document: it "sells" a proposed action and your services or the services of your company to carry out that action. A proposal has several parts:

- Description of the problem or need
- Description of, and justification for, the proposed service, product, or solution
- Specific plan for providing the proposed service or product or for solving the identified problem
- Timetable for carrying out the plan
- Budget (if the project is for a fee)
- Description of the people who will carry out the plan and, if applicable, of the company that employs them

You might write a proposal in response to several scenarios. Let's look at five scenarios and how the writers responded:

Scenario 1   Bill Martinez works for a large construction company. His company is building a new manufacturing plant. The manufacturing process will create large amounts of ash. According to EPA guidelines, the company must dispose of the ash properly. Bill is responsible for hiring a company to develop recommendations for disposing of the ash. Therefore, he sends out requests to several environmental service companies, inviting them to submit their qualifications to develop the recommendations. (The sample proposal in Figure 13.9 is a proposal from one of the environmental service companies.)

Scenario 2   A government agency in Wisconsin decides that it should renovate its office building. The building is fifty years old and has several problems: it doesn't meet current fire code regulations; the windows and outside doors provide little insulation from the weather; the bathrooms have plumbing problems; and the offices are not appropriately wired for current computer technology. The agency wants to find a qualified construction company to renovate the building at a reasonable price. The agency advertises the proposed work in newspapers across Wisconsin. Any companies interested in submitting bids can then request the specifications of the project.

Scenario 3   The United States Army solicited proposals for manufacturing night vision sight for the M24 Sniper Weapon System. The army put an RFP (request for proposals) in *Commerce Business Daily* (see Figure 13.1). The RFP describes the specifications for the night vision sight, gives the

Figure 13.1

An RFP from
*Commerce Business
Daily*

US Army CECOM, Command, Control, Communications and Intelligence (C31) Acquisition, Fort Monmouth, New Jersey 07703-5008
59–59 • NIGHT VISION SIGHT FOR M24 SNIPER WEAPON SYSTEM SOL DAAB07•93-R-K533 DUE 122293 POC Contact Michael L. Lang, Contract Specialist, (908) 532-4042. Matthew Meinert, Contracting Officer, (908) 532-4043. The US Government intends to issue a solicitation to interested sources who have the capability to manufacture a Night Vision Sight for the M24 Sniper Weapon System (SWS). The sight must incorporate third generation image intensifier technology and appropriate magnification power and maximum possible field of view thus enabling the SWS to meet the requirements of paragraph 3 below.

Specifications —

The night vision sight: 1. Shall be either (a) a module that connects with and uses the current M24 Leupold day optics, OR (b) an integrated systems that contains both day and night optics. 2. Shall have a maximum weight of 6.3 required, 4.5 lbs desired. Weight includes day sight and mounts for clip-on configuration night sight, or total system weight for integrated day/night configuration. 3. When mounted to the M24 SWS, the M24 SWS must achieve a daytime probability of hit (PH) between 0.95 and 0.85 on an averaged basis, over a course of fire with stationary known distance targets out to 800 meters. The M24 SWS must also achieve a minimum nighttime PH of 0.70 on an averaged basis, over a course of fire with stationary known distance targets out to 600 meters under clean air, starlight to quarter moonlight conditions. 4. Shall demonstrate the following performance characteristics: (a) image tube center resolution:)55 lp/mm, (b) magnification:)7X, (c) field of view:)2 degrees, (d) elevation and windage adjustment: One minute of arc per click. The zero position of the reticle shall not move more than 0.55 minutes of angle (MOA) from the optical axis when each knob (both elevation and windage) is cycled from 0 to the extreme adjustments and returned, for 10 cycles. The Government is interested in obtaining comments from industry who have the capability to provide a device meeting the above requirements as part of a category B (Adaptation) Non-Developmental Item (NDI) procurement. Two hardware samples will be required and are to be delivered concurrent with submission of the proposal.

Due date for proposal —

Proposals are due 30 days after the date of solicitation which is tentatively scheduled for 22 Nov 93. Any deviations from the requirements of the solicitation must be addressed in the offeror's written proposal, and will be considered in the Government's proposal evaluation. Specific information regarding the Government's test procedure and evaluation criteria for the hardware samples will be included in the forthcoming solicitation. The Government provides this data without assuming responsibility for its accuracy of for any conclusion/interpretation which may be drawn from the data which is provided solely for information purposes and should not be relied upon as a basis for interpretation of a bid.

Information for obtaining specific information about the request —

The solicitation may include more detailed information concerning price history. Therefore, telephone or other requests for price history will not be accepted. Respond in writing only to AMSEL-ACCC-C-CR (LAN). No Phone calls will be accepted. A solicitation will be provided to all interested bidders on or about 22 Nov 93. The solicitation will include Government requirements for a two-year multi-year procurement. A pre-proposal conference will be held approximately 15 days after issuance of the solicitation. All responsible sources may submit a bid/quote/proposal which shall be considered by this agency. Only written requests will be accepted. (0307)

Source: Commerce Business Daily. PSA-0967. 5 November 1993:21.

due date for the proposal, and provides information about obtaining specifics about the request.

Scenario 4   Susan Rowland writes software documentation. In recent months, her workload—as well as that of the other documentation writers—has dramatically increased. Susan knows that her company currently has a hiring freeze, so she can't hire another writer. She believes that the only way to help with the increased workload is to update the computer software and hardware used to write and produce the documentation. Therefore, she writes a proposal to her regional supervisor requesting updated software and hardware for her department.

Scenario 5   Leanne Gong wants to research whether or not the concentrations of mercury and lead allowed by the government are safe. She wants to determine whether people living in areas with allowable concentrations of mercury or lead have a history of health problems. To conduct this research, Leanne needs funds. She looks for RFPs in the *Federal Registry* and other sources. She can't find an RFP that matches her proposed research, so she prepares a proposal to send to various private and public agencies, hoping these agencies will fund her research.

Those five scenarios illustrate the two primary types of proposal situations: solicited and unsolicited. Scenarios 1 through 3 illustrate situations requiring solicited proposals. **Solicited proposals** originate when a person, company, or government agency requests qualified companies and individuals to submit their qualifications to do work (Scenario 1), to submit bids to complete proposed work (Scenario 2), or to submit proposals for manufacturing equipment according to specifications (Scenario 3). In each of these scenarios, the companies and individuals write proposals based on the requests and specifications of another company, individual, or government agency.

Scenarios 4 and 5 illustrate situations requiring **unsolicited proposals**—proposals *not* requested by the company, individual, or government agency that receives them. Unlike solicited proposals, unsolicited proposals must convince readers that a specific need or problem exists, before explaining a plan, cost, or qualifications. You can write unsolicited proposals to people in your own company as in Scenario 4, or you can write them to people outside your company as in Scenario 5. In Scenario 5, Leanne Gong decides to send unsolicited proposals because she can't find any RFPs that request the kind of research that she wants to conduct. Therefore, she targets a group of agencies that fund research and sends them her proposal.

Susan Rowland's and Leanne Gong's task—writing an unsolicited proposal—can be more difficult than writing a proposal in response to a specific request. Susan and Leanne not only have to convince readers that they have good projects and can carry out those projects at a reasonable cost, but also have to persuade readers that their projects are worthwhile and will fulfill a need. Susan wants to convince her readers that her department has an increased workload and that the computer software and hardware used by the documentation writers is preventing the department from completing that workload in a reasonable time and with the quality the company expects. Leanne wants to persuade her readers that the allowable levels of mercury and lead may be too high and that a scientific study can determine whether or not the levels actually are too high.

The five scenarios illustrate how proposals originate and the possible locations of the readers. Readers of proposals can work within or outside your company. If the readers work within your company as in Susan's scenario (Scenario 4), the proposal is *internal*, written to someone within the writer's company or institution. If the readers work outside your company as in Scenarios 1, 2, 3, and 5, the proposal is *external*. The following principles will help you to write effective proposals whether they are solicited or unsolicited, or internal or external.

PRINCIPLE 1: FIND OUT ABOUT THE READERS OF YOUR PROPOSALS

Before writing any proposal, find out about the people who are most likely to read it. You can write an effective proposal only if you understand your readers and have some idea about how they will respond to the problem and to the work that you propose. To find out about readers, ask yourself these questions, which will help you to customize your proposal:

- **What positions do your readers hold in the company? If the readers work in the company that employs you, where are their positions in relation to yours in the organizational hierarchy?** If you know readers' positions in the hierarchy, you can more accurately determine who will approve or disapprove your proposal, who will understand the topic and the background of your proposal, and who will be your primary and secondary readers. Are your readers above you, below you, or at the same level as you in your organization? If they outrank you, you may want to use a more formal approach or to have your immediate supervisor read a draft of your proposal before you send it to your primary readers. If you and your readers are at the same level in the organization, or if you outrank them, they may expect a less formal approach.

- **Will more than one group read the proposal? If so, what sections of the proposal will each group read?** Often, several groups of readers may read a proposal. For example, managers or executives may read the summary to determine whether the proposal has potential merit. If they decide that it has merit, they may send the proposal to the accountants to look at the budget and to technical experts to look at the solution and the plan.

- **What do your readers know about the problem or need that prompted your proposal?** If your proposal is unsolicited, readers probably will know little about the problem or need addressed in your proposal. If your proposal is solicited, readers will understand the problem.

- **What do your readers know about you or your company? Have their previous experiences with your company or with you been positive? If not, why?** Find out whether your readers have had previous experiences with your company. Was the experience extended or brief, positive or negative? What impression are the readers likely to have of you or your company? Knowing the answers to these questions will help you write the qualifications section of the proposal and lessen any negative concerns your readers may have about you or your company.

If you are aware of the answers to all these questions, you can write a proposal that meets your readers' needs and expectations. Once you have found out about your readers, you can determine what they may ask about your proposal.

PRINCIPLE 2: PREPARE TO ANSWER READERS' QUESTIONS

The success of your proposal depends on how

- Persuasively and logically you argue for your proposed solution, product, or service
- Convincingly you argue that you or your company is best qualified to carry out the plan
- Persuasively you argue that you or your company can complete the work within a reasonable time and at a reasonable cost

How can you provide readers with the information they need, without overstating what your company can provide? First determine what your readers expect and what questions they will seek answers to as they read your proposal, and then decide what you or your company can reasonably propose. You have a responsibility to explain specifically and accurately the work that you or your company can provide, so readers will not expect more or less than you intend to deliver and will not hold you or your company responsible for more or less work than you propose. In your eagerness to get a proposal accepted, don't exaggerate or overestimate the work that you can perform.

A series of questions relating to three areas—the problem or need addressed in the proposal; the proposed solution, product, or service; and the plan of work—will help you to anticipate what readers expect from your proposal and what they may ask as they read it.

The Problem or Need

If the proposal is solicited: What do readers expect from your proposal?

If the proposal is unsolicited: Why should readers be interested in your proposal?

What problem or need does your proposal address?

Why is the problem or need important to readers?

Proposed Solution, Product, or Service

How will you solve the problem or satisfy the need? Specifically, what do you propose to make or to do?

Are other solutions, products, or services possible? If so, why have you chosen the solution, product, or service presented in the proposal? How does your choice compare with the other possible solutions?

How will readers view the solution, product, or service you've selected?

The Plan of Work

What will you do?

How long will the plan take?

Is the plan reasonable?

Why should readers believe that you can do what you propose?

How much will the proposed solution cost?

Is the proposed solution worth that cost to readers?

Why should readers believe that they can depend on you or your company to do what you propose?

To answer those questions, you need to research the readers and their organization. You might find out about the organization's history, its financial standing and goals, and its organizational hierarchy. You also can research the organization's corporate culture to see how it might affect readers' perspectives and ideas. With this information, you can better anticipate readers' questions and provide persuasive answers.

In addition to anticipating reader's questions, consider what you and your organization can realistically propose and the strengths and weaknesses of your proposal. These questions will help you to evaluate what you are proposing:

The Problem or Need

How can the proposal demonstrate that you understand the problem or need?

Should you restate the problem or need to show readers that you understand it?

Proposed Solution, Product, or Service

How can you reasonably solve the problem or meet readers' needs?

What are the strengths of your solution, product, or service? How can you emphasize them?

What are the weaknesses of your solution, product, or service? How can you counter them and readers' possible objections to them?

How does your solution, product, or service meet readers' needs?

THE READER'S CORNER

Presidential Proposals

As one of three equal branches in the federal government, the president of the United States often has exerted executive power only by persuading the other branches, especially the legislature, to act in concert with his office. Many famous presidential addresses to Congress were essentially proposals, and some were more successful than others. One notable failure occurred in January 1918 when President Woodrow Wilson proposed that his "Fourteen Points" were the "only possible" program for world peace after the end of the Great War—World War I. A fierce moralist, Wilson struck many members of Congress as too overbearing when he presented his principle of universal justice as the only solution, without which "no part of the structure of international justice can stand. The people of the United States could act upon no other principle." His Fourteen Points did in fact become the basis for the League of Nations, but—to Wilson's deep disappointment—Congress refused to allow America to join. Would the result have differed if Wilson's proposal had been more diplomatic—more "reader oriented"?

President Franklin Delano Roosevelt was a more canny politician, as his proposal of war against Japan, after the attack on Pearl Harbor, shows. Even though Congress was almost certain to approve his proposal, Roosevelt was noticeably more diplomatic—more "reader oriented"—than Wilson in his presentation: "I believe I interpret the will of the Congress and of the people when I assert that we will . . . make very certain that this form of treachery shall never endanger us again . . . I ask that the Congress declare [a state of war to now exist]."

Can you and your company reasonably carry out the solution, product, or service?

How can you make the solution, product, or service attractive to readers without compromising what you and your company can actually do?

The Plan of Work

What are the strengths of your plan?

What are the weaknesses of your plan? How can you counter the weaknesses and readers' objections to them?

How can you demonstrate that you and your company are qualified and that readers can depend on you to do what you propose?

Is the plan one that you and your company can reasonably carry out?

How can you make your plan attractive to readers without overstating what you and your company can do?

Does the budget reflect the actual cost of the plan? Have you justified your budget and anticipated readers' possible objections to it?

Those questions will help you to develop and then to evaluate your proposal. You want to make sure that your proposal will appeal to readers without compromising what you and your company can actually do. Figure 13.2 relates the questions presented in this section to the conventional elements of proposals, discussed in the next section.

Figure 13.2 Readers' and Writers' Questions About the Conventional Elements of a Proposal

Element	Writers' Questions	Readers' Questions
Introduction and problem definition	How can the proposal demonstrate that you understand the problem or need? Should you restate the problem or need to show readers that you understand it?	*If the proposal is solicited:* What do readers expect from your proposal? *If the proposal is unsolicited:* Why should readers be interested in your proposal? What problem or need does your proposal address? Why is the problem or need important to readers?
Proposed solution, product, or service	How can you reasonably solve the problem or meet readers' needs? What are the strengths of your solution, product, or service? How can you emphasize those strengths? What are the weaknesses of your solution, product, or service? How can you counter those weaknesses and readers' objections to them? How does your solution, product, or service meet readers' needs? Can you and your company reasonably carry out the solution, product, or service? How can you make the solution, product, or service attractive to readers without compromising what you and your company can actually do?	How will you solve the problem or satisfy the need? Specifically, what do you propose to make or to do? Are other solutions, products, or services possible? If so, why have you chosen the solution, product, or service presented in the proposal? How does your choice compare with the other possibilities? How will readers view the solution, product, or service you've selected? *(continued on next page)*

Figure 13.2 (cont.)

Element	Writers' Questions	Readers' Questions
Plan of work	What are the strengths of your plan? What are the weaknesses of your plan? How can you counter those weaknesses and the readers' objections to them? Is the plan one that you and your company can reasonably carry out? How can you make your plan attractive to readers without overstating what you and your company can do?	What will you do? How long will the plan take? Is the plan reasonable?
Qualifications	How can you demonstrate that you and your company are qualified and that the readers can depend on you to do what you propose?	Why should readers believe that you can do what you propose? Why should readers believe that they can depend on you or your company to do what you propose?
Budget	Does the budget reflect the actual cost of the plan? Have you justified your budget and anticipated readers' possible objections to it?	How much will the proposed solution cost? Is the proposed solution worth that cost to readers?

PRINCIPLE 3: CONSIDER THE CONVENTIONAL ELEMENTS OF PROPOSALS

As the five scenarios presented earlier illustrate, you may write proposals in response to many different situations. The formats for the proposals vary with the situations. If your proposal is formal, you might choose to include a letter of transmittal, title page, table of contents, and summary. If your proposal is informal, you might select a letter or memo format (see Chapter 17 for information on letters and memos). Whether you use a format with front matter or a letter or memo format, your proposal will have some or all of the conventional elements discussed in this chapter. From one organization to another, these elements may have different names; but their purpose remains the same. For example, instead of *problem definition* your company may use the phrase "scope of work," and instead of *budget* your company may use "cost estimates." If your company prefers certain names for the elements or requires certain elements to appear in its proposals, use those names and include those elements. If you are responding to a request for a proposal (RFP) or a request for a bid, the request may specify the elements and the format that you should follow. Follow the specifications of the requesters; otherwise, they may reject your proposal or bid.

Most readers generally want a description of the project—including a statement of the problem; the proposed solution, product, or service; your plan for solving the problem or providing the proposed product or service; and the cost. Many readers also will want to know whether you and your company are qualified to do what you propose. Most proposals contain these conventional elements:

Summary

Description of the proposed project

    Introduction

    Problem definition

    Proposed solution

    Plan of work

Qualifications

    Personnel

    Resources

Budget

Conclusion

The following sections describe these conventional elements. These elements correspond to the questions that readers may ask and questions that you should ask (see Figure 13.2).

Summary

The summary is a condensed version of your proposal. Because readers will look at the summary first, it is often crucial to the success of a proposal. Based on the summary, many readers may decide whether or not to consider a proposal. In fact, many readers may read only the summary. Readers who have many proposals in response to one request for proposals (RFP) may use the summaries to determine which proposals to consider seriously.

The summary contains essential information about the proposed solution, product, or service; the plan of work; and the cost of the proposal. In other words, the summary

- Concisely states the problem or need addressed in the proposal
- Summarizes the proposed solution, product, or service, and shows how it meets readers' needs and requirements
- Describes your plan for carrying out the proposed solution, work, product, or service
- Summarizes the qualifications of you and your organization (optional)
- Summarizes the budget (optional)

Figure 13.3

The Summary from an Unsolicited Proposal

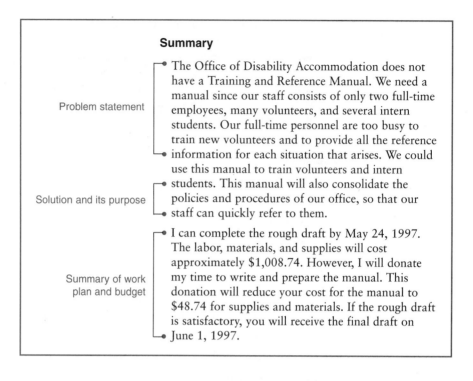

Summary

Problem statement

The Office of Disability Accommodation does not have a Training and Reference Manual. We need a manual since our staff consists of only two full-time employees, many volunteers, and several intern students. Our full-time personnel are too busy to train new volunteers and to provide all the reference information for each situation that arises. We could use this manual to train volunteers and intern

Solution and its purpose

students. This manual will also consolidate the policies and procedures of our office, so that our staff can quickly refer to them.

Summary of work plan and budget

I can complete the rough draft by May 24, 1997. The labor, materials, and supplies will cost approximately $1,008.74. However, I will donate my time to write and prepare the manual. This donation will reduce your cost for the manual to $48.74 for supplies and materials. If the rough draft is satisfactory, you will receive the final draft on June 1, 1997.

The summary is a powerful tool. An effective summary persuades readers to read more about your proposed project. Figure 13.3 presents the summary from an unsolicited proposal for a training and reference manual for a university Office of Disability Accommodation.

Description of the Proposed Project

The description of the proposed project is the heart of the proposal. It presents detailed information about the problem or need; the solution, product, or service; and the plan. The description may include an introduction, problem description, proposed solution, and work plan.

Introduction

The introduction briefly describes the project that you are proposing and tells why you are proposing it. For example, you might state that you are writing in response to a request from readers or to a specific request for proposals. In the introduction, you also can tell readers what follows in the proposal. The writers of the example shown in Figure 13.4 combine the introduction and the summary; this combination is common in short and informal proposals. The writers identify the problem that they are addressing: "to develop a conceptual closure plan for the Caney Branch Ash Disposal Area." They then give some

Figure 13.4

The Introduction to a
Solicited Proposal

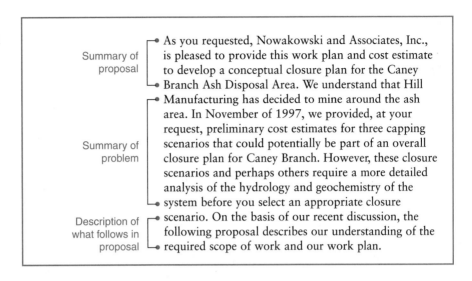

Summary of proposal — As you requested, Nowakowski and Associates, Inc., is pleased to provide this work plan and cost estimate to develop a conceptual closure plan for the Caney Branch Ash Disposal Area. We understand that Hill

Summary of problem — Manufacturing has decided to mine around the ash area. In November of 1997, we provided, at your request, preliminary cost estimates for three capping scenarios that could potentially be part of an overall closure plan for Caney Branch. However, these closure scenarios and perhaps others require a more detailed analysis of the hydrology and geochemistry of the system before you select an appropriate closure

Description of what follows in proposal — scenario. On the basis of our recent discussion, the following proposal describes our understanding of the required scope of work and our work plan.

details about how they will develop the plan. They also describe what follows in the proposal: "the following proposal describes our understanding of the required scope of work and our work plan."

Problem Definition

Once you have told readers what you are proposing, convince them that you understand the work that you are proposing and that you designed your solution and work plan after studying their needs. If the proposal is unsolicited, convince readers that the proposal addresses a significant problem or need and demonstrate how that problem or need affects them. Persuade them first that a problem or need truly exits and then that it is important to them.

Anticipate and answer any questions that readers may have, so they know that you clearly understand their situation. (Figure 13.2 lists questions that readers might ask as they read any problem description. Your readers may have other questions about the specific matter addressed in your proposal.) Depending on whether the proposal is solicited or unsolicited, the problem definition may

- Define the problem—in detail for an unsolicited proposal and with less detail for a solicited proposal.
- Give the background of the problem or need or explain how it developed (primarily for unsolicited proposals). The background may help readers to understand that a significant problem exists or that you understand their needs.
- Explain why the work that you propose is necessary (for unsolicited proposals). For instance, if you are proposing a research project, explain why the research is important.

Figure 13.5

The Problem-
Definition Section of a
Solicited Proposal

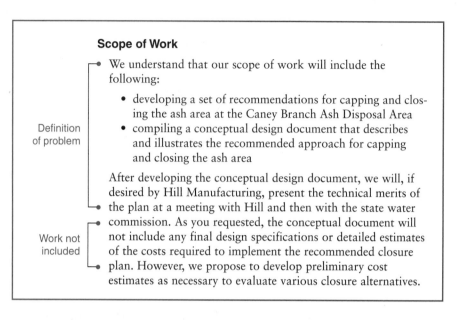

Figure 13.5 presents the problem-definition section of a solicited proposal. The readers know what their needs are, so the primary purpose of this problem-definition section is to show that the writers understand the readers' needs. Thus, the writers restate the work that the readers expect of them.

Figure 13.6 shows the problem-definition section of an unsolicited proposal sent to the Office of Disability Accommodation. Using examples and terms the readers will understand, the writer specifically explains the problems resulting from the turnover of volunteers and students. This problem-definition section (called "Current Problems") points out why the problems are significant. The writer explains, for example, that these problems prevent the office from creating "the positive image that the students and the faculty need" and "slow the work of the office."

Proposed Solution and Work Plan

After describing the problem or need, explain the proposed solution, product, or service. Link the proposed solution to the problem by explaining how that solution will solve the problem or meet readers' needs. As you describe the proposed solution, product, or service, explain how you plan to do the proposed work. The work plan will help readers who are trying to determine whether you really understand the scope of the work you are proposing. Therefore, present a detailed, step-by-step plan for carrying out the work, justifying your plan and anticipating readers' questions (see Figure 13.2).

In some work plans, you may want to explain not only what you and your company will do but also what you will not do. Your readers have a legal and ethical right to understand what you and your company are proposing and also what you are not proposing. If you do not tell readers what you will and

Figure 13.6
The Problem-
Definition Section of
an Unsolicited
Proposal

Current Problems at the Office of Disability Accommodation

The Office of Disability Accommodation uses many volunteers and students. These volunteers and students may work in the office for only a semester, creating a large turnover. They may work as few as 5 or as many as 20 hours per week. With the number of these volunteers and students and the high turnover, the office frequently has workers who do not understand how to do the various tasks assigned to them. To complete their assigned tasks, the volunteers and students frequently must interrupt you and your administrative assistant or other workers. These frequent interruptions slow the work of the office. The volunteers and students have to interrupt others because they do not understand how to

- handle most student and faculty problems independently
- operate the various office computers and equipment correctly
- administer basic office policies and procedures.

Frequently, the volunteers and students will decide to handle a faculty or student problem independently even though they do not completely understand how to handle that problem. Such actions can create other problems that you or your administrative assistant must then handle. For example, a new volunteer might tell a faculty member that the office will be happy to monitor an exam for any student with a disability when in fact we only monitor exams for students who must use the technology in the computer lab for disability accommodation. Such mishandling is frustrating for you, your assistant, students, and faculty members. The volunteers and students frequently must also ask questions about simple tasks such as running the copy machine or processing a student or faculty request because they have not received any training and do not have any written source of information about office machinery or policies and procedures.

The purpose of this office is to help students with disabilities by informing faculty and students about appropriate and necessary accommodation and also to help faculty to understand how to accommodate. When this office runs inefficiently and makes mistakes because of uninformed and untrained volunteers and students, we don't create the positive image that the students and the faculty need.

---

will not do, they may expect more than you intend. You can prevent such miscommunication by spelling out exactly what you are and are not proposing.

The proposed solution and work plan in the proposal for Hill Manufacturing appear in the sections titled "Work Plan" and "Schedule" in Figure 13.9 (see page 345). In this proposal the writer links the proposed solution and work plan to the problem. Figure 13.7 shows how the writer (Nowakowski) links the solution and work plan directly to the reader's (Hill's) problems and needs. In the problem-definition section (called "Scope of Work" in Figure 13.9), the writer mentions three areas of work: "developing a set of recommendations for capping and closing the ash area," "compiling a

Figure 13.7

The Link Between the
Problems of Hill
Manufacturing and
the Work Proposed
by Nowakowski and
Associates

Hill's Problems/Needs	Nowakowski's Solution/Work Plan to Solve the Problem/Need
Set of recommendations for capping and closing the ash area at the Caney Branch Ash Disposal Area	Task 1. Review data and develop preliminary closure options Task 2. Collect and analyze additional data Task 3 (partial). Evaluate closure alternatives
Conceptual design document that describes and illustrates the recommended approach for capping and closing the ash area	Task 3 (partial). Develop a conceptual closure plan
Presentation of the technical merits of the plan at meetings with Hill and the state water commission	Task 4. Attend strategic planning meetings

conceptual design document," and "a meeting with Hill and then with the state water commission." In the "Work Plan" section the writer mentions these three areas in the list of tasks and explains how the tasks will fulfill the work requested by Hill. The proposal writer lists and describes the tasks necessary to carry out the work and then presents a schedule.

Many proposal writers include a visual aid, such as a time line or chart, of the schedule. Whether you do or not include a visual aid, as you prepare the schedule for a proposal, allow ample time to complete each phase of the work plan. Be careful not to underestimate the amount of time you or your company needs. Readers will prefer a realistic schedule instead of an overly optimistic schedule that is impossible to meet.

Qualifications

The qualifications section, also called project organization, facilities, or personnel, is important for readers who want to know whether you and your company are capable of carrying out the work that you propose. This section generally includes some or all of the following information:

- **Qualifications of the people (including yourself, if necessary) who will carry out the work plan.** You can include a paragraph summarizing each person's qualifications for the project, or you can attach résumés in an appendix. If you attach résumés, use the qualifications section to introduce the project personnel and refer readers to the appendix, or summarize each person's qualifications and then refer readers to the résumés in the appendix.

ISSUES IN CONTEXT

The Future of Proposals

With the explosion of software and of electronic communication via the Internet and the World Wide Web, the process of creating proposals is changing, especially in companies whose business depends in part on proposals (Cobb; Fry). Neil Cobb, a manager and proposal developer for a telecommunications company, has been writing proposals since the early 1990s. In the early 1990s, his teams for the most part wrote each proposal "from scratch," occasionally using pieces from previously written proposals. In the mid 1990s, his teams began to use electronic "libraries" and software to create some types of proposals. His teams created an online library of product descriptions, solutions, plans of action, budgets, and so on from successful proposals. Proposal writers and coworkers throughout the company could access this library to create "cut and paste" proposals. His teams also created software that would create small business proposals for some of the company's services. Other companies are also using proposal software to help their employees create proposals (Fry).

As Cobb and his teams move toward 2000, they are developing an online proposal center that employees can access by way of the Internet. Their employees can use this online center to create proposals for all the services offered by the company. Will their potential customers also work by way of the Internet and the Web? Will they expect companies to send proposals and to respond to requests for proposals (RFP) online? Some companies are already sending requests for proposals online and asking those responding to do so by way of the Web. This online trend is certainly changing the process of writing proposals and will perhaps change the medium for delivering proposals.

- **Qualifications of the company.** For some proposals, you may need to "sell" your company's qualifications. You can demonstrate to readers that the company has carried out similar work and has the facilities and knowledge to successfully and efficiently complete the work. In this section, you might give readers a brief background of your company and projects that it has completed successfully. You also can include information on specific facilities that the company will use to complete the work—especially if those facilities compare favorably with industry standards or your competitors.

Figure 13.8 shows the qualifications section from the Hill Manufacturing proposal. The writers summarize the qualifications of the people who will carry out the proposed work. The writers also include specific information

Figure 13.8
The Qualifications
Section of a Proposal

Qualifications

Bob Congrove, P.E., Senior Engineer, will serve as project manager and will provide much of the technical analysis and input for developing the conceptual closure plan. Mr. Congrove served as project manager for the Caney Branch Phase II Investigation and knows the conditions and water commission permitting processes and requirements.

Alejandro Martinez, P.E., Senior Civil Engineer, will provide conceptual design input on engineered components of the closure plan, such as capping specifications, and will assess the technical and financial feasibility of various closure options. Mr. Martinez has over 22 years of applied engineering experience, including designing landfill caps, liner systems, and slurry walls, and developing landfill closure plans.

Brandon McCarroll, Principal Hydrogeologist, will provide input about geochemical processes affecting the mobility of ash leachate constituents. In addition, Donna Camp, Ben Armstrong, and Terry Huey (support staff) have recently worked on ash disposal projects and associated water commission permitting. As necessary, they will provide technical input and review. They will also participate in meetings with Hill Manufacturing and the water commission.

about each person's responsibilities on the project and explain why each person is uniquely qualified to work on the project. The writers don't present résumés in an appendix because their company has previously worked with Hill Manufacturing.

Budget

The budget, sometimes called cost estimate or cost proposal, is an itemized list of the estimated costs of the work plan. When you prepare a budget, carefully estimate the cost of labor, equipment, and any materials needed to carry out the work plan. For some proposals, readers will expect a justification along with the budget. The budget justification explains each budgeted item and its purpose for the proposed solution. Estimate as accurately as possible; don't underestimate your costs in trying to get a proposal accepted. If readers accept the proposal, you will be bound by your estimate. If it is too low, you and your new company could lose money.

The budget for the Hill Manufacturing proposal (see Figure 13.9) is in a section titled "Cost Estimate." There, the writers present a total estimate for the project and separate estimates for each task.

Conclusion

In most proposals, a conclusion briefly restates the problem or need and the proposed solution. The conclusion also restates

- What the proposal offers readers
- How the proposal will benefit readers
- Why readers should accept the proposal
- Why readers should accept you and your company to carry out the proposed solution

For short proposals in memo or letter format, the conclusion is likely to be a brief statement of whom readers should call if they have questions.

TWO SAMPLE PROPOSALS

The two sample proposals in Figures 13.9 and 13.10 illustrate conventional proposal elements. In Figure 13.9, an environmental sciences and engineering firm is responding to a request for proposals (RFP). The writers propose to prepare a plan for capping and closing an ash area at a lignite mine owned by Hill Manufacturing. In Figure 13.10, a student proposes a manual for the Office of Disability Accommodation at her university. This office helps students with disabilities receive appropriate accommodation from the university and helps faculty members who have these students in their classes. The readers of her proposal are the director and assistant director of that office.

WORKSHEET for Planning and Writing Your Proposals

Principle 1: Find Out About the Readers of Your Proposals

- Will more than one group of readers read the proposal? If so, what sections will each group read?
- What do readers know about the problem or need that led to the proposal?
- What do readers know about you or your company? Have previous experiences been positive? If not, what can you do to counter the experiences?

Principle 2: Prepare to Answer Readers' Questions

- Have you answered all the writers' questions in Figure 13.2?
- Have you answered all the readers' questions in Figure 13.2?

Principle 3: Consider the Conventional Elements of Proposals

- Does the summary summarize the problem or need; the proposed solution, product, or service; and the work plan?
- Does the introduction briefly describe the proposed work and its purpose?

- Does the problem definition define the problem or need, present any necessary background, and explain why the work is necessary?
- Do the proposed solution and work plan directly relate to the problem or need? Do the proposed solution and work plan clearly demonstrate this relationship? Are the solution and work plan detailed, clear, and reasonable?
- Does the qualifications section clearly detail relevant skills and experience of you, other participants, and your company? Does the qualifications section detail your company's equipment and facilities (if necessary)?
- Is the budget complete and accurate?

Figure 13.9 A Solicited Proposal Prepared by Nowakowski and Associates for
Hill Manufacturing

Nowakowski & Associates, Inc.
243 26th Street, Suite 808
Montrose, Colorado 80303-2317
303/555-1823 Fax: 303/555-1836

March 24, 1998

Ms. Ginny Thompson
Hill Manufacturing
400 North Vintage Street
St. Louis, Missouri 75201

The writer identifies the document as a proposal.

Re: Work Plan and Cost Estimate to Develop a Conceptual Closure Plan for
the Caney Branch Ash Disposal Facility, Martin Lake

Dear Ms. Thompson:

The writer combines the summary and introduction. Here, the writer describes the problem, the proposed work, and the organization of the proposal.

As you requested, Nowakowski and Associates, Inc., is pleased to provide this
work plan and cost estimate to develop a conceptual closure plan for the
Caney Branch Ash Disposal Area. We understand that Hill Manufacturing has
decided to mine around the ash area. In November of 1997, we provided, at
your request, preliminary cost estimates for three capping scenarios that could
potentially be part of an overall closure plan for Caney Branch. However,
these closure scenarios and perhaps others require a more detailed analysis of
the hydrology and geochemistry of the system before you select an appropriate
closure scenario. On the basis of our recent discussion, the following proposal
describes our understanding of the required scope of work and our work plan.

Scope of Work

Because the proposal is solicited, the writer only briefly states the scope of work. The writer also states the work that the project will not *include.*

We understand that our scope of work will include the following:

- developing a set of recommendations for capping and closing the ash
  area at the Caney Branch Ash Disposal Area (Caney Branch)
- compiling a conceptual design document that describes and illustrates
  the recommended approach for capping and closing the ash area

After developing the conceptual design document, we will, if desired by Hill
Manufacturing, present the technical merits of the plan at a meeting with Hill
and then with the state water commission. As you requested, the conceptual
document will not include any final design specifications or detailed estimates
of the costs required to implement the recommended closure plan. However,
we propose to develop preliminary cost estimates as necessary to evaluate
various closure alternatives.

Work Plan

The writer provides an overview of the work plan.

To develop the conceptual closure plan, we will balance the level of effort and
associated costs for preparing the plan with the requirements to provide
sufficient documentation and justification for addressing possible questions

Figure 13.9 (cont.)

from the state water commission. We will work closely with Hill to ensure that the level of effort and work are consistent with Hill objectives. We will complete four tasks to complete the work that Hill requires.

The writer describes in detail each task in the work plan.

Task 1. Reviewing Data and Developing Preliminary Closure Options

We request that Hill Manufacturing provide any water level data, sump discharge volume data, and sump water quality data obtained at Caney Branch since the Phase II Investigation (1996–1997). We will review these data, along with the historical data provided in the Phase II Report, to further develop possible closure options. In developing a preliminary list of closure options, we will review correspondence from the state water commission and registration papers regarding Caney Branch. We will also examine the water commission's precedents for closure of ash disposal areas at other lignite mines in the state. We will also use these reviews to further evaluate possible data gaps in the various closure options.

Task 2. Collecting and Analyzing Additional Data

During task 2, we will evaluate the need for collecting additional data; we currently envision two specific needs. The latest water-level readings, taken in selected ash and overburden wells at Caney Branch, were measured in early May of 1997. The last complete set of readings for all wells occurred in October of 1997. Historically, water levels in the ash have generally exhibited an upward trend but may be approaching a quasi-static condition. The quasi-static water level in the ash under present stratigraphic conditions is important because it serves as a "baseline" when estimating the long-term water-level conditions in a post-mining scenario. Therefore, we propose to obtain another set of water-level measurements in wells within and near Caney Branch to evaluate the "baseline" condition.

We also foresee the need for new data on the ground-water chemistry for ash and overburden wells. Because attenuation of ash leachate constituents will likely be a critical basis for limiting the scope of closure activities, we will collect samples from selected wells to confirm that ash leachate constituents are continuing to attenuate. We presently anticipate that collecting and analyzing the samples from six monitoring wells will be sufficient to document that attenuation.

We will collect and analyze the samples in the same manner as in the Phase II Investigation. Field analyses would include Ph, Eh, specific conductance, and temperature. However, we will analyze the samples in the lab for a shorter list of constituents than those evaluated during the Phase II Investigation. The proposed list of constituents includes calcium (dissolved), magnesium (dissolved), sodium (dissolved), potassium (dissolved), chloride, sulfate, alkalinity, boron (dissolved), and selenium (dissolved). We will be most interested in the key parameters of sulfate, boron, and selenium. To estimate cost, we have assumed that Core Laboratories, which analyzed the water samples for Phase II, will analyze the samples. However, if desired, the Hill Manufacturing lab could analyze the samples.

Figure 13.9 (cont.)

G. Thompson   3   March 24, 1998

Task 3. Evaluating Closure Alternatives and Developing a Conceptual Closure Plan
The current mine plan calls for mining within 400 feet of Caney Branch. This plan will have substantial effects on both the short- and long-term hydrogeologic conditions near the ash area. Therefore, we will consider these effects when evaluating the closure options:

- effects of mining on the rate of ash water leaching
- extent of ash area dewatering caused by adjacent mining and the possible effects on induration of the ash
- time required to resaturate the spoil and ash material after mining
- post-mining hydrologic conditions (effects of spoil characteristics, ponds, etc., on post-mining hydrology)
- historical and future attenuation of ash water constituents
- hydrologic effects of constructing a flow barrier between the ash area and Barrier Lake (A slurry wall is currently not a preferred option, but we will review it to address possible questions from the water commission or to provide an alternative.)
- cost-feasibility of various construction options
- applicability of the water commission's Draft Risk Reduction Rules to Caney Branch
- potential post-closure care requirements and costs.

Although we don't anticipate substantial modeling efforts associated with developing the conceptual plan, the existing model developed during the Phase II Investigation will help us to address some of the hydrologic issues. In some cases, we can use previous model simulations to assess an issue; and in other cases, we anticipate performing additional simulations. We anticipate using the HELP (Hydrologic Evaluation of Landfill Performance) model to evaluate the hydrology of various capping scenarios. In other cases, we will draw on experience at the Barrier Lake Mine and perhaps simple hydraulic calculations of water balance to develop estimates. The actual level of effort and list of critical issues will depend upon which closure options we evaluate.

We anticipate developing a narrative to justify and describe the conceptual closure plan and simple conceptual design drawings to illustrate the closure concept. We will present the draft closure plan to Hill Manufacturing at a meeting (Task 4). The report to Hill will not include complete documentation of model results and analytical analyses as part of the conceptual planning.

Task 4. Attend Strategic Planning Meetings
We will estimate the time and material expenses required to prepare for and present the technical merits of the proposed conceptual closure plan in meetings with Hill Manufacturing and the water commission. Our cost estimate assumes two meetings, one with Hill Manufacturing and one with the water commission.

Figure 13.9 (cont.)

G. Thompson   4   March 24, 1998

The writer describes the schedule for completing the work.

Schedule

We estimate 8 weeks for drafting the conceptual closure plan. We assume that Hill Manufacturing can provide during the first week of the project any additional data that they have collected since 1997 (see Task 1). We anticipate performing the field work associated with Task 2 within the first two weeks of the project. We will proceed with Tasks 1 and 3 while the lab analyzes the additional water samples (two- to three-week turnaround). After we receive the sample results, we estimate that we can finalize the conceptual closure plan in approximately three weeks.

The writer introduces the budget.

Cost Estimate

We propose to execute the work plan on a time and materials basis according to our 1998 Schedule of Charges. We will provide periodic reports to the Hill Manufacturing Project Manager detailing the progress of the project and will work closely with Hill Manufacturing personnel to streamline the work effort and ensure that the project deliverables are consistent with Hill Manufacturing expectations. We will not exceed the following total cost estimate without authorization from Hill Manufacturing. If the project requires less effort, the invoiced amount will be less than the estimated budget.

The writer presents a detailed budget for each task.

Task 1: Labor

Principal	4 hrs. @ $110/hr.	$ 440
Senior	24 hrs. @ $90/hr.	2,160
Staff	4 hrs. @ $55/hr.	220
Support Staff	3 hrs. @ $30/hr.	90
		$2,910

Task 1: Expenses

Communication/Shipping	$ 75
Photocopies	25
	$ 100

TASK 1 TOTAL   **$3,010**

Task 2: Labor

Principal	2 hrs. @ $110/hr.	$ 220
Senior	16 hrs. @ $90/ hr.	1,440
Staff	30 hrs. @ $55/hr.	1,650
Support Staff	2 hrs. @ $30/hr.	60
		$3,370

Task 2: Expenses

Vehicle		$ 250
Per Diem	2.5 days @ $70/day	175
Sampling Equipment		100
Communication/Shipping		200
Photocopies		25
		$ 750

Figure 13.9 (cont.)

G. Thompson   5   March 24, 1998

Task 2: Outside Services

Lab Analyses	6 samples @ $108/sample	$ 648
10% Handling		65
		$ 713

TASK 2 TOTAL   **$4,833**

Task 3: Labor

Principal	32 hrs. @ $100/hr.	$ 3,200
Senior	140 hrs. @ $90/hr.	12,600
Project	16 hrs. @ $75/hr.	1,200
Staff	40 hrs. @ $55/hr.	2,200
Drafting	24 hrs. @ $40/hr.	960
Support	12 hrs. @ $30/hr.	360
		$20,520

Task 3: Expenses

Communication/Shipping	$ 200
Photocopies/Reproducing	200
	$400

TASK 3 TOTAL   **$20,920**

Task 4: Labor

Principal	20 hrs. @ $100/hr.	$2,000
Senior	20 hrs. @ $90/hr.	1,800
Support Staff	4 hrs. @ $30/hr.	120
		$3,920

Task 4: Expenses

Travel	$ 200
Communication/Shipping	$150
Photocopies/Reproducing	25
	$375

TASK 4 TOTAL   **$4,295**

ESTIMATED PROJECT TOTAL   **$33,058**

The writer describes the qualifications of all the people who will complete the tasks.

Qualifications

Bob Congrove, P.E., Senior Engineer, will serve as project manager and will provide much of the technical analysis and input for developing the conceptual closure plan. Mr. Congrove served as project manager for the Caney Branch Phase II Investigation and knows the conditions and water commission permitting processes and requirements.

Alejandro Martinez, P.E., Senior Civil Engineer, will provide conceptual design input on engineered components of the closure plan, such as capping specifications, and will assess the technical and financial feasibility of various closure options. Mr. Martinez has over 22 years of applied engineering experience, including designing landfill caps, liner systems, and slurry walls, and developing landfill closure plans.

Figure 13.9 (cont.)

G. Thompson 6 March 24, 1998

Brandon McCarroll, Principal Hydrogeologist, will provide input about geochemical processes affecting the mobility of ash leachate constituents. In addition, Donna Camp, Ben Armstrong, and Terry Huey (support staff) have recently worked on ash disposal projects and associated water commission permitting. As necessary, they will provide technical input and review. They will also participate in meetings with Hill Manufacturing and the water commission.

If you have any questions about our recommended approach for developing the conceptual plan or about any other aspect of this proposal, please feel free to call.

Sincerely,

Tom J. Nowakowski
Senior Engineer
Project Manager

Figure 13.10 An Unsolicited Proposal Written by a Student

Proposal to Create a Training and Reference Manual
for the Office of Disability Accommodation

The writer summarizes the problem, solution, schedule, and budget.

Summary

The Office of Disability Accommodation does not have a Training and Reference Manual. We need a manual since our staff consists of only two full-time employees, many volunteers, and several intern students. Our full-time personnel are too busy to train new volunteers and to provide all the reference information for each situation that arises. We could use this manual to train volunteers and intern students. This manual will also consolidate the policies and procedures of our office, so that our staff can quickly refer to them.

I can complete the rough draft by May 24, 1998. The labor, materials, and supplies will cost approximately $1,008.74. However, I will donate my time to write and prepare the manual. This donation will reduce your cost for the manual to $48.74 for supplies and materials. If the rough draft is satisfactory, you will receive the final draft on June 1, 1998.

The writer uses informative headings.

The writer describes the nature of the problems and then cites specific examples of the problems.

Current Problems at the Office of Disability Accommodation

The Office of Disability Accommodation uses many volunteers and students. These volunteers and students may work in the office for only a semester, creating a large turnover. They may work as few as 5 or as many as 20 hours per week. With the number of these volunteers and students and the high turnover, the office frequently has workers who do not understand how to do the various tasks assigned to them. To complete their assigned tasks, the volunteers and students frequently must interrupt you and your administrative assistant or other workers. These interruptions slow the work of the office. The volunteers and students have to interrupt others because they do not understand how to

- handle most student and faculty problems independently
- operate the various office computers and equipment correctly
- administer basic office policies and procedures

Frequently, the volunteers and students will handle a faculty or student problem independently even though they do not completely understand how to handle that problem. Such actions can create other problems that you or your administrative assistant must then handle. For example, a new volunteer might tell a faculty member that the office will be happy to monitor an exam for any student with a disability, when in fact we only monitor exams for students who must use the technology in the computer lab for disability accommodation. Such mishandling is frustrating for you, your assistant, students, and faculty members. The volunteers and students frequently must also ask questions about simple tasks such as running the copy machine or processing a student or faculty request because they have not received any training and do not have any written source of information about office machinery or policies and procedures.

Figure 13.10 (cont.)

2

The purpose of this office is to help students with disabilities by informing faculty and students about appropriate and necessary accommodation and also to help faculty to understand how to accommodate. When this office runs inefficiently and makes mistakes because of uninformed and untrained volunteers and students, we don't create the positive image that the students and the faculty need.

The writer links the solution to the problems listed in "Current Problems."

Proposed Solution: A Training and Reference Manual

The proposed Training and Reference Manual will provide new volunteers and intern students with the training and information to

- handle most student and faculty problems independently
- operate the various office computers and equipment correctly
- quickly learn the basic policies and procedures.

I will write the Training and Reference Manual from my experience and will consult with your administrative assistant for technical information. The Training and Reference Manual will include the following sections.

The writer presents a detailed outline to show how she will complete the proposed manual.

Answering Student Inquiries
- Telephone Inquiries
- In-House Visits

Working with New Students
- Necessary Forms and Procedures
- Campus Offices of Assistance

Working with Faculty Members
- Pre-Semester Notification Packets
- Faculty Guide

Using Office Equipment and Computers
- Equipment and Furniture
- Computers

Understanding Procedures
- Registering Students
  Early Registration
  Regular Registration

- Testing
  Regular Semester Exams
  Final Exam Procedures

- Filing
  Confidentiality
  Location of Different Files

- Issuing Elevator Keys
  Assigning Keys
  Returning Keys

Figure 13.10 (cont.)

3

Working with Various Groups with Disabilities
- Hearing Disabilities
- Visual Disabilities
- Motor/Mobility Disabilities
- Learning Disabilities
- Head-Injury Disabilities
- Hidden Disabilities
- Speech Disabilities

Working with Volunteers
- Applications
- On-Campus Service Groups

The writer includes a schedule.

I can complete the Training and Reference Manual during the next seven weeks. During the week of May 17, the office volunteers and students will use the rough draft and give me their comments. I will then submit the draft to you on May 24. If the draft is satisfactory, you will receive the completed manual on June 1, 1998.

My Qualifications for Writing the Proposed Manual

The writer describes her experience.

I have worked in the Office of Disability Accommodation and in the computer lab for disability accommodation for three years as a student volunteer. I have seen and experienced first-hand the problems and frustrations of not understanding how to handle a student or faculty problem. I have worked in all phases of the office and am able to write the proposed manual. In addition, I am a Senior majoring in rehabilitation therapy, so I understand the legal and ethical issues involved in working with students with disabilities.

Budget

The writer uses a table to present the budget.

The following table reflects the estimated cost of writing and printing the manual:

Items	Time and Supplies	Cost (dollars)
Writing and Editing the Manual	160 hours @ $6.00 per hour	960.00
Binding Costs	Vinyl Front and Back Spiral Binding	5.18
Colored Illustrations	10 pages @ $2.50 per page	25.00
Tab Inserts	$.89 for 5 pages x 4 packets	3.56
Copying Costs	300 pages @ $.05 a page	15.00
Total Cost		**$1,008.74**

Figure 13.10 (cont.)

4

I will donate my time in return for a receipt for my donation. Your cost for materials and supplies will be $48.74.

Conclusion

I am excited about the possibility of preparing this much-needed manual for our office. This manual will resolve our ongoing problem with training volunteers and students. I look forward to the possibility of working with you on this manual.

Source: Courtesy of LeNeva Bjelde Steiner.

EXERCISES

1. For your technical writing class, you will prepare a report. Follow these steps to select a topic and write a proposal for that report.

   - Make a list of possible topics, and gather some information about each one. You might select topics related to your major or to your current job.
   - Brainstorm about the feasibility of each topic. As you brainstorm, you might list the pros and cons of each topic and consider the amount of time you will have to complete the project and the importance of the topic to you, your career, and your field or workplace.
   - After you've thought about the pros and cons of each possible topic, select a topic and write a memo asking your instructor to approve your choice. In your memo, give your instructor enough information to understand and evaluate the topic.
   - After your instructor approves your topic, write a proposal to your instructor. Include all the con-

   ventional elements relevant to your proposal. (Your instructor may prefer that you write your proposal for a reader other than him or her. For instance, if you are proposing to research a problem at work, you might address the proposal to your manager.)

2. Evaluate your proposal using the questions listed in the "Worksheet for Planning Your Proposals." After you have evaluated your proposal, revise it based on your answers to the questions.

3. To complete this exercise, bring three copies of the proposal that you revised in Exercise 2. Using the copies of your proposal, three of your classmates will read and evaluate your proposal based on questions in the "Worksheet for Planning and Writing Your Proposals."

4. Based on your classmates' answers to the questions in Exercise 3, revise your proposal if necessary. Then prepare a final draft for your instructor.

CASE STUDY Working for the Community

Background

You probably are aware of many problems and needs on your college campus or in the surrounding community. For instance, your campus may have a shortage of parking places for commuter students or the computer labs may close too early in the evening. In the surrounding community, some children may not receive new toys at Christmas; or some families may not have enough food. These are only a few of the possible problems and needs that you might encounter.

Assignment

You or your team will write a proposal to solve a problem on your campus or in the surrounding community. To write this proposal, complete these steps:

1. Select a problem on campus or in the surrounding community. Make sure that you and all members of your team are familiar with the problem and that team members can gather the needed information about the problem to propose a solution in the allotted time.

2. Gather information about the problem and about readers of the proposal. Develop possible solutions to the problem.

3. Discuss the advantages, disadvantages, and feasibility of each solution. Then determine the most effective solution for the readers.

4. Write the proposal.

Chapter 14

Planning and Writing Reader-Oriented Progress Reports

CHAPTER OUTLINE

Progress reports describe the current status of a project. Readers of progress reports may be managers, clients, coworkers, or sponsors of a project. These reports have three primary purposes:

- To describe progress on one or more projects so readers can monitor the work
- To provide a written record of progress
- To document problems with, and changes to, a project

You may write progress reports in two types of contexts: when reporting your progress on one project or on several projects assigned to you. For example, Tom is an engineer for an architectural engineering firm. He spends 60 percent of his time working as the lead engineer on a plant design project for a power-generating company and 40 percent assisting on three other design projects. Once a month, Tom submits a progress report to the lead mechanical engineer of the power-generating company. In addition to this monthly progress report, Tom writes a biweekly progress report, where he reports not only on the plant project, but also on the other three design projects.

Besides helping readers to monitor Tom's progress, these reports provide a written record of that progress. This record gives readers evidence of Tom's work and a history of his work on the projects. Suppose Tom's company decides to postpone work on the power plant for one year. The monthly progress reports that he wrote before the delay will provide a record of the work previously done; so when the project starts up again, Tom or other engineers will be able to refer to the reports to determine where to resume work. The reports could prevent Tom or others from duplicating work completed before the company postponed the project.

Whether you write a progress report on one project or on several projects, consider your readers. Why will they read your report? How will they use it? What questions will they want it to answer? To help you meet these needs of your readers, this chapter presents three principles.

PRINCIPLE 1: FIND OUT ABOUT THE READERS OF YOUR PROGRESS REPORTS

You may submit a progress report to various readers who have different concerns as they read it. Let's consider Tom's progress reports again. When Tom submits his monthly progress report to the mechanical engineer outside his company, the engineer will want to know whether Tom has encountered any problems in his work and whether Tom's work is progressing according to schedule. The engineer may use the report to monitor Tom's efficiency—to make sure that Tom and his company are completing the planned work in the time promised. When Tom reports his progress on all his projects, he submits his biweekly report to several people in his company: to his supervisor, who uses these reports to ensure that the work in the division is progressing at an acceptable rate; to project leaders who will use the reports to monitor his work and his time management; and to managers who read the reports to monitor work flow and to decide when the division can begin new projects.

Figure 14.1

Readers' Questions About the Conventional Elements of a Progress Report

Element	Readers' Questions
Introduction	What project does the report cover?
	What time period does the report cover?
	What are the objectives of the project?
Discussion of the progress	What work have you accomplished since the beginning of the project or since the last progress report?
	Is the project progressing as planned?
	What work have you planned for the next reporting period or for the remainder of the project?
Results and problems*	What are the results of the work?
	What problems, if any, have you encountered?
Conclusions	What changes, if any, do you recommend?
	How will these changes affect the project?
	What is the overall status of the project?

* Results and problems generally appear in the "conclusions" and "discussion of progress" sections.

Before writing a progress report, find out who will read it and then try to anticipate the questions those readers may ask. Figure 14.1 presents questions that readers may ask and relates those questions to the conventional elements of a progress report, discussed later in this chapter.

PRINCIPLE 2: PREPARE TO ANSWER READERS' QUESTIONS

Whether you are reporting on one project or several, readers will ask questions about the project or work that the report covers, your progress, future work, and the overall status of the project.

To help readers understand your progress report, mention the time period and the specific project or projects that the report covers. Readers also want to know the objectives or purpose of the project, so they can determine how it relates to their responsibilities and to their company. This information helps readers to put your report in context. To create this context, consider these questions:

- What project does the report cover?
- What time period does the report cover?
- What are the objectives of the project?

Readers are interested in your specific accomplishments during the reporting period to see whether your work is progressing as planned. Readers will want to know your schedule and possibly your budget for the next reporting period or for the remainder of the project if you will not be writing any other progress reports. They also may want to know what kinds of results they can expect during the next reporting period. To describe your progress and to report work planned, consider these questions:

- What work have you accomplished since the beginning of the project or since the last progress report?
- Is the project progressing as planned?
- What work have you planned for the next reporting period or for the remainder of the project?

Readers also want to know the overall status of the project. If the project is not progressing as planned, they want to know what specific problems you have encountered, the effect of these problems on the project, and your recommendations for handling these problems. Some readers also will want to know the results of your work. This information may help readers to determine the future work on your projects and others. If you have recommendations for improving the project—regardless of whether it is progressing as planned or you have encountered problems—your readers may want to know your ideas. Readers may use the information about the overall status and your recommendations to determine whether to adjust the project, budget, schedule, and personnel. To report the overall status of your project, consider these questions:

- What are the results of the work?
- What problems, if any, have you encountered?
- What changes, if any, do you recommend?
- How will these changes affect the project?
- What is the overall status of the project?

PRINCIPLE 3: CONSIDER THE CONVENTIONAL ELEMENTS OF PROGRESS REPORTS

brief ltr

Progress reports vary in format and structure. Progress reports may be only brief letters, memos, e-mail, or even a telephone call. Some companies have preprinted forms for reporting on progress. Progress reports may be several pages long and may need some of the front matter and end matter described in Chapter 12. Most progress reports contain these conventional elements: introduction, discussion of the progress, and conclusions. This section describes how to include these elements in a reader-oriented progress report.

Introduction

In the introduction, you

- Identify the project or projects that the report covers
- State the time period that the report covers
- State the objectives of the project or projects (if readers need this information)

ISSUES IN CONTEXT

Progress Reports and Telecommuting

Does working at home and saving hours of driving sound appealing? Many companies are finding that their employees are more productive when they work at home—when they telecommute (Weber). However, telecommuting is not without its pitfalls. To improve productivity, employees and their managers need to set some guidelines. One of the most important of these guidelines is open lines of communication—before and during a project. At the beginning of the project, the team might follow these guidelines:

- Define the working relationship and role of each team member—if possible in a face-to-face meeting (Tumminello and Carlshamre; Weber).
- Make sure that each team member has explicit goals and weekly assignments (Weber).

Once a team has defined roles and set goals and assignments, the telecommuters can "go to work." To ensure that the project is successful, your team can follow these guidelines to keep the lines of communication open.

- Report your progress (or lack of progress) to your team and your manager. "Keeping in contact with team members is vital—your coworkers need to know what you are doing and that you are keeping up your share of work" (Weber 23).
- Honor checkpoints and deadlines. These become even more important when team members are working in different locations (Weber).
- Inform your team members and your manager "of where you are," how they can contact you, and when you won't be available during the working day (Weber 23).

During your career, you may be a telecommuter. Remember that communicating—especially your progress—will be key to your success.

Frequently, you can identify a project and its time period in one sentence such as, "This report covers progress on the Midwest Relocation project from January 1 through March 31." You would explain the objectives of your project to help readers put your report in context or to remind them of its purpose. For example, you might explain the problem you are trying to solve or the situation you are studying. You also can state the objectives as you defined them in the project proposal. Figure 14.2 shows a paragraph in which the writer states the objectives of a project and also identifies the project and the time period that the progress report covers.

Figure 14.2

The Introduction to a Progress Report

>   This letter describes the current status of, and progress on,
> Project information→ the lignite-handling system for the Old Eagles plant. The
> Objective of project→ purpose of this project is to renovate the current lignite-
> handling system at the plant. This letter covers our work
> on the obsolescence study, the mechanical engineering, the
> structural engineering, and the electrical engineering from
> Time period of→ July 1, 1998, to August 30, 1998.
>   project

Discussion of the Progress

The discussion of the progress answers readers' questions about how the project is proceeding and about what work you've planned for the next reporting period or for the remainder of the project (see Figure 14.1). Readers will be especially interested in

- How your progress compares with what you planned to accomplish during the reporting period
- Any problems that you have encountered
- The results of your work

Whether your progress report covers one project or several projects, you can organize the discussion of the progress in two ways:

- By the progress made during the reporting period and the progress expected during the next reporting period (see Figure 14.3)
- By the tasks or projects to be completed (see Figure 14.4)

Using the *progress-made/progress-expected pattern,* shown in Figure 14.3, you can organize the discussion around the progress made on one or several tasks or projects during the reporting period and the progress expected during

Figure 14.3

The Progress-Made/Progress-Expected Pattern

> I. Progress made during the current reporting period (the work that you accomplished during the time period covered by the progress report)
>
>   A. Task 1 (or Project 1)
>   B. Task 2 (or Project 2)
>   C. Task 3* (or Project 3)
>
> II. Progress expected during the next reporting period (the work that you expect to complete during the next reporting period)
>
>   A. Task 1 (or Project 1)
>   B. Task 2 (or Project 2)
>   C. Task 3 (or Project 3)
>
> *Your project may have more or fewer than three tasks.

Figure 14.4
The Task/Project
Pattern

> I.   Task 1 (or Project 1)
>
>   A. Progress made during the current reporting period (the work that you accomplished during the time period covered by the progress report)
>   B. Progress expected during the next reporting period (the work that you expect to complete during the next reporting period)
>
> II.   Task 2 (or Project 2)
>
>   A. Progress made during the current reporting period
>   B. Progress expected during the next reporting period
>
> III.   Task 3 (or Project 3)
>
>   A. Progress made during the current reporting period
>   B. Progress expected during the next reporting period

the next reporting period. Using the *task/project pattern,* shown in Figure 14.4, you can organize the discussion around one or several tasks or projects, discussing the progress made and expected on task or project 1, then moving to task or project 2, and so on.

The progress-made/progress-expected pattern emphasizes the total amount of progress you have made as well as the work you expect to do during the next reporting period. If progress has been slow during the period covered by the report, you may want to choose the task/project pattern. This pattern deemphasizes the amount of your progress or lack of progress.

Results and Problems

Readers are interested in any major results or problems that you encountered during the reporting period. They need information about results and problems, so they can approve or change the project, budget, schedule, or personnel. By including information about problems, you document those problems and possibly lay the foundation for changes later in the project.

In most progress reports, the results and problems appear in the discussion of the progress and then again in the conclusion. In long progress reports, however, this information may appear in a separate section titled "Results and Problems" or "Evaluation of the Progress."

Conclusions

The conclusion summarizes the overall progress on the project and, if necessary, recommends changes. Specifically, the conclusion

- Summarizes the progress made on the project
- Summarizes any problems experienced during the reporting period
- Evaluates the overall progress on the project
- Recommends ways to improve or change the project or future work, if necessary

THE READER'S CORNER

Dramatizing Progress Reports

The progress report has surprising dramatic qualities. In Joseph Conrad's novella *The Heart of Darkness* (1902), Charlie Marlow recounts his work as skipper of a river steamboat on the Congo River. Part adventure story, part detective story, the novella is also part progress report: The skipper reports his meetings with the bookkeeper and the manager, the repairs he made to the steamboat, and finally his progress shipping goods upriver. The real progress, though, is the narrator's gradual psychological awakening to the horrifying emptiness of life (the "heart of darkness"), symbolized by his predecessor, Kurtz. Having severed all contact with his employers, Kurtz has become a brutal and insane god to an African tribe deep in the Congo; Kurtz's own progress report concludes, "Exterminate all the brutes."

A powerful critique of heartless bureaucratic imperialism, Conrad's novella was revived to serve a similar purpose in the 1979 film *Apocalypse Now.* Criticizing America's imperialism in Vietnam, the film portrays a U.S. military captain sent on a clandestine mission to "terminate" a renegade "Colonel Kurtz" holed up in a remote Cambodian compound. In the captain's voice-over, we can still hear elements of the progress report: dutiful reports of an efficient but senseless village bombing so an officer can go surfing, the endless "securing" of Do Lung Bridge, and of course the voyage upriver. Colonel Kurtz's own progress report concludes with an echo of his namesake's: "Drop the bomb."

In this section, you might recommend ways to overcome problems that you are experiencing, or you might suggest ways to alter the project to get better results. You also can briefly mention these recommendations in the introduction or at the beginning of the discussion of the progress.

TWO SAMPLE PROGRESS REPORTS

The two sample progress reports presented in this chapter illustrate the conventional elements. In Figure 14.5, a student reports on her progress on a manual for the Double Oaks Golf Shop; she uses the progress-made/progress-expected pattern. In Figure 14.6, an engineering company reports on its progress on a lignite-handling system; it uses the task/project pattern.

WORSHEET for Planning and Writing Your Progress Reports

Principle 1: Find Out About the Readers of Your Progress Reports

- Who are the readers of your progress report?
- What are your readers' goals in reading your report?
- What do your readers know about your project?

Principle 2: Prepare to Answer Readers' Questions

- What project does the report cover?
- What time period does the report cover?
- What are the objectives of the project?
- What are the results of the work?
- What problems, if any, have you encountered?
- What changes, if any, do you recommend?
- How will these changes affect the project?
- What is the overall status of the project?

Principle 3: Consider the Conventional Elements of Progress Reports

- Have you identified the project the report covers?
- Have you identified the time period the report covers?
- Have you identified the objectives of the project, if necessary?
- Have you discussed the work you have accomplished since the beginning of the project or since the last report?
- Have you discussed the major results?
- Have you explained the significant problems, if any, you have experienced?
- Will these problems affect future work on the project? If so, have you explained this effect?
- Have you discussed the work planned for the next reporting period or for the remainder of the project?
- Have you evaluated the overall progress in a "conclusions" section?
- Can you recommend any changes to the project? If so, have you included your recommendations in the "conclusions" section?
- Have you explained how these recommendations might affect the remainder of the project?

Figure 14.5 A Progress Report Written by a Student

MEMO

March 5, 1998

To: Professor Patricia McCullough
From: Nicole Sanders
Subject: Progress report on the employee manual for Double
              Oaks Golf Shop

Introduction

This report covers my progress on an employees' manual for the ● ─ Project
Double Oaks Golf Shop since February 15. This manual will   ● ─ Time period
include up-to-date procedures for opening, maintaining, and
closing the shop and for maintaining the inventory; it will also
include the current policies for the employees. Although my
work is progressing satisfactorily, I have experienced some problems in gathering information from the management of the shop.

My Progress During the Past Three Weeks

During the past three weeks, I had planned to interview the sales
staff and the manager of the shop and to update and revise the
procedures and policies for the shop. I have completed the interviews; and based on the information gathered in these interviews, I have updated the procedures currently in writing.
However, I have not updated and revised all the procedures and
policies because from the interviews, I learned that many of the
procedures are not in writing. To write the remaining procedures, I need information from the manager and from the managers of other small golf shops.

Interviews with the Sales Staff and the Manager

Progress made

I interviewed five members of the sales staff—Bart Thompson,
Stella Smith, Melissa Connors, Dan Sandstedt, and Bradley
Davis. My interviews with Bart and Melissa were most revealing.
They explained that few of the current procedures and policies
appear in writing. Before the interview, I assumed that the current employees' manual contained most of the procedures and
policies but that the procedures and policies were out of date.
However, Bart and Melissa explained that the manual did not
contain any inventory procedures—a major responsibility for the
sales staff.

I also interviewed the manager of the club, Donna Shoopman. She
explained how the manual differed from the current policies of the
shop. She also confirmed that the procedures for maintaining the
inventory and closing the shop were not in writing.

Updating and Revising the Policies and Procedures

I have updated and revised the policies on employee dress, customer satisfaction, substance abuse, disciplinary issues, and work

Description of progress

Figure 14.5 (cont.)

P. McCullough   2   March 5, 1998

Progress made

schedules. I updated and revised these policies based on information from Donna, the shop manager. I have also up-dated and revised the opening procedures for the shop. These were the only procedures in writing.

Problems with Updating and Revising the Procedures ●—| Problems encountered

I cannot completely update the procedures for maintaining the inventory and for maintaining and closing the shop because they are not in writing. Donna, the shop manager, plans to give me the procedures for maintaining the inventory, closing the shop, and maintaining the shop by March 12. These procedures will serve as a foundation for the procedures section of the manual. I cannot finish the procedures section of the manual without the information from Donna.

Description of progress

Progress Expected During the Next Three Weeks

During the next three weeks, I will

- interview managers of other small golf shops
- finish updating and revising the procedures
- prepare a completed draft of the manual.

Interviewing Managers of Other Golf Shops

Future work

I will interview Don Price, manager of Briarwood Golf Shop, and Bonnie Barger, manager of Brentwood Golf Shop. These interviews will help me appropriately revise the procedures for maintaining the inventory and the shop.

Completing the Updating and Revising of the Procedures

I will update and revise the procedures for maintaining inventory and for maintaining and closing the shop after receiving the procedures from Donna. I will also use the information from the interviews with the managers of Brentwood and Briarwood Golf Shops to help me appropriately revise these procedures.

Conclusions

Conclusion

My interviews with the sales staff and with the manager gave me ●— Overall status valuable information and guidelines for writing the manual. Even though I am behind schedule, I can complete the draft of the manual by March 30 if Donna gives me the procedures by March 12.

Figure 14.6 A Progress Report from an Engineering Company

Material Handling Systems Division
4000 Highline Court
Chalfant, Pennsylvania 18914
(412) 555-4200

October 15, 1998

Mr. William Holtz
Morris and Associates, Inc.
400 East Fifth Street
Midwest City, Iowa 65091

Subject: Progress on the lignite handling system at the Old Eagle plant

Dear Mr. Holtz:

Introduction

This letter describes the current status of, and progress on, the lignite-handling system for the Old Eagles plant. The purpose of this project is ◄— Project
to renovate the current lignite-handling system at the plant. This letter covers our work on the obsolescence study, the mechanical engineering, the structural engineering, and the electrical engineering from July 1, ◄— Time period
1998, to August 30, 1998.

Obsolescence Study

We identified all obsolete equipment. This equipment includes the Merrick scales, heating vents and air conditioning, Wesman level detectors, and rotary plow relay logic.

Mechanical Engineering

We have submitted 90 mechanical drawings to Britt Engineers. They have approved or approved with comments all the drawings. These drawings show the following items:

Description of progress

- changes to conveyors C-3A, C-3B, BF-16, BF-17, BF-18, and BF-19 because of obsolete speed reducers.
- revised conveyor C-2 because of obsolete fluid couplings.
- small scale drawings with 1998 changes and additions.
- drawings with miscellaneous 1998 changes and additions to the Active Storage Building, Rotary Plow Area, Reclaim Hoppers, Crusher House, and Transfer Vault.
- miscellaneous minor pre-1998 changes to the Boiler Surge Bin Tower and Transfer Towers 1A and 1B.

Progress made

Figure 14.6 (cont.)

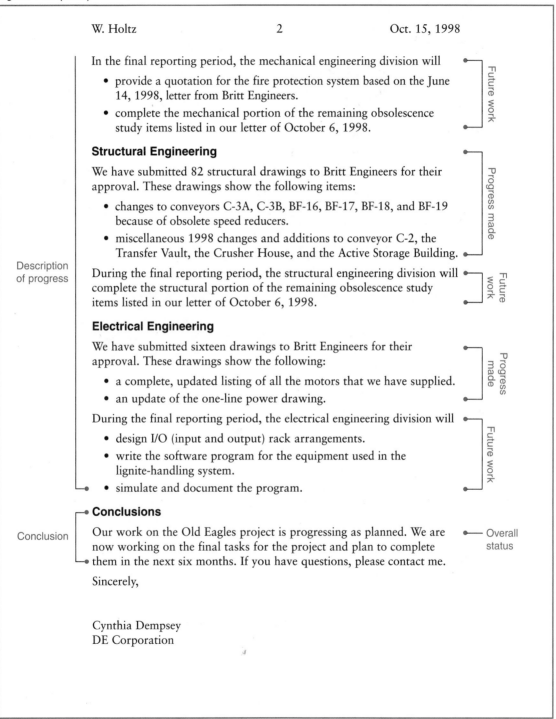

W. Holtz   2   Oct. 15, 1998

In the final reporting period, the mechanical engineering division will

- provide a quotation for the fire protection system based on the June 14, 1998, letter from Britt Engineers.
- complete the mechanical portion of the remaining obsolescence study items listed in our letter of October 6, 1998.

Structural Engineering

We have submitted 82 structural drawings to Britt Engineers for their approval. These drawings show the following items:

- changes to conveyors C-3A, C-3B, BF-16, BF-17, BF-18, and BF-19 because of obsolete speed reducers.
- miscellaneous 1998 changes and additions to conveyor C-2, the Transfer Vault, the Crusher House, and the Active Storage Building.

During the final reporting period, the structural engineering division will complete the structural portion of the remaining obsolescence study items listed in our letter of October 6, 1998.

Electrical Engineering

We have submitted sixteen drawings to Britt Engineers for their approval. These drawings show the following:

- a complete, updated listing of all the motors that we have supplied.
- an update of the one-line power drawing.

During the final reporting period, the electrical engineering division will

- design I/O (input and output) rack arrangements.
- write the software program for the equipment used in the lignite-handling system.
- simulate and document the program.

Conclusions

Our work on the Old Eagles project is progressing as planned. We are now working on the final tasks for the project and plan to complete them in the next six months. If you have questions, please contact me.

Sincerely,

Cynthia Dempsey
DE Corporation

Margin annotations: Future work · Progress made · Future work · Progress made · Future work · Description of progress · Conclusion · Overall status

EXERCISES

1. With your team, list the strengths and the weaknesses of the progress report shown in Figure 14.7. The writer of this report is a college student who works part-time as a trainer for Magic Computers, a computer repair service. The owners of the service asked the writer to prepare a manual for their repair teams and managers. They want to have the manual by May 15 when they will begin training two new teams.

2. Recommend ways to improve the progress report shown in Figure 14.7. The readers are busy owners who also work full-time at other jobs. In your recommendations, comment on the organization of information, the style, and the page design.

3. Revise the progress report shown in Figure 14.7, incorporating your team's recommendations from Exercise 2.

4. Write a progress report for the project that you proposed in Exercises 1, 2, and 3 in Chapter 13.

Figure 14.7 The Progress Report for Exercises 1, 2, and 3

Memo

Date: March 19, 1998
To: Barbara and Don Simpson, Owners of Magic Computers
From: Carol Arnold
Subject: Progress report on my manual for Magic Computers

During the last three weeks, I have worked on a managers' and repair teams' manual for Magic Computers. I began by looking for other similar residential computer repair services in other cities. I found four such services: Computer Doc in Flower Mound, 24-Hour Computer Repairs in Carson City, Computer FixIt in Desoto, and Boswell's Computer Repair in Estes. I called these four services to set up appointments to visit with their owners and managers. I was able to set up appointments with only three services; Boswell's cannot set up an appointment with me until the owner returns from vacation on March 30.

My interview with Jim Smith, owner of Computer Doc, was quite helpful. Jim showed me the office space and the equipment that Computer Doc uses. They use a wide variety of equipment. The most helpful part of my interview with Jim was the information he gave me for the procedures for the repair teams. He helped me to determine a list of the major procedures that the repair teams must know to repair a personal computer.

My interview with Jane Price, manager of 24-Hour Computer Repairs, was also quite helpful. Jane also showed me her office and the equipment that her repair teams use. They also use a wide variety of diagnostic software. The most helpful part of my interview with Jane was the information that she gave me about the manager's duties. She helped me to define and to list the daily, weekly, and monthly duties of the manager.

I also interviewed Jim and Alice Wilson, owners of Computer FixIt. My interview with the Wilsons was a little disappointing because they only had 30 minutes to spend with me. They did not have time to discuss the specific procedures followed by their repair teams or their managers.

Along with the interviews, I also accompanied two repair teams from Magic Computers. I accompanied each team for one day. I followed the team members as they took repair calls, entered the customers' business or home, listened to the customers, diagnosed the problems either by examining the computer or by using diagnostic software, and then made repairs on site. I asked them questions about their responsibilities and procedures. I made notes as I watched and questioned them. Accompanying these teams was quite helpful. I learned some specific procedures for questioning the computer owner and for creating a checklist for the owners to fill out. I also learned where the teams seem to work differently when diagnosing problems, working with the customers, and billing the customer. For example, one team bills customers for an entire hour even if the team works for only 15 minutes while the other team prorates the hourly fee. I will talk to you about what you expect and then write the procedures accordingly.

During the next three weeks, I will set up an appointment with the owner of Boswell's Computer Repair. I will also draft a set of procedures for the repair teams and then have the teams test these procedures. I will also visit with the manager of Magic Computers to determine her responsibilities before I begin writing the manager's section of the manual. Overall, I am pleased with the progress I am making. I am a little behind schedule because I could not meet with the owner of Boswell's and because I spent an extra day with the repair teams. However, I don't think these delays will prevent me from completing the manual before May 15, when our new teams come on board.

CASE STUDY   Relocating an Office

Background

Charles Patterson works part-time at the Global Travel agency. The agency experienced rapid growth during the past year, and its current location—one large office and a small storage area—is too small. The office originally housed only three employees but now houses six. These employees cannot work easily with clients because of noise and insufficient space.

The owners of Global Travel asked Charles to investigate possible new locations for the agency and then to recommend the best of these locations. Charles began work on this project two weeks ago. Since that time, he has interviewed the owners and the manager; they want the new location to have these characteristics:

- An outer office for a receptionist.
- A waiting area and six small offices for the travel agents and the manager. Each office should accommodate two chairs for clients, one desk, and a computer table.
- A large walk-in closet for storage.
- An area where employees can eat lunch and take their breaks.

After interviewing the owners and the manager, Charles contacted the managers of three office buildings: the Kirby Building, the Cumberland Building, and San Jacinto Tower.

He met with Nathaniel Ross, manager of the San Jacinto Tower on February 10. Mr. Ross showed Charles office space that would meet Global Travel's needs and gave him the rental and deposit information for that office space. Charles made appointments with Diana Alcorn, manager of the Kirby Building, and with Dianne McCarroll, manager of the Cumberland Building, for the week of February 23.

Charles also contacted three moving companies—AM/PM Vanlines, Cross-Country Moving and Storage, and Johnson Vanlines. He asked each company to bid on moving Global Travel to each of these three buildings. He expects to receive these bids by February 25.

Once Charles meets with the managers of the Kirby Building and the Cumberland Building and receives the bids from the moving companies, he will study the office space available in each of the three office building and the cost involved in moving to these buildings. He then will decide on the best location for the company and write his findings and recommendations in a report to the owners of Global Travel.

Assignment

Write a progress report in memo form to the owners and manager of Global Travel. Use the "Worksheet for Planning and Writing Your Progress Reports" to plan this report.

Chapter 15

Planning and Writing Reader-Oriented Completion Reports

CHAPTER OUTLINE

Cassie and Jon are technical writers employed by an engineering firm that works with companies to renovate and rebuild manufacturing plants. Cassie's group is working with a company to find out why a tower collapsed at one of its plants. Cassie will write a report explaining possible reasons for the collapse. Jon is working with another group to prepare a report recommending various ways to repair the tower. Cassie and Jon are working on the same project but are preparing two different types of reports: Cassie is writing an informative, investigative research report; Jon is writing a report that analyzes and interprets information.

Like Cassie and Jon, you may write completion reports that present research or recommendations. You write completion reports when you've completed the research, study, or project. Completion reports document your work, so that others can refer to it. The term *completion report* can refer to many types of reports. For example, completion reports like Cassie's present information from original research conducted in the field or laboratory. They might also present information from research conducted by others—information gained through library or online research. Sometimes called *research reports,* such reports frequently appear in scientific and technical journals.

Completion reports like Jon's analyze and interpret information and then recommend a particular option or course of action. Such reports are feasibility reports, sometimes called recommendation reports. *Feasibility reports* evaluate various options based on appropriate criteria and then recommend the most feasible or preferable option.

You will read and write many types of completion reports when you enter the workplace. These reports may not fit into neat categories with predetermined arrangements and conventional elements. Many of the completion reports you will write may not have a specific label such as "completion report" or "feasibility report." Instead, you may write a report documenting the completion of a design of a new product or of a study of locations for opening a new branch for your company. Your managers probably won't specifically tell you to write a completion report documenting and analyzing your new design or recommending the most effective location for the new branch. Instead, they will assign you the project and expect you to know what type of report to write when you've completed the work. Even if you don't have a specific label for the report, you can determine a general category and thus organization because most completion reports have one of three general objectives: to inform, to analyze, or to both inform and analyze.

Informational reports inform readers, report data, or document a particular problem or situation. *Analytical reports* do more than simply inform readers; these reports also analyze and interpret information and data. You may encounter several types of analytical reports. If a report analyzes information and then recommends a specific course of action or solution, it is a recommendation report. If a report evaluates options based on certain criteria and then determines the most feasible option for a specific situation or problem, it is a feasibility report. Other analytical reports may record and interpret the work the writer did to design a product or test a hypothesis. These reports are research reports.

Many of the reports that you read or write both inform and analyze. For example, the progress reports you learned about in Chapter 14 combine these two functions. They give readers information about the work completed and the work to be completed during the next reporting period. Progress reports also evaluate the progress made during the current reporting period and may recommend changes to the schedule or budget for a project. Other reports that both inform and analyze are lab reports and personnel reports. Lab reports document what the writer did or observed in the lab and then may evaluate or interpret the results of the experiment or observations. Personnel reports describe and evaluate the work of an employee and the employee's potential for promotion or continued employment.

In this chapter, you will learn two principles for writing any type of completion report that informs and/or analyzes. You also will learn the conventional elements of two completion reports: feasibility and research. You can adapt these elements for various reports that you will write in the workplace.

PRINCIPLE 1: DETERMINE THE PURPOSE OF YOUR REPORTS

As a professional, you will determine the purpose for your completion reports. Once you know the purpose, you can better identify how to meet readers' needs and what information you will need for the report. The following scenarios illustrate how the purpose helps you to know what type of report you will write and what information readers will expect.

Scenario 1   Gwen is reporting on the space problems in a computer lab at her university. The lab just received ten new computers, but the computers are too close together. As Gwen analyzes her writing situation, she considers what information readers will expect. She thinks they might expect information documenting the space problem, so the general purpose of her report will be to inform. However, she thinks readers might expect the report to examine and evaluate the various options for solving the space problem, so another purpose of the report will be to analyze. Gwen also decides to talk to the lab managers to determine what they expect in the report.

Scenario 2   Taylor will write a report discussing the major problems in selecting an effective flood control plan for a large residential area that has experienced severe flooding in the past five years. As she begins planning, she thinks about what readers will expect. Will they expect her just to analyze the major problems, or will they also expect her to document the problems? Like Gwen's report, Taylor's report doesn't neatly fit into either the informative or the analytical category because it probably will both inform and analyze. Before writing the report, Taylor decides to discuss it with some of the people who will be reading it, or at least with the person who assigned it, to determine its purpose.

As those situations illustrate, the best way to identify the purpose of a report is to talk to readers or to the person who asked you to write the report. However, what should you do if you don't have access to the readers or to the person assigning the report, or if you have decided to write an unsolicited report (in other words, no one has assigned the report to you)? If you don't have access to these people or if the report is unsolicited, consider these questions to help you determine the purpose:

- What do you want readers to know, do, or learn from the report?
- Do you want to document or to describe a situation or problem?
- Do you want to present and evaluate possible solutions or options? Do you want to recommend a particular solution or option?

These questions will help you to decide whether your report will inform, analyze, or do both. After you gather information about readers and their expectations, you will want to identify a more specific purpose.

PRINCIPLE 2: PREPARE TO MEET READERS' EXPECTATIONS

You will write a more effective report if you spend time gathering information about readers and their expectations. Your report will have a greater chance of succeeding if you find out what your readers know about your topic and what they expect. Consider these general questions (you will want to add more specific questions as you identify the specific type of report to write):

- What do readers know about the topic?
- How much detail will readers need or expect? Does this need or expectation differ among the various readers? If so, how?
- Do readers expect you to evaluate, analyze, or recommend?

Information about two important factors will help you to discover what readers need or expect: readers' familiarity with the topic and their purpose for reading (Holland, Charrow, and Wright 27–54). Readers who are familiar with the topic of your report will "find it easier to grasp new material about the topic than readers" who are not familiar with it (Holland, Charrow, and Wright 30). If readers are not familiar with, or do not understand, your field, include adequate detail and explain technical terms and concepts. If you know that the knowledge level will vary among your readers, consider three options:

- Writing separate reports
- Directing the language and detail to readers with the lowest level of knowledge
- Compartmentalizing the report (Holland, Charrow, and Wright 37–38)

Writing separate reports is rarely an option because it would be time-consuming and expensive. If you direct the language and details to readers with the lowest level of knowledge, readers highly familiar with the topic may become bored by or impatient with what they see as simplistic and tedious explanations. Thus, compartmentalizing the report is the most efficient and effective method for writing for varied readers. When you compartmentalize, you create a separate section for each group of readers. You can compartmentalize by simply using headings, tables of contents, summaries, and indexes to help readers find the sections that will interest them (Holland, Charrow, and Wright 38). You also can place definitions and explanations of technical terminology and concepts in footnotes, glossaries, appendixes, or other special sections within the report (Holland, Charrow, and Wright 38).

After you have a sense of what your readers know about the topic of your report, find out whether they will prefer you to just present information or to evaluate, analyze, or recommend. When you know what they expect, you can decide what type of information to include, how to organize that information, and what elements to include. If you know whether to evaluate, analyze, or recommend, you will know whether your report must persuade your readers to accept your evaluation, analysis, or recommendation—especially if the report is unsolicited.

PRINCIPLE 3: CONSIDER THE CONVENTIONAL ELEMENTS OF REPORTS

In this section, you will examine the conventional elements of two types of completion reports that both inform and analyze: a report for decision makers, a *feasibility report*; and a report of empirical research, a *research report*. In a report for decision makers, use the *executive organization* to help readers make decisions based on your work (see Figure 15.1). In this type of report, the conclusions and recommendations appear before the discussion. Decision makers are more interested in the "bottom line" than in how you arrive at your conclusions and recommendations. In reports of empirical research, use the *standard organization*. Readers of these reports are interested not only in your conclusions and recommendations but also in your methods; so the conclusions and recommendations appear after the discussion (see Figure 15.1). These readers want to understand how you set up your study or project and how you arrived at your conclusions and recommendations. In reports of scientific research, readers may expect a discussion of the literature (research

Figure 15.1
Two Basic
Organizational
Structures for
Completion Reports

Executive Organization	Standard Organization
Introduction	Introduction
Conclusions/recommendations	Discussion
Discussion	Conclusions/recommendations

in scientific journals and books) that supports or relates to your research. You can adapt the executive or standard organization for any type of completion report in the workplace.

Feasibility reports help readers decide between two or more options or actions; therefore, they follow the executive organization. Feasibility reports have an informative and an analytical purpose. They inform readers of the criteria used to evaluate options and of the methods used to gather and analyze information. Feasibility reports answer questions such as these: "Which location would be best for our branch laboratory?" "Should we repair the tower or build another one?" "Which method is best for repairing the tower?" "Should we buy a new computer or update the current one?" Some feasibility reports may seem to offer readers only one option. For example, Jon (the technical writer mentioned at the beginning of this chapter) originally studied the feasibility of repairing the tower. Although he seemed to be studying only one option, he actually was studying two—whether the company should repair or not repair the tower. After considering his report, his readers decided to repair the tower and then had several repair options.

Research reports follow the standard organization. They explain primary research conducted in a laboratory or in the field. A lab report that you might prepare for a biology or chemistry class is similar to a research report, except in primary research the writer comes up with an untested idea or hypothesis. The writer tests that hypothesis and records and interprets the results of the

Figure 15.2

Readers' Questions About the Conventional Elements of Feasibility and Research Reports

Element	Readers' Questions
Introduction	What is the topic of the report?
	What is the purpose of the report?
	How does the report affect the readers?
	What is the background of the report?
	What other research relates to the report (for research reports)?
	What follows in the report?
Methods	How did you do the research or conduct the study?
	How did you gather the information that led to your conclusions and recommendations?
Results	What did you find out?
	What did you learn?
Conclusions	What do the results mean?
Recommendations	Given the results and the conclusions, what should occur?

tests. Research reports provide a permanent record of the research, the methods used to test the hypothesis, and the results of the test. These reports also draw conclusions based on the results and often recommend either further research or a particular course of action.

For example, a group of scientists wanted to determine safe levels of mercury in the sediment and soil in the floodplain of East Fork Poplar Creek in Oak Ridge, Tennessee. The scientists looked at the research on mercury and couldn't find federal or state regulations suggesting an allowable or safe level, so they developed their own equation to discover a safe level of mercury and tested the equation. The scientists presented the results of their study in a research report.

Research and feasibility reports have these conventional elements:

- Introduction
- Methods
- Results
- Conclusions
- Recommendations

Figure 15.2 presents questions that may occur to readers as they read each element.

Introduction

The introduction sets the stage or prepares readers for the information presented in the report. The introduction

- Identifies the purpose of the report
- Identifies the topic of the report
- Indicates how the report affects or relates to readers
- Presents background information, possibly including a review of current research (or literature) to demonstrate that the writer understands relevant research on the topic and to prepare readers for the topic of the report
- Presents an overview or preview of the report

Figure 15.3 presents an effective introduction to an internal feasibility report from Southwestern Bell. In the first paragraph, the writer introduces the general topic of the report: changing procedures in the proposal centers to improve productivity. The first paragraph also tells how the report affects the reader, who is the division manager who oversees the proposal center. The first and second paragraphs give the reader background about the need to increase productivity without increasing costs. The third paragraph states the specific topic and purpose of the report: to evaluate three options for improving productivity by completing boilerplate text for the proposals and then to recommend one of the options. The introduction doesn't include the conclusions and recommendations because they appear in an executive summary. The introduction also tells the reader what follows in the report.

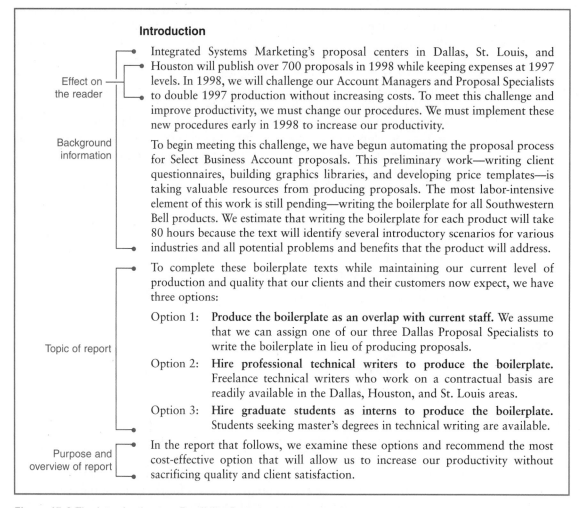

Figure 15.3 The Introduction to a Feasibility Report
Source: Courtesy of Neil Cobb and Southwestern Bell Telephone Company.

Methods

The methods section of a report answers the question "How did I do the research or conduct the study?" Readers of feasibility reports want to know the criteria that you used to evaluate the options and the methods used to gather information for evaluating the options. From the methods section of either type of report, readers want to learn exactly how you gathered your information. Many readers of research reports are as interested in your

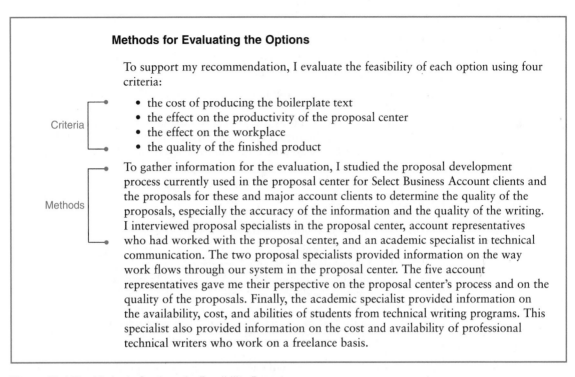

Methods for Evaluating the Options

To support my recommendation, I evaluate the feasibility of each option using four criteria:

Criteria
- the cost of producing the boilerplate text
- the effect on the productivity of the proposal center
- the effect on the workplace
- the quality of the finished product

Methods
To gather information for the evaluation, I studied the proposal development process currently used in the proposal center for Select Business Account clients and the proposals for these and major account clients to determine the quality of the proposals, especially the accuracy of the information and the quality of the writing. I interviewed proposal specialists in the proposal center, account representatives who had worked with the proposal center, and an academic specialist in technical communication. The two proposal specialists provided information on the way work flows through our system in the proposal center. The five account representatives gave me their perspective on the proposal center's process and on the quality of the proposals. Finally, the academic specialist provided information on the availability, cost, and abilities of students from technical writing programs. This specialist also provided information on the cost and availability of professional technical writers who work on a freelance basis.

Figure 15.4 The Methods Section of a Feasibility Report
Source: Courtesy of Neil Cobb and Southwestern Bell Telephone Company.

methodology as in your results; so use specific, detailed language when describing your methodology. The language should be specific enough that readers could reproduce your research methods.

Figure 15.4 presents the methods section of the feasibility report from Southwestern Bell. The writer lists four criteria for evaluating the options and describes the two methods he used to evaluate each option:

- Interviewing
- Studying the proposal development process currently used for Select Business Account clients and the quality of current proposals

Figure 15.5 shows an excerpt from a lengthier methods section of a research report prepared for the U.S. Department of Energy by scientists at the Oak Ridge National Laboratory in Tennessee. The report presents the results of a study of macroinvertebrates and fish in streams near two oil retention ponds. This portion of the methods section includes specific references to the procedures used to collect water samples and identify and quantify benthic macroinvertebrates.

Figure 15.5

The Methods Section
of a Research Report

Methods for Sampling Benthic Macroinvertebrates

To sample the benthic macroinvertebrates at Stations 1B–4B (three samples per site), we followed these procedures:

1. Placed a 27 × 33 cm metal frame on the bottom of the stream in the riffle area.
2. Held a 363-m mesh drift net at the downstream end of the metal frame while agitating the stream bottom (within the frame) with a metal rod. The stream flow transported suspended materials into the net.
3. Washed the net three times with the stream water to concentrate the sample and remove fine sediments.
4. Transferred the sample to glass jars which contained approximately 10% formalin to preserve the sample.

In the laboratory, we followed these procedures to analyze the samples:

1. Washed each sample using a standard No. 35 mesh (500 m) sieve and placed the washed sample in a large white tray.
2. Examined large pieces of debris (e.g., leaves and twigs) for organisms and then removed the debris not containing organisms.
3. Covered the contents of the tray with a saturated sucrose solution and agitated the tray to separate the organisms from the debris.
4. Identified all organisms that floated to the surface by taxonomic order or family.
5. Collectively weighed (to the nearest 0.1 g) the individuals in each taxonomic group.

Source: Adapted from J. M. Loar and D. K. Cox, *Biotic Characterization of Small Streams in the Vicinity of Oil Retention Ponds 1 and 2 Near the Y-12 Plant Bear Creek Valley Waste Disposal Area* (Oak Ridge, TN: Oak Ridge National Laboratory, 31 Jan. 1984).

Results

The results section answers the question "What did you find out?" or "What did you learn?" This section presents the data that you gathered from your research. When writing this section, only present the results; interpret them in the conclusion or discussion section. Readers are most likely to understand your logic and your conclusions if you present all the results before you interpret them. If you mix the results with your interpretations, readers may not be able to separate the results from your interpretations.

The arrangement of a results section varies with the topic and the purpose of the report. For research reports, present the results in a series of paragraphs and supporting visual aids, such as tables and graphs. If you used a variety of methods in your research, you can organize the results section around those methods. You then can structure your discussion of the results in the order in which you present the methods. For example, in the report presented in Figure 15.12, the writers discuss the methodology for sampling first benthic macro-

ISSUES IN CONTEXT

Personal Computers, the Web, and Corporate Information

James I. Cash, Jr., chair of the MBA program at Harvard, states:

> In the 1950s, the family car, TV, and supermarkets changed the way we thought about and shopped for daily provisions. In the 1960s and 1970s, the shopping mall replaced Main Street as the place where people gathered. In the 1980s, toll-free phone numbers and database marketing created an explosion in direct-mail commerce and forced mall and department store managers to rethink their strategies. . . . As mass-customization becomes a reality, the opportunity to add value to information-intensive products and services becomes limitless (60).

In the 1990s, the personal computer, technology, and global communication are revolutionizing how companies conduct daily business—how they distribute information to their employees and to those outside the company. As the use of personal computers and the Web grows, so will the "user's expectation for information availability on or through that machine" and the Web (Foy 24). Users are increasingly demanding information and services that put information directly into their hands via the computer (Foy 24). While this concept of providing universal access to information seems alluring for you and for companies, the real issue may be more work and mediocrity (Foy 25). For many companies, the issue is twofold:

- Deciding how best to create, share, protect, and distribute information
- Making the right information easy to get

Companies want to "put their best foot forward." Therefore, they want to put out information in the best format for the user and for the information. They want the information to add value to the company and to avoid the less desirable "data dump"—making all information available regardless of its value. As companies consider making information available in the coming century, new formats for the traditional report will evolve—you may help to create these new formats.

invertebrates and then fish. In the results section, they again discuss the results of the benthic macroinvertebrates sampling first.

In feasibility reports, the most effective way to present research results is by means of a comparison/contrast (see Chapter 7, "Arranging Information for Your Readers"). Using this basic arrangement, you have two patterns to choose from: comparing by alternatives or comparing by criteria. Comparing by criteria (see Figure 15.6) works best if you are evaluating only a few

Figure 15.6

Comparing by Criteria
in a Results Section

Cost of producing the boilerplate text (*criterion*)

- Option 1: Produce the work as an overlap with current staff
- Option 2: Hire professional technical writers to do the work
- Option 3: Hire graduate students as interns to do the work

Effect on the productivity of the proposal center (*criterion*)

- Option 1: Produce the work as an overlap with current staff
- Option 2: Hire professional technical writers to do the work
- Option 3: Hire graduate students as interns to do the work

Effect on the workplace (*criterion*)

- Option 1: Produce the work as an overlap with current staff
- Option 2: Hire professional technical writers to do the work
- Option 3: Hire graduate students as interns to do the work

Quality of the finished product (*criterion*)

- Option 1: Produce the work as an overlap with current staff
- Option 2: Hire professional technical writers to do the work
- Option 3: Hire graduate students as interns to do the work

options. If you are evaluating more than three options, comparing by alternatives (see Figure 15.7) will probably be more effective and accessible. When you compare by criteria, the criteria by which you evaluate each option are the organizing focus of the comparison, and the options are subsections of each criterion. When organizing by options, the options are the organizing focus, and the criteria are the subsections. When you use either organization, you can help readers to understand your results by creating a chart or table that compares each option criterion by criterion.

Conclusions

The conclusions section answers the question "What do the results mean?" In research reports, this section is sometimes titled "Discussion of the Results." It interprets and explains the significance of the results. The conclusions and the recommendations sections are often the most important sections of both feasibility and research reports; therefore, as mentioned earlier, they often appear at the beginning of the report.

State your conclusions and recommendations clearly and confidently, for you have results and research to support them. Avoid words and phrases that may undermine readers' confidence in what you say. Readers may think that the following conclusion shows the writer's lack of confidence:

Option 1: Produce the work as an overlap with current staff

- Cost of producing the boilerplate text (*criterion*)
- Effect on the productivity of the proposal center (*criterion*)
- Effect on the workplace (*criterion*)
- Quality of the finished product (*criterion*)

Option 2: Hire professional technical writers to do the work

- Cost of producing the boilerplate text (*criterion*)
- Effect on the productivity of the proposal center (*criterion*)
- Effect on the workplace (*criterion*)
- Quality of the finished product (*criterion*)

Option 3: Hire graduate students as interns to do the work

- Cost of producing the boilerplate text (*criterion*)
- Effect on the productivity of the proposal center (*criterion*)
- Effect on the workplace (*criterion*)
- Quality of the finished product (*criterion*)

Figure 15.7 Comparing by Alternatives in a Results Section

Lack of confidence	We believe that Option 1 will maintain current expense levels and may build on current expertise to reduce the time for writing boilerplate text. However, we think that Option 1 fails to appreciably improve the quality of the text and could disrupt the work group.

The grammatical subject of both sentences in this conclusion is "we": "We believe" and "we think." When the sentences focus on the options, not on the writer, the conclusions are more direct and confident:

No lack of confidence	Option 1 maintains current expense levels and builds on current expertise to reduce the time for writing boilerplate text. However, Option 1 fails to appreciably improve the quality of the text and could disrupt the work group.

As you write the conclusions section, you may discover that the results are inconclusive, that none of the options studied meets the criteria, or that the methodology was poor. The conclusions won't always fit into the neat categories that you expected. Nevertheless, you have an ethical responsibility to report clearly what the results mean, even when the conclusions are not what you or your readers expect or want. Figure 15.8 presents the conclusions of the feasibility report from Southwestern Bell. The style of the conclusions is clear, the tone confident.

Figure 15.8
The Conclusions
Section of a
Feasibility Report

Each of the three options has definite advantages and disadvantages. Option 1 (produce the work as an overlap with current staff) maintains current expense levels and builds on current expertise to reduce the time for writing boilerplate text. However, Option 1 fails to appreciably improve the quality of the text and could disrupt the work group. Option 2 (hire professional technical writers to do the work) offers the highest quality text at the highest level of productivity, yet could cause the most friction in the workplace. It also carries the highest price tag on a "per-unit" basis. Option 3 (hire graduate students as interns to do the work) delivers improved quality and productivity at minimal cost with the most positive potential effect on the workplace. In fact, the quality of text written by interns and the speed at which they produce it will rival that of the professional writers if we screen the applicants properly.

Based on our evaluation of the options in light of the criteria, productivity and cost are secondary issues. The savings that we realize from automating the proposals will recover the up-front costs of creating the boilerplate text. Therefore, the center's primary concern is with the quality of the boilerplate and the effect of the option on the workplace.

Source: Courtesy of Neil Cobb and Southwestern Bell Telephone Company.

Recommendations

The recommendations section answers the question "Given the results and the conclusions, what should occur?" In this section the writer recommends some type of action (or perhaps inaction) based on the results and the conclusions. The recommendations section may be shorter than the conclusions section and the results section. Some writers combine the recommendations and conclusions sections.

The recommendations may not be what you or your readers expect. In a feasibility study, you might recommend more than one option if the results warrant such a recommendation; or, if none of the options meets the criteria set up in the study, you might be unable to make any recommendations. In a research report, you might recommend further research or a revised study because your results are inconclusive. Your readers may not expect such recommendations; but you have a responsibility to give them honest, well-supported recommendations.

Figure 15.9
The Recommenda-
tions Section of a
Feasibility Report

Because Option 3 offers the highest quality for the dollar with potentially no impact on the morale of the work groups, we recommend hiring two technical writing interns in January 1998 to write boilerplate text for Select Business Account (SBA) automated proposals.

Source: Courtesy of Neil Cobb and Southwestern Bell Telephone Company.

Figure 15.10
The Recommendations Section of a Research Report

Recommendations

We recommend additional studies to address several important issues:

- More extensive season sampling of the benthic macroinvertebrates and fish communities to obtain a complete inventory of the aquatic biota in the Bear Creek watershed, to investigate the potential recovery of biotic communities downstream of the confluence of Stream 1A, and to identify specific sources of impact to aquatic biota in Bear Creek above the confluence with Stream 1A.
- In situ and acute bioassays to assist with identifying potential sources of impact.
- Chronic bioassays to determine the effects on biota of long-term exposure to various effluent sources.
- Studies of storms and their role in transporting contaminants downstream and in establishing and/or recovering of the biotic communities in Bear Creek.

Source: Adapted from J. M. Loar and D. K. Cox, *Biotic Characterization of Small Streams in the Vicinity of Oil Retention Ponds 1 and 2 Near the Y-12 Plant Bear Creek Valley Waste Disposal Area* (Oak Ridge, TN: Oak Ridge National Laboratory, 31 Jan. 1984).

Figure 15.9 presents the recommendations section from the feasibility report from Southwestern Bell. The writer simply states the recommendations in one sentence, offering little explanation because he clearly supports the recommendations in the results section. Figure 15.10 presents the recommendations section from the research report prepared for the Department of Energy. The writers recommend more studies and explain what those studies should be.

TWO SAMPLE REPORTS

You will write many completion reports as a professional in your field. Although the subject matter and purpose of the reports will vary, the principles presented in this chapter will help you to write any report that informs, analyzes, or does both. To create effective reports, think about your readers' needs and expectations and the purpose for writing.

Figures 15.11 and 15.12 present reports that met the readers' needs and expectations as well as the writers' purpose. Figure 15.11 is an internal feasibility report prepared for a division manager at Southwestern Bell. The writer analyzes three options for writing boilerplate text for Select Business Account proposals. The writer uses the executive organization; therefore, the conclusions and recommendations appear in a summary at the beginning of the report. Figure 15.12 is a research report prepared for the U.S. Department of Energy by scientists at the Oak Ridge National Laboratory. The report details a study of fish and benthic macroinvertebrates in streams near a landfill. The writers use the standard organization, putting the recommendations at the end.

THE READER'S CORNER

Reports and the Free Press

Early reports played a significant role in the development of the modern newspaper. Before the printing press, when literacy rates were low, newspapers did not exist. Instead, ancient emperors (including the rulers of the Romans and the Chinese) dictated news that was to be read aloud, posted, or read throughout their empire. An independent free press—so crucial to modern democracies—began to develop during the late Middle Ages when elite European trading families began to exchange information among themselves. One family, the Fuggers, owned an important financial house in the German city of Augsburg. Their regular newsletters mostly provided commercial reports on the availability and prices of goods and services, but they also occasionally reported political developments that might affect commerce. Such commercial newsletters became regularly printed newspapers in Dutch hands during the early 1600s. Their *corantos* ("current news") helped this geographically central nation to dominate European commerce. English and French translations of the *corantos* quickly became available, and national papers soon followed in England and France. The history of press censorship begins shortly thereafter. No longer able to control the press as earlier autocrats could, European monarchs began to repress these first free presses, sometimes replacing the papers with their own official "news" publications. In 1766, Sweden established the first law to guarantee the freedom of the press.

WORKSHEET for Planning and Writing Your Reports

Principle 1: Determine the Purpose of Your Reports

- What do you want readers to know, do, or learn from the report?
- Do you want to document or to describe a situation or problem?
- Do you want to present and evaluate possible solutions or options? Do you want to recommend a particular solution or option?

Principle 2: Prepare to Meet Readers' Expectations

- What do readers know about the topic?
- How much detail will readers need or expect? Does this need or expectation differ among the various readers? If so, how?

- Do readers expect you to evaluate, analyze, or recommend?

Principle 3: Consider the Conventional Elements of Reports

- Will you use the executive or the standard organization?
- In the introduction: Have you identified the purpose and topic of the report? Have you indicated how the report relates to readers? Have you presented background information and a review of current research (or literature) if necessary? Have you presented an overview of the report?
- In the methods section: Have you specifically explained how you did the research or conducted the study?
- In the results section: Have you explained what you found out or what you learned from the research or study?
- In the conclusions section: Have you explained what the results mean? Have you explained the results in terms readers will understand?
- In the recommendations section: Have you told your readers what should occur based on the results and conclusions?

Figure 15.11 A Sample Feasibility Report

The writer uses a → memo format and identifies the subject of the report in the memo heading.

Memo

To:	Charlie Divine, Division Manager
	101 Pine, Room 1234
	St. Louis, MO 63101
From:	Neil Cobb
	Account Manager, ISM
Date:	November 21, 1997
Subject:	Feasibility of hiring technical writing interns to create boilerplate text for automated proposals

The writer uses → the executive organization. The writer summarizes the report and states his recommendation.

Summary

I have investigated the feasibility of using current staff, hiring freelance technical writers, and hiring student interns to generate low-cost boilerplate texts for automated proposals. Because interns will work for a low hourly wage with no benefits in exchange for experience, we can produce high-quality, low-cost boilerplate text. By using this boilerplate text, the productivity of Proposal Specialists who serve the Select Business Accounts (SBA) will ultimately increase.

Universities in the Dallas, Houston, and St. Louis areas have programs that can provide these interns. Ninety percent of the students in these programs are looking for intern opportunities to complete their degree requirements. These programs will provide a continuous resource for capable writers to serve as interns.

I recommend hiring two technical writing interns in January 1998 to create boilerplate for SBA automated proposals.

Introduction

Integrated Systems Marketing's proposal centers in Dallas, St. Louis, and Houston will publish over 700 proposals in 1998 while keeping expenses at 1997 levels. In 1998, we will challenge our Account Managers and Proposal Specialists to double 1997 production without increasing costs. To meet this challenge and improve productivity, we must change our procedures. We must implement these changes early in 1998 to increase our productivity.

The writer → explains the background and the purpose of the report.

To begin meeting this challenge, we have begun automating the proposal process for Select Business Accounts. This preliminary work—writing client questionnaires, building graphics libraries, and developing price templates—is taking valuable resources from producing proposals. The most labor-intensive element of this work is still pending—writing the boilerplate for all Southwestern Bell products. We estimate that writing the boilerplate for each product will take 80 hours because the text will identify several introductory scenarios for various industries and all potential problems and benefits that the product will address.

Figure 15.11 (cont.)

C. Divine   2   Nov. 21, 1997

To complete these boilerplate texts while maintaining our current level of production and quality that our clients and their customers now expect, we have three options:

The writer highlights the options in a list.

Option 1: **Produce the boilerplate as an overlap with current staff.** We assume that we can assign one of our three Dallas Proposal Specialists to write the boilerplate in lieu of producing proposals.

Option 2: **Hire professional technical writers to produce the boilerplate.** Freelance technical writers who work on a contractual basis are readily available in the Dallas, Houston, and St. Louis areas.

Option 3: **Hire graduate students as interns to produce the boilerplate.** Students seeking master's degrees are available from area universities.

The writer tells the reader what follows in the report.

In the report that follows, we examine these options and recommend the most cost-effective option that will allow us to increase our productivity without sacrificing quality and client satisfaction.

Methods for Evaluating the Options

The writer lists the criteria and then explains his methods.

To support my recommendation, I evaluate the feasibility of each option using four criteria:

- The cost of producing the boilerplate text
- The effect on the productivity of the proposal center
- The effect on the workplace
- The quality of the finished product

To gather information for the evaluation, I studied the proposal development process currently used in the proposal center for Select Business Account clients and the proposals for these and major account clients to determine the quality of the proposals, especially the accuracy of the information and the quality of the writing. I interviewed proposal specialists in the proposal center, account representatives who had worked with the proposal center, and an academic specialist in technical communication. The two proposal specialists provided information on the way work flows through our system in the proposal center. The five account representatives gave me their perspective on the proposal center's process and on the quality of the proposals. Finally, the academic specialist provided information on the availability, cost, and abilities of students from technical writing programs and of professional technical writers who work on a freelance basis.

The writer organizes the results by criteria.

Results of the Evaluation

To determine the feasibility of hiring interns, I evaluated the three options according to the criteria of cost, productivity, quality of the finished proposal, and effect on the workplace.

Figure 15.11 (cont.)

C. Divine   3   Nov. 21, 1997

Cost of Producing the Boilerplate Text

Option 1, using the current staff, is least expensive. Option 2, hiring freelance technical writers, is the most expensive.

The writer uses specific, actual figures to clearly explain the cost of each option. He tells the reader how he arrived at the figures.

Option 1: Overlap with Current Staff

Proposal Specialists (SG-22) earn on the average $48,700 per year. Loaded for relief and pension benefits, their total compensation is equivalent to $72,000 per year, or $34.60 per hour. With Option 1, the initial boilerplate for a single product would cost approximately $2,800.[1] Since loaded salaries for the Proposal Specialist are an embedded cost, Option 1 would not affect expenses.

Option 2: Hire Technical Writers on a Contractual Basis

Professional technical writers charge between $35 and $50 per hour, depending on their experience. With this option, the initial boilerplate would cost between $2,800 and $4,000 and would raise our departmental expenses accordingly.

Option 3: Hire Student Interns

Graduate interns will work for $10–$15 per hour in exchange for on-the-job experience. These interns will be classified as part-time employees, so the company will not pay them benefits. With Option 3, the initial boilerplate text for a single product would cost between $800 and $1,200 and would raise our expenses accordingly.

In the results section, the writer uses the same order for the options as in the Introduction. The writer also uses the same order for the criteria throughout the Results and clearly identifies each criterion and option in a heading.

Effect on the Productivity of the Workplace

Option 2, hiring freelance technical writers, would be most productive. Option 1, using current staff would be the least productive.

Option 1: Overlap with Current Staff

When Account Representatives fill out forms and pricing tables, Proposal Specialists can produce a proposal in eight hours. If we take Proposal Specialists from their regular proposal-writing tasks to write boilerplate text (80 hours of work), we will produce 10 fewer proposals every two weeks until the boilerplate is complete. This option will reduce potential revenues. With this option, the proposal center will not meet the immediate needs of the Account Representatives and thus discourage them from using the center.

This option does have an advantage. Because the proposal specialists are familiar with our products and the proposal-writing process, they may be able to create the boilerplate for a product in less than the estimated 80 hours.

Option 2: Hire Technical Writers on a Contractual Basis

Professional technical writers should be able to produce boilerplate for a

---

[1] I am using an 80-hour estimate for development time for determining the cost of producing the boilerplate text.

Figure 15.11 (cont.)

C. Divine   4   Nov. 21, 1997

single product with the 80-hour benchmark. Some of the writers may require less time, depending on the writers' expertise in telecommunications and how long they work for us. Option 2 may be the most productive scenario overall because it will free Proposal Specialists to continue writing proposals while spending minimal time working with the hired writers to develop and edit the boilerplate.

Option 3: Hire Student Interns

Like the professional technical writers, the interns will lack experience with our products and proposal style. Because they are relatively less experienced writers, we expect their productivity to be less than that of the professional writers. However, student interns are professional writers in training. They will have considerable academic and practical experience from at least 20 hours of technical writing courses. Because much of the course work is "real-world" oriented, the difference in productivity may not be significant. Like Option 2, Option 3 will free Proposal Specialists to continue producing proposals although the specialists may spend more time guiding the process.

Effect on the Quality of the Finished Product

Options 2 (hiring freelance technical writers) and 3 (hiring student interns) will provide the highest quality in the finished product.

Option 1: Overlap with Current Staff

Account representatives praise the effectiveness of SBA proposals, keying on the "looks" of the documents. However, the quality of the text is presently inferior to that of proposals for major accounts. The content is technically correct—the Proposal Specialists know the products well—but they often write in passive voice and have difficulty writing clear prose. Unfortunately, because the Proposal Specialists know the material so well, they tend to let some difficult concepts and technical descriptions flow unedited into the final document.

Option 2: Hire Technical Writers on a Contractual Basis

Professional technical writers should greatly improve the quality of the written text of SBA proposals. Their writing skills and a fresh perspective on our documents would ensure that the proposals meet the needs of the non-technical readers.

Option 3: Hire Student Interns

Interns would improve the quality of the written text for the same reasons discussed for Option 2. We would see work of higher quality because the interns' graduate advisers would evaluate the text. Their text would have to pass two layers of edits: edits from the advisers and from our Proposal Specialists.

Figure 15.11 (cont.)

C. Divine   5   Nov. 21, 1997

Effect on the Workplace

Option 3, hiring student interns, could positively affect the workplace. Option 1, using current staff, and Option 2, hiring freelance technical writers, could negatively affect the workplace.

Option 1: Overlap with Current Staff
Option 1 will affect the workplace negatively for two reasons. First, taking one Proposal Specialist from the group to write boilerplate will require the others to do additional work or to turn one out of three prospective clients away. Neither result would be acceptable long term, and turning away clients could cripple the automation project before it starts. Second, choosing one Proposal Specialist to write the boilerplate might bruise the egos of the others. This choice could irreparably divide the group.

Option 2: Hire Technical Writers on a Contractual Basis
Option 2 could help to avoid the negative effects of Option 1, but could also cause problems. The Proposal Specialists might resent management hiring another writer to do "their" work, especially if the freelance writers receive higher wages.

Option 3: Hire Student Interns
Like Option 2, Option 3 should prevent the negative effects of Option 1. Interns could also help us to avoid the problems of Option 2 because the Proposal Specialists would more readily accept the interns as subordinates and take on the responsibility of supervising their work. The interns themselves also will more readily accept the role as subordinates.

The writer presents and justifies the conclusions.

Conclusions

Each of the three options has definite advantages and disadvantages. Option 1 (produce the work as an overlap with current staff) maintains current expense levels and builds on current expertise to reduce the time for writing boilerplate text. However, Option 1 fails to appreciably improve the quality of the text and could disrupt the work group. Option 2 (hire professional technical writers to do the work) offers the highest quality text at the highest level of productivity, yet could cause the most friction in the workplace. It also carries the highest price tag on a "per-unit" basis. Option 3 (hire graduate students as interns to do the work) delivers improved quality and productivity at minimal cost with the most positive potential effect on the workplace. In fact, the quality of text written by interns and the speed at which they produce it will rival that of the professional writers if we screen the applicants properly.

Based on our evaluation of the options in light of the criteria, productivity and cost are secondary issues. The savings that we realize from automating

Figure 15.11 (cont.)

C. Divine   6   Nov. 21, 1997

the proposals will recover the up-front costs of creating the boilerplate text. Therefore, the center's primary concern is the quality of the boilerplate and the effect of the option on the workplace.

The writer states ⟶ and justifies his recommendations.

Recommendations

Because Option 3 offers the highest quality for the dollar with potentially no impact on the morale of the work groups, we recommend hiring two technical writing interns in January 1998 to write boilerplate text for Select Business Account (SBA) automated proposals.

Source: Courtesy of Neil Cobb and Southwestern Bell Telephone Company.

Figure 15.12 A Sample Research Report

<table>
<tr>
<td>

Because the
readers are
biologists, the
writers use
technical
terminology the
readers will
understand and
expect.

The writers use
the standard
organization.
Therefore, the
writers do *not*
summarize the
conclusions and
the recommenda-
tions at the
beginning of the
report.

The writers list
the specific sites
studied.

</td>
<td>

Biotic Characterization of Small Streams in the Vicinity of Oil Retention Ponds 1 and 2 Near the Y-12 Plant

Introduction

This report provides data on the aquatic biota in the streams near the oil retention ponds west of the Y-12 plant at Oak Ridge National Laboratory. Built in 1943, the Y-12 plant originally produced nuclear weapon components and subassemblies and supported the Department of Energy's weapon-design laboratories. In the production of the subassemblies, the plant used materials such as enriched uranium, lithium hydride, and deteride. The plant disposed of both solid and liquid wastes in burial facilities in Bear Creek Valley—approximately one mile west of the plant site. This report fulfills the Department of Energy's commitment to assess the aquatic biota near the man-made oil retention pond in the valley.

Methods

The Environmental Sciences Division conducted quantitative sampling of benthic macroinvertebrates and fish at the following sites:

- Bear Creek above and below the confluence with Stream 1A, a small tributary that drains Oil Retention Pond 1 (Stations 1 and 2, respectively)
- Stream 1A just above the confluence with Bear Creek (Station 3)
- Stream 2, a small uncontaminated tributary of Bear Creek that flows adjacent to Bear Creek Road (Station 4, the control station)

We also conducted qualitative sampling at the following sites in the watersheds of Oil Retention Ponds 1 and 2:

- Stream 1A, immediately below Pond 1 (Station 5)
- The diversion ditch that carries surface runoff from portions of Burial Grounds B, C, D, and the area north of Burial Ground A to Stream 1A just below the pond (Station 6)
- Stream 1A above the diversion ditch (Station 7)
- Oil Retention Pond 2 (Station 8)

We could not sample above or below Pond 2 because of insufficient flows. We did not sample Oil Retention Pond 1.

</td>
</tr>
</table>

Methods for Sampling Benthic Macroinvertebrates

The writers use lists
and subheadings
to identify the
methods for
sampling benthic
macroinvertebrates
and fishes.

To sample the benthic macroinvertebrates at Stations 1B–4B (three samples per site), we followed these procedures:

1. Placed a 27×33 cm metal frame on the bottom of the stream in the riffle area.
2. Held a 363-m mesh drift net at the downstream end of the metal frame while agitating the stream bottom (within the frame) with a metal rod. The stream flow transported suspended materials into the net.

Figure 15.12 (cont.)

2

3. Washed the net three times with the stream water to concentrate the sample and remove fine sediments.

4. Transferred the sample to glass jars that contained approximately 10% formalin to preserve the sample.

In the laboratory, we followed these procedures to analyze the samples:

The writers use specific, detailed language, so that readers could duplicate their methods. This language also helps to justify their conclusions and recommendations.

1. Washed each sample using a standard No. 35 mesh (500 m) sieve and placed the washed sample in a large white tray

2. Examined large pieces of debris (e.g., leaves and twigs) for organisms and then removed the debris not containing organisms

3. Covered the contents of the tray with a saturated sucrose solution and agitated the tray to separate the organisms from the debris

4. Identified all organisms that floated to the surface by taxonomic order or family

5. Collectively weighed (to the nearest 0.1 g) the individuals in each taxonomic group

Methods for Sampling Fishes

We used a Smith-Root Type XV backpack electroshocker to sample the fish community at Stations 1F–3F. This electroshocker can deliver up to 1200 V of pulsed direct current. We used a pulse frequency of 120 Hz at all times and adjusted the output voltage to the optimal value, based on the water conductivity at the site. We measured the conductivity with a Hydrolab Digital 4041. This instrument also concurrently measured the water temperature and pH.

At each of the sampling stations, we followed these methods to sample the fish community:

1. Made a single pass upstream and downstream using a representative reach. The length of the reach varied among sites (from 22 to 115 m).

2. Held captured fish in a 0.64-cm plastic-mesh cage until we completed the sampling.

3. Anesthetized the fish in the field with MS-222 (tricane methane sulfonate).

4. Counted the fish by species and collectively weighed the individuals of a given species to the nearest 0.5 g on a triple-beam balance.

5. Released the fish to the stream.

In a preliminary sampling we collected representative individuals of each species by seining and preserved the fish in 10% formalin. In the laboratory, we identified the fish using these methods:

1. Identified species using unpublished taxonomic keys of Etnier (1976)

2. Compared the mountain redbelly dace (*Phoxinus Oreas*) and the common shiner (*Notropis Cornutus*) with specimens collected from Ish

Figure 15.12 (cont.)

3

Creek, a small stream on the south slope of West Chestnut Ridge, and identified as *Phoxinus Oreas* and *Notropis Cornutus*

Results

This section presents the results of the sampling and analyzing of the benthic macroinvertebrates and of the fishes in the study sites.

Benthic Macroinvertebrates

The writers → summarize the results in tables. The writers use parenthetical notes to refer the readers to tables.

Qualitative sampling at the sites near Oil Retention Pond 1 and in Pond 2 resulted in few samples (see Table I). We also found low densities in the quantitative samples taken from Stream 1A, which drains Oil Retention Pond 1, and in Bear Creek near the confluence with Stream 1A (see Tables II and III). Relatively high densities and biomass of benthic organisms appeared in Stream 2, a small uncontaminated tributary of Bear Creek (Station 4). Some of the differences in the composition of the benthic community between this site and the others may have occurred because of substrate differences (e.g., the large amounts of detritus in Stream 2 when compared to the predominately small rubble and gravel at Stations 1 and 2). However, a depauperate benthic fauna existed in Bear Creek and Stream 1A.

Fishes

The four fish species collected at the four sample sites commonly inhabit small streams on the Department of Energy Oak Ridge Reservation. For

Station	Location	Method	Sampling results
5	Stream 1A just below Oil Retention Pond 1	Kick-seining	No organisms found
6	Diversion ditch just west of Oil Retention Pond 1	Kick-seining	No organisms found
7	Stream 1A above the diversion ditch	Kick-seining	Few Isopoda; unidentified salamander
8	Oil Retention Pond 2	Dip-netting; removal of sediment/litter from margins of ponds	No organisms found

Table I Description of qualitative sampling conducted near Oil Retention Ponds 1 and 2 west of the Y-12 Plant (previous study)

Figure 15.12 (cont.)

4

Sample no.	Sampling station			
	1B	2B	3B	4B
1	0	0	0	63(0.8)
2	0	2(0.1)	3(0.1)	46(2.2)
3	0	2(1.8)	0	25(1.0)
Mean no./m^2 (g/m^2)	0	14.9(7.1)	11.2(0.4)	501.3(15.3)
Substrate	Coarse gravel embedded in sand and silt; leaf packs uncommon	Same as Station 1B	Sand, silt, mud, and detritus/ leaves	Deep soft mud covered by leaves and woody debris

Table II Total number and weight (g, in parentheses) of benthic macro-invertebrates in each of three 27 × 33 cm bottom samples collected from four sampling sites in the vicinity of Y-12 Oil Retention Pond 1

Taxon	Sampling station			
	1B	2B	3B[a]	4B
Amphipoda	NC	NC	NC	67.3(0.6)
Annelida	NC	7.5(0.4)	NC	NC
Chironomidae	NC	NC	NC	273.1(0.7)
Decapoda	NC	NC	NC	22.4(7.1)
Isopoda	NC	NC	NC	86.1(1.9)
Oligochaeta	NC	NC	11.2(0.4)	NC
Sialidae	NC	3.7(1.5)	NC	NC
Tipulidae	NC	3.7(5.2)	NC	7.5(3.7)
Tricoptera	NC	NC	NC	44.9(1.3)

[a]Damselfly nymph collected by kick-seining.

Table III Density (mean no./m^2) of various benthic macroinvertebrate taxa in bottom samples collected from four sampling sites in the vicinity of Y-12 Oil Retention Pond 1. Biomass (wet weight, g/m^2) in parentheses. NC = None collected

Figure 15.12 (cont.)

5

example, these four species were the most abundant fishes found by electrofishing in Ish Creek, a small, undisturbed tributary of the Clinch River that drains the south slope of Chestnut Ridge. The presence of fish in the lower reaches of Stream 1A is consistent with the results of a bioassay conducted on the water from Oil Retention Pond 1. This bioassay showed no mortality to bluegill sunfish after 96 hours (Giddings). The high density and biomass of fish at Station 3F may relate to the abundant periphyton growth observed in the winter and to the chemistry of the effluent from Oil Retention Pond 1.

We found no aquatic species listed as threatened or endangered by either the U.S. Fish and Wildlife Service or the State of Tennessee. However, the Tennessee Wildlife Resources Agency has identified the mountain redbelly dace (*Phoxinus Oreas*) as a species needing management. The agency assigns this classification to those species which, though not considered threatened within the state, may not currently exist at or near their optimum carrying capacity (see Table IV).

Species	Sampling station		
	1F	**2F**	**3F**
Blacknose dace (*Rhynichthys atratulus*)	8 (21.0)	1 (1.5)	2 (2.5)
Common shiner (*Notropis cornutus*)	3 (22.5)	0	1 (6.5)
Creek chub (*Semotilus atromaculatus*)	42 (204.5)	4 (76.5)	10 (64.0)
Mountain redbelly dace (*Phoxinus oreas*)	39 (64.0)	1 (3.5)	35 (51.0)
Total (all species combined)			
Density (no./m²)	0.30	0.03	1.68
Biomass (g/m²)	1.00	0.41	4.33
Physical characteristics of sampling site			
Length of stream sampled (m)	115	91	22
Mean width (m)	2.7	2.2	1.3
Mean depth (cm)	19	13	10
Conductivity (S/cm)	260	1005	477
Water temperature (°C)	8.5	0.5	1.5
pH	7.1	7.6	7.5

Table IV Species composition, as numbers and biomass (g, in parentheses), of the fish community at four sampling sites near Y-12 Oil Retention Pond 1

Figure 15.12 (cont.)

6

Conclusions

The Y-12 Plant operations have had an adverse impact on the benthic communities of Bear Creek and some of its tributaries. The low benthic densities at Station 2B just above the confluence with Stream 1A suggest that the source of impact is not limited to the effluent from Oil Retention Pond 1. The relatively low fish density at Station 2F also implies an upstream perturbation (such as the S-3 ponds).

Further evidence of upstream impact(s) is available from the results of a similar study conducted 10 years prior to this study. In this study, researchers sampled benthic macroinvertebrates and fish at two sites located 50 m above and 100 m below the Y-12 sanitary landfill site. The west end of the landfill is approximately 1.4 stream kilometers above the confluence of Stream 1A with Bear Creek. No benthic organisms or fish were collected at either of the two sites, and in situ fish bioassays conducted just above and 500 m below the landfill resulted in 100% mortality after 24 hours.

The results of the earlier study differ significantly from those of the present study. The current presence of fish at Station 2F, which is approximately 500 m below the site of the earlier bioassays, may indicate changes in water quality over the past 10 years. However, the occurrence of fish in this region of Bear Creek may only be a temporary phenomenon (such as from a storm), reflecting short-term changes in water quality. The limited sampling in the present study may not have detected such a phenomenon. In view of the information currently available, both explanations of the difference in results seem equally plausible.

Recommendations

We recommend additional studies to address several important issues:

- More extensive season sampling of the benthic macroinvertebrate and fish communities to obtain a complete inventory of the aquatic biota in the Bear Creek watershed, to investigate the potential recovery of biotic communities downstream of the confluence of Stream 1A, and to identify specific sources of impact to aquatic biota in Bear Creek above the confluence with Stream 1A
- In situ and acute bioassays to assist with identifying potential sources of impact
- Chronic bioassays to determine the effects on biota of long-term exposure to effluent sources
- Studies of storms and their role in transporting contaminants downstream and in establishing and/or recovering of the biotic communities in Bear Creek

Figure 15.12 (cont.)

7

Works Cited

Etnier, David A. 1976. Family cyprinidae. Department of Zoology, University of Tennessee, Knoxville, Tennessee. Unpublished.

Giddings, J. M. Short-term survival of bluegill sunfish in water from Y-12 Oil Retention Ponds. Attachment to memorandum dated 13 January 1984, from C. W. Gehrs to G. A. Gillis.

Source: Adapted from J. M. Loar and D. K. Cox, *Biotic Characterization of Small Streams in the Vicinity of Oil Retention Ponds 1 and 2 Near the Y-12 Plant Bear Creek Valley Waste Disposal Area* (Oak Ridge, TN: Oak Ridge National Laboratory, 31 Jan. 1984).

EXERCISES

1. Working with your team, identify a problem at your university, in your community, or at your workplace. Write a feasibility report that examines options for solving this problem. As your team works, follow these guidelines:

   - Make sure that all team members are familiar with the problem and can gather the needed information.
   - Set up reasonable and appropriate criteria for evaluating the options.
   - Decide what methods your team will use to gather the needed information for evaluating the options.
   - Assign each team member an information-gathering task. For example, if your team decides to develop and distribute a survey, decide who will write the survey, who will prepare and distribute the copies, and who will tabulate the returned copies.

   - Use the "Worksheet for Planning and Writing Your Reports" as you plan and evaluate your feasibility report.

2. Working with a team of peers in your major field, identify a problem to research. After identifying the problem, decide how to approach the research. For example, you might identify the methods you would use to research the problem, the means for verifying your results, and so on. Write a memo to your instructor describing the problem and your approach to researching it.

3. Some information appears in more than one section of a research or feasibility report. For example, the summary repeats information given in greater detail in the conclusions and recommendation sections. Write a memo to your instructor identifying possible areas where repetition may occur in these reports and explaining the necessity for it.

Deciding Where to Live in the Fall[1]

Background

Each spring, students at your college or university decide where they will live in the fall. Usually they have at least four options:

- Living off campus in an apartment or house and eating off campus
- Living off campus in an apartment or house and using the board plan on campus
- Living on campus in a dorm and using the board plan
- Living on campus in a dorm without using the board plan

These options vary slightly for each college or university. For example, some universities allow students to live only in certain dorms when not using the board plan, and some universities don't offer a board plan to students not living on campus.

Assignment

Your instructor will ask you to prepare either an individual or a team feasibility report recommending the best housing option for undergraduate students at your university.

Individual Reports

If your instructor asks you to prepare an individual feasibility report, follow these steps:

1. Revise the housing options listed in the "Background" section to match those available to students at your college or university.
2. Determine the criteria you will use to evaluate the options.

3. Gather the information necessary to evaluate each option, based on the criteria.
4. Analyze the information about each option according to the criteria.
5. Write a feasibility report for students at your college or university.

Team Reports

If your instructor asks your team to write a feasibility report, follow these instructions.

At the first team meeting . . .

1. Revise the housing options listed in the "Background" section to match those available to students at your college or university.
2. List the characteristics of the readers of the report.
3. Determine the criteria you will use to evaluate the options.
4. Decide how the team will gather the necessary information for evaluating the options. For example, the team might write a questionnaire and administer it to students on campus or meet with the director of housing and food services to get costs of food, housing, and parking. Team members might interview students about the advantages and disadvantages of each option, or they might survey different apartments to determine an average cost for rent and utilities.
5. Assign each member an information-gathering task. (Each member should be ready to report on that information at the second team meeting.)

---

1. Adapted from Brenda R. Sims, *Technical Writing: A Handbook of Examples and Exercises* (Denton: University of North Texas Press, 1995).

At the second team meeting . . .

1. Analyze the information gathered by each member, and determine the best housing option for students.

2. Assign a section or part of a section of the report for each team member to write. (Each team member should complete his or her assignment before the next team meeting.)

At the third team meeting . . .

1. Read all sections of each team member's report.

2. Compile one report.

3. Edit and proofread the report.

Chapter 16

Planning and Writing User-Oriented Instructions and Manuals

We follow instructions at home and in the workplace. Whether we are cooking microwave popcorn or installing new software, we use instructions. Some instructions are short, simple, and informal—perhaps only a few steps or sentences. For example, Figure 16.1 presents simple instructions that accompany a registration form for activities sponsored by a city parks and recreation department. Other instructions may be hundreds of pages long and more complex. Many of these longer instructions are in the form of manuals. Figure 16.2 is an excerpt from a manual for a dishwasher. This brief excerpt tells readers how to change the dishwasher's front panels.

The instructions that you write may be as simple as the list shown in Figure 16.1 or as complex as an entire manual. You might write instructions for tasks that you want your coworkers to complete or for tasks that customers will follow when using your company's products. Regardless of the number and complexity of the tasks, the same principles apply. In this chapter, you will learn five principles to help you write effective, reader-oriented instructions.

PRINCIPLE 1: FIND OUT HOW MUCH READERS KNOW ABOUT THE TASK

Before you can write effective instructions, find out how much readers know about the task. This information will help you decide how much detail readers will need to perform the task correctly and easily. In preparing to write your instructions, you might also find out about readers' background and training by answering these questions:

- Have readers performed the task before? Have they performed similar tasks?
- Do readers have the same background or knowledge of the task? Will they have different purposes for using the instructions? Will their purposes for reading change?

Figure 16.1
Simple Instructions

Registering for FunEd Classes

1. Complete the registration form. Please print clearly or type.
2. Determine the appropriate fee for each class on the form. (You can find the fees in the class listings on page 16.)
3. Write your driver's license number and date of birth on the front of the check.
4. Make your check payable to the City of Albany.
5. Write the class number in the lower-left corner of the check.
6. Mail or take your completed registration form and check to Redbud Recreation Center before December 30, 1998. (The mailing address appears on page 18.)

How to Change the Front Panels

The writers briefly introduce the task of changing panels.

If you are redecorating, you can change your dishwasher's front panels to match or blend with your new colors by turning them over. Each side of the panel is a different color. You may also paint a panel with a color of your choice.

 **NOTE: Do not operate dishwasher while changing panels or when lower access panel is removed.**

The writers have subdivided the task into two subtasks: changing the top panel and changing the bottom panel.

How to Change the Top Panel

1. Take out the four trim screws on the sides of the dishwasher door. (Use the standard screwdriver.)
2. Remove the side trim.
3. Slide the top panel out. (Caution—The edges may be sharp.)
4. Turn the panel to the color you want in front.
5. Slide the panel back into place.
6. Replace the side trim and screws.

How to Change the Bottom Panel

Drawings with labels show readers where to find the panels and the screws.

1. Remove the two bottom panel screws. (Use the standard screwdriver.)
2. Remove the two top trim screws. (Use the standard screwdriver.)
3. Remove the top trim.
4. Slide the bottom panel up and out.
5. Turn the panel to the color you want in front.
6. Slide the panel back into place.
7. Replace the top trim and screws.

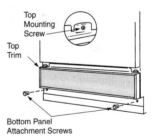

Figure 16.2 An Excerpt from an Instruction Manual
Source: General Electric Company, *Dishwasher Use and Care Guide,* 12.

- How much detail do readers need to complete the task? Do they want only minimal instructions?
- What are readers' attitudes toward the task and toward the equipment used for the task? (Brockmann 101)

If you know how much readers know about the task, you can select the appropriate amount of detail. For example, if you know readers have used a

ISSUES IN CONTEXT

A Note About Paper Versus Online Instructions

As we depend more on computers, more instructions are appearing online instead of on paper. Online instructions—often called online documentation—appear not on paper but on a computer monitor. Readers access these instructions from their computer and use the keyboard or mouse to move through the instructions. Online instructions, however, aren't just paper instructions displayed on screen. Paper and online instructions differ in several ways:

- Because of the size of most computer screens, writers chunk information presented online in smaller pieces than they do information presented on paper. On-screen line lengths and paragraphs may be shorter.
- Writers use more white space on screen than they do on paper. Otherwise, on-screen text would be hard to read because the ascenders and descenders of letters are often compressed, and the space between lines is less than in most paper documents, making each line blur into the lines immediately above and below it.
- Writers use different typefaces on screen than they might use for paper documents. The screen diminishes the resolution, or sharpness, of letters. On a typeset page, around 17,500 dots create a letter; and on a laser-printed page, about 1,000 dots create the same letter; but on a computer screen, about 63 dots create the same letter. Thus many typefaces that are readable on paper are not readable on screen.
- Writers organize effective online instructions differently than they do paper instructions. Effective online instructions may have a tree-type, nonlinear structure; so readers can decide how to move through the document. Readers are "lost much more easily in the organization" of online documents, especially when confronted with multiple screens and choices (Brockmann 70). Thus writers of online instructions must give readers clear navigation tools and offer them different ways of navigating through the documents.

Most of the information presented in this chapter applies to online instructions—except in organization and layout. Therefore, if you are asked to write online instructions, learn more about the various computer software authoring packages that will help you write such instructions and about the differences in the organization and layout of paper and online instructions.

Bunsen burner, you won't have to tell them how to work the burner; however, if you know they have never used a Bunsen burner, you will need to include basic instructions for operating one. You can also help your readers if you know whether they have performed similar tasks or used similar equipment. You can build on this similarity when giving instructions or introducing equipment. If you know readers are familiar with similar tasks, you can compare the familiar tasks with the new task to help readers feel comfortable. You also can help readers feel comfortable with a task if you know their attitudes toward the task and the equipment (Brockmann 101). For instance, if you know readers may resist a change in routine or habits caused by the instructions, frequently reassure them and whenever possible link the new task to what they already know.

Depending on the needs of your readers, you may want to include detailed instructions and explanations or perhaps even the theory behind a procedure. A novice may need detailed information to perform a task correctly, whereas a more expert reader may need—and want—only minimal instructions. Some readers may want or need to know the theory underlying a procedure or to understand how the equipment used for the procedure operates; other readers want only the basic instructions.

As you decide how much detail and explanatory information to provide, consider readers' reasons for reading your instructions or manual. Davida Charney, Lynne Reder, and Gail Wells found that "readers with specific tasks in mind need little or no elaboration," but "readers without specific goals benefit from explanations of "how to apply procedures," not from elaborations that describe general concepts (63). Thus, readers who have specific tasks to complete need little if any explanation of the procedure or the concept behind the procedure, and readers without specific tasks will benefit from "how-to" statements, not from "why" and "when" statements.

Consider the elaboration in a document on controlling thatch (Koop and Duble).

General elaboration	Mowers tend to scalp lawns that have excess thatch.
How-to elaboration	Use vertical mowers specifically designed to remove thatch. When using these mowers, make sure the blades penetrate through the thatch to the soil surface.

The general elaboration will not help readers to control thatch. However, the how-to elaboration gives readers specific information about the type of mower to use and how to use that mower to remove thatch.

Find out whether readers are likely to have the same background and knowledge of the task and the same purpose for reading. If readers don't, find out how they differ in background and knowledge of the task or in their purpose for using the instructions. This information will help you to determine how to organize the instructions to best meet the needs of all readers. You also need to consider whether readers' needs may change over time. For instance, new users of a software application may first consult the manual to learn how to get started, so they will want basic information. As these users learn more about the software, they may have questions about more advanced commands, so they will want to use the manual as a reference guide, not as a tutorial. The manual thus needs a tutorial-type section for new users and a reference section for users who have become more familiar with the software.

PRINCIPLE 2: USE AN ACCESSIBLE DESIGN

As you plan your instructions and manuals, decide on an appropriate typeface, layout, color, and page size for your purpose and your readers (Brockmann 139). As you plan these visual elements, ask yourself how and where readers will use the instructions. For example, will they use the instructions at a computer workstation? If so, use a spiral binding so the pages will lie flat, and perhaps use a smaller-than-traditional page size so the instructions fit easily at a computer workstation. Perhaps readers will use the instructions not in a typical office environment but in a power plant, a manufacturing plant, or a maintenance facility. To select the design that best suits readers' needs, consider these questions:

- Will readers use the instructions in an environment in which the instructions may become soiled or the pages easily crumpled?
- What typeface is appropriate for the instructions? Do readers require a particular type size or page size to use the instructions effectively?
- What layout will help readers find and follow the instructions?

Design Instructions Suitable for Readers' Environment

If readers will use documents outside typical office environments, select paper, a typeface, a type size, and a page size that will make the instructions easy to use. For example, if readers will use the instructions in a environment such as a manufacturing floor or a maintenance facility, use laminated paper or card stock that they can easily clean and a hard cover or notebook to protect the pages.

Choose a typeface that doesn't call attention to itself—a conservative typeface such as Times Roman, Bookman, or Palatino (Brockmann 141–42). If readers must read the instructions from a distance, the type size and page size may need to be larger than usual. For example, the instructions for clearing the air passages of a choking victim in a restaurant might be on a large poster in large type; so readers can see the instructions while working with the victim. If readers will use the instructions in a small area, the pages must be small enough to fit easily in the work space. For example, quick-reference information for some computer software programs is printed on the front and back of a card that readers can lay next to the computer.

Design Layouts to Help Readers Use the Instructions

As you design your instructions, create task-oriented headings and an accessible layout. Consider these headings:

Not task oriented	Deletion, Modification, and Addition
Task oriented	Deleting, Modifying, or Adding a Record

The first heading does not use verbs to identify the tasks described in the section that it introduces. The task-oriented heading uses verbs to identify the tasks. Task-oriented headings suggest activities that users may already understand and can find immediately applicable (Brockmann 100). Task-oriented headings also help readers who are using instructions as a reference tool to learn how to perform specific tasks.

To display your task-oriented headings, devise a layout that will let readers easily search through your document to locate specific instructions. When reading instructions, readers generally have a problem to solve or a task to complete. For example, they may need to learn how to install a software program onto a hard disk drive, how to maximize the storage space on a hard drive, or how to install a new airbag in a car. Whatever the task or problem, readers want to quickly and easily locate the information they need.

A logical, consistent layout like the one in Figure 16.3 helps readers find the information they need. The layout of this page from a user's guide is effective because of the task-oriented wording of the headings, the position of the headings on the page, the use of lists, and the use of color. The headings suggest tasks that readers will understand, and the modified hanging format makes the first-level headings easy to see. The second-level headings are also effective because the icon and the color draw attention to each specific task. The numbered lists visually separate each step, so readers can easily identify and perform it.

To create an effective visual design for instructions, follow these tips and also review Principles 3 and 4 in Chapter 10:

- Use a serif typeface such as Times Roman, Palatino, or Bookman for the text.
- Use no more than two typeface families. If you use two, use a serif typeface for the text and a sans-serif typeface such as Helvetica or Univers for the headings.
- Use the modified hanging or left-hanging format for headings (see Figure 10.7).
- When possible, use color consistently to highlight important elements such as first-level headings and lists. Use the same color throughout so that readers won't wonder what different colors mean (Brockmann 161).
- Use typefaces, type sizes, color, and other design elements consistently.

Figure 16.3 An Effective Layout for Instructions

The writer has used task-oriented headings with verbs to focus the action.

The writer uses color consistently to highlight headings, bullets, and step-by-step directions.

The writer uses a consistent layout for headings and subheadings. Notice the blue rule following each subheading.

A copy of the screen helps readers to follow the directions.

Deleting a File from a Print Queue

You can use the Delete button in the Print Manager window to delete a file from a print queue at any time.

▶ **To delete a file from a print queue**

1. Select the information line for the file from the print queue.
2. Choose the Delete button.
   Or press ALT + D.
   A dialog box appears, asking you to confirm the deletion.
3. Choose OK.

▶ **To delete all files from all print queues**

1. Choose Exit from the Options menu.
   A dialog box appears, asking you to confirm the deletion.
2. Choose OK.
   If you do not choose OK, Print Manager will continue to operate, and the files will continue to print.

CAUTION If you delete a file currently printing in graphics mode, you might need to reset your printer to ensure that the printer's buffer is clear. (Turn it off and back on again or select the Reset option, if available.)

Changing the Printing Speed

You can specify the rate at which information is transferred from Print Manager to the printer ports by using the Low Priority, Medium Priority, and High Priority commands on the Options menu.

A checkmark next to a command indicates the current setting.

Print Manager				▼ ▲
Options View Help				

Low Priority		Delete	The Postscript printer on \\PRT31155\APL31155(LPTs) is Active
✓**Medium Priority**			on LPT1 [Idle]
High Priority			
Alert Always			
✓**Flash if Inactive**			
Ignore if Inactive			
Network...			
Exit			

Figure 16.3 (cont.)

The writer uses typeface and type size consistently for the headings.

▶ **To increase printing speed and slow down applications**

■ Choose High Priority from the Options menu.

This setting uses more of your computer's processor time for Print Manager, causing other applications to run more slowly.

▶ **To print and run applications equally**

■ Choose Medium Priority from the Options menu.

This setting shares your computer's processor time as equally as possible between Print Manager and other applications that are running. This is the standard setting.

▶ **To decrease printing speed and run applications faster**

■ Choose Low Priority from the Options menu.

This setting uses more of the computer's processor time to run applications, causing Print Manager to slow down.

Source: Microsoft ® Windows 3.0 User's Guide, 202–203. Reprinted with permission from Microsoft Corporation.

PRINCIPLE 3: USE READER-ORIENTED LANGUAGE

As you write your step-by-step instructions, use reader-oriented language. Use a "talker" style: Write as if you were speaking directly to your readers (Brockmann; Haramundanis). The following examples contrast *talker style* with *writer style*:

Use Talker Style . . .	Not Writer Style
Press the <return> key for help.	The user should press the <return> key for assistance.
Press the shutter-release button.	The user should press the shutter-release button.
Tighten the knobs on each side of the handle.	The knobs on each side of the handle should be tightened.

Talker style is concise. It uses action verbs, imperative sentences (or commands), and simple and specific language.

Use Action Verbs

Action verbs tell readers what to do. When writing step-by-step instructions, use verbs like *run, adjust, press, type*, and *loosen*—not verbs like *is* or *have*. Notice the action verbs (in boldface type) in these instructions:

Replace the battery with a new one.

Dial the phone number that you want to store in memory.

Disconnect the sparkplug wire, and **move** it away from the sparkplug.

Each action verb clearly indicates the action that the reader should perform. Each action verb is in the active voice (to review the difference between the active and passive voice, see Principle 1 in Chapter 8).

Use Imperative Sentences

Effective step-by-step instructions consist of talker-style sentences whose grammatical subject is the pronoun *you*, which, however, doesn't appear—as in "Replace the battery." Sentences in which the grammatical subject is understood to be *you* are called **imperative sentences.** An imperative sentence is a command. Its main verb tells the reader to carry out some action. Imperative sentences focus attention on what the reader is to do, not on the reader or person who will perform the action.

Compare these two sentences:

Writer-style sentence	You should locate a wall stud in the area where you want to install your telephone.
Imperative sentence	**Locate** a wall stud in the area where you want to install your telephone.

The writer-style sentence focuses the reader's attention on the subject "You," the first word of the sentence. In the imperative sentence, the reader understands the subject to be "you" and focuses on the main verb, which expresses the action.

Let's look at two more examples:

Writer-style sentence	Testing of emergency numbers should be performed during off-peak hours, such as in the early morning or late evening.
Imperative sentence	**Test** emergency numbers during off-peak hours, such as in the early morning or late evening.

In the writer-style sentence, the verb is in the passive voice ("should be performed"), and the action that the reader is to perform is in the noun *testing*. The imperative sentence expresses the action in the verb *test*. By using imperative sentences, the writer eliminates passive-voice constructions and focuses the reader's attention on the action.

Use Simple and Specific Language

Try to resist the temptation to use "fancy" words. Figure 16.4 lists alternatives to some "fancy" words that you otherwise might use. When writing instructions and manuals, use words that readers can quickly and easily understand. If you are unsure whether readers will understand a word, choose some other word or provide a definition that they will understand.

When writing instructions and manuals, be specific. Otherwise, readers might not gather the proper equipment and materials, or they might misunderstand the instructions and injure themselves or damage the equipment. Consider these instructions for changing the oil in an automobile:

> Before changing the oil, run the engine until it reaches normal operating temperature. The engine has reached this temperature when the exhaust pipe is warm to the touch. You should run the engine to mix the dirt and sludge with the oil in the crankcase, so the dirt and sludge drain along with the oil.

Experienced automobile mechanics would know how long to let the engine run before the exhaust pipe became so hot that it burned their hands. Other readers using these instructions might not know how long to let the engine run. Thus the writer should specifically state how long to let the engine run, so that novice readers are less likely to burn themselves on a hot exhaust

Figure 16.4
Fancy and Simple
Words

Instead of These Fancy Words . . .	Use These Simple Words
assistance	help, aid
construct	build
facilitate	help
indicate	show
initial	first
initiate	begin, start
modify	change
perform	do
proceed	go
subsequent	next, later
terminate	end, stop
transmit	send
utilize	use

THE READER'S CORNER

Liability and Instructional Writing: Can You or Your Company Be Liable?

Are companies liable for financial damages when instructions for their products are imprecise or inaccurate? In *Martin v. Hacker*, the New York Court of Appeals unanimously decided that companies are definitely liable. This decision is especially interesting to those who write instructions because the court carefully analyzed the language of instructions in a lawsuit over a drug-induced suicide. Eugene Martin was taking hydrochlorothiazide and reserpine for high blood pressure; although he "had no history of mental illness or depression, [he] shot and killed himself in a drug-induced despondency" (Caher 6). His widow alleged that the written warnings supplied with the drugs hydrochlorothiazide and reserpine were insufficient. The court stated that the case centered on the drug manufacturer's obligation to fully reveal the potential hazards of its products. Therefore, the court specifically examined the accuracy, clarity, and consistency of the warnings. In its examination, the court scrutinized specific language that the writers used. The court dismissed the lawsuit, stating that the warnings "contained language which, on its face, adequately warned against the precise risk" (Martin v. Hacker).

According to this case and a growing trend, courts will carefully analyze the specific language of technical documents and will hold companies liable for that language (Parson). Companies and writers, then, must be diligent in writing technical instructions—especially in terms of accuracy, clarity, and consistency because the "stakes are substantial" (Caher 10). When a writer's "work is unclear, [and] an operator inadvertently reformats a hard drive, that's unfortunate"; but if a writer's inaccurate or unclear language "claims a life, that's another matter altogether" (Caher 10).

pipe. Specific language is crucial if readers are to correctly and safely follow instructions.

Use Language Readers Will Understand

Use terminology that readers will understand. To determine how "technical" your manual or instructions can be, consider these questions:

- What sort of background and training do your readers have? Will they understand technical terminology related to the task?
- Are the readers native or expert speakers of technical/business English?

If you know that readers have background or training in a field related to the task, use technical terms that they know and will expect. If your readers have little relevant background or training, try to avoid technical terms and instead use language that they will understand. If your readers are not native or expert speakers of technical/business English, avoid connotative and ambiguous language and terms that may have different meanings in other languages.

Also be sensitive to the tone of your writing. For instance, imperative sentences will make readers in some cultures uncomfortable. For some readers, you might use labeled drawings, especially when the instructions are relatively simple and require few words (Brockmann 115).

PRINCIPLE 4: TEST YOUR INSTRUCTIONS

When time and money allow, test your instructions before you release them to your primary readers. One method of testing is to let some readers try out the instructions to see whether the instructions are effective. This type of testing can uncover places where readers cannot understand what you have written, where you have given too much information, or where readers need you to give more. Many companies, especially software development companies, have specific procedures for testing instructions.

You can test instructions several times during the writing process:

- Test the prototype, or first draft, of a chapter or section. Prototype testing occurs early in the writing process before you draft the entire document. Prototype testing helps you to see whether the layout, design, and style you have selected will work for your readers.
- Test a complete but preliminary draft of the instructions.
- Test a revised but not yet final draft of the instructions.

Prototype testing is extremely valuable because it provides early feedback before you write the entire document. If you wait to test until you are completely satisfied with the instructions, you probably will be near your final deadline and will not have time to revise the document after it is tested.

To conduct the test, follow these guidelines:

- Select as testers people who will be typical readers or users of the instructions (Brockmann 262).
- Explain the purpose of the test, either orally or in writing, and tell the testers how they should note problems or make suggestions.
- Tell the testers what they should consider as they use the instructions. For instance, you might ask them to evaluate the clarity, accuracy, and completeness of the step-by-step instructions or to evaluate the visual aids. Many writers provide a questionnaire or checklist for the testers to fill out as they test the instructions.
- Observe the testers while they are using the instructions. Watch for any problems they have as they use the instructions.

PRINCIPLE 5: USE THE APPROPRIATE CONVENTIONAL ELEMENTS OF INSTRUCTIONS AND MANUALS

The structure, length, and formality of instructions varies depending on the procedure and readers. If you want to explain to your coworkers how to use the new fax machine, you might first briefly introduce the procedure and then present the step-by-step instructions. You could send these instructions to the readers in a memo or by way of e-mail, or you might write the instructions on a card placed next to the fax machine itself. Your coworkers just want to know how to use the fax machine. They probably aren't interested in how a fax machine operates, and they don't need a formal list of materials and equipment. However, suppose you are writing instructions that come in the carton with a fax machine that a customer will buy. These instructions will need to be more formal than the ones for your coworkers and will need to meet the needs of a diverse group of readers. These instructions might appear in a manual that has a table of contents and an index. Such a manual will also list the materials, equipment, and instructions for installing and using the fax machine. The manual is likely to have a troubleshooting section for solving common problems.

The sections and format that you use will vary with the procedure that you are describing and the needs of your readers. Simple, informal instructions to a homogeneous group of readers may just be a step-by-step list. To write complex, formal instructions for diverse groups of readers, you might decide to include any or all of these conventional elements:

- Introduction
- Theory of operation/description of equipment
- Safety alerts
- Step-by-step directions
- Troubleshooting guide
- Reference aids

Introduction

The introduction gives readers the basic information they need to understand how to use the instructions. Introductions for manuals often have titles other than "Introduction." They might have the title "Preface" or "How to Use This Manual." In the *User's Guide* for Microsoft® Windows 3.0, the title of the introduction is "Welcome to Windows." The introduction may include any or all of the following information:

- **The purpose of the instructions.**
- **The intended readers and their assumed level of skill and knowledge of the task:** Clearly state who should use the instructions and what they should know about the task. For example, the installation guide for a garbage disposal states that the instructions are "for electricians with a Level 3 or higher certification according to Section 3 of the state electrical code." In other words, the writers assume that readers know how to install

The writer uses drawings (instead of photographs) to identify the tools and fasteners.

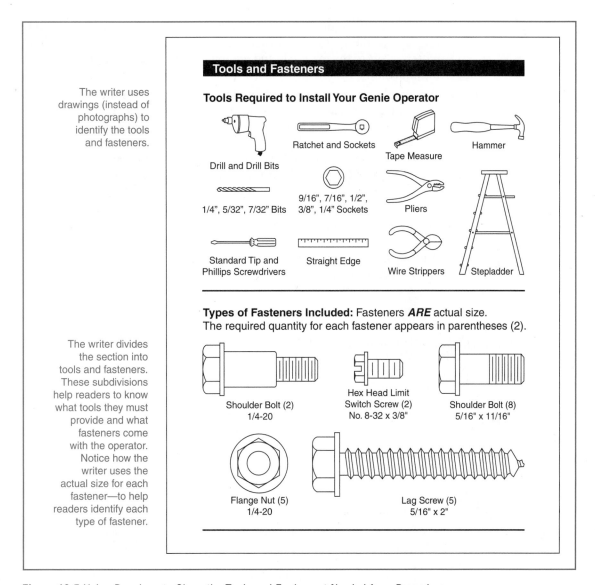

The writer divides the section into tools and fasteners. These subdivisions help readers to know what tools they must provide and what fasteners come with the operator. Notice how the writer uses the actual size for each fastener—to help readers identify each type of fastener.

Figure 16.5 Using Drawings to Show the Tools and Equipment Needed for a Procedure

Source: Adapted from *Genie Automatic Screw Drive Garage Door Operator System* (Alliance, OH: Genie, n.d.) 5. Used by permission of Genie.

similar equipment and that they understand the electrical code and related ordinances.

- **Materials and equipment that readers need:** List all the materials and equipment in one place, so readers can gather them together before beginning the task. You can use drawings of some materials and equipment to ensure that readers understand what they need. For example, the parts identification page shown in Figure 16.5 uses drawings and words to make sure readers know what tools they need to install a garage door opener. The figure also shows the types of fasteners included in the installation kit. Some writers identify the materials and equipment in a separate section after the introduction.

- **Typographical conventions and terminology used in the instructions:** If you use any typographical conventions, icons, or terminology that your readers may not understand or recognize, explain them in the introduction. If you use many terms that readers may not understand, you can define them in a glossary and introduce the glossary in the introduction. Figure 16.6 shows how the *User's Guide* for Microsoft® Windows explains in its introduction the various typographical conventions, icons, and terminology used throughout the manual.

- **Any other information necessary to help readers use and understand the instructions:** For instance, if you've divided the manual into sections, tell readers what information each section includes and perhaps when and how to use each section.

Figure 16.6 Explaining Typographical Conventions, Icons, and Terminology in an Introduction

Visual Cues

You will find the following typographic conventions throughout the *User's Guide.*

Type style	Used for
italic	Anything that you must type exactly as it appears. For example, if asked to type *dir\windows,* you would type all the italicized characters exactly as they appear in the guide.
	Italic type also signals a new term. An explanation immediately follows the italicized term.
bold	Placeholders for information you must provide. For instance, if asked to type **filename,** you would type the actual name for a file instead of the word shown in bold print.
ALL CAPITALS	Directory names, filenames, and acronyms.
SMALL CAPITALS	The names of keys on your keyboard. For example, CTRL, ESC, or HOME.
Initial capitals	Menu items, command names, and dialog-box names and options. For example, File menu, Save command, or Line Wrap option.

Symbol	Used for
▶	Signals the beginning of a procedure.
■	Signals a procedure that has only one step.
Mouse	Instructions for mouse users.
Keyboard	Instructions for keyboard users.

Figure 16.6 (cont.)

Keyboard Formats

Key combinations and key sequences appear in the following format:

Format	Meaning
KEY1 + KEY2	A plus sign (+) between key names means to hold down the first key while you press the second key. For example, Press ALT + ESC means to hold down the ALT key and press the ESC key. Then release both keys.
KEY1, KEY2	A comma (,) between key names means to press and release the keys one after the other. For example, Press ALT, F means to press and release the ALT key. Then press and release the F key.

Terminology

The following terms take on special meanings in the context of Windows.

Term	Meaning
Application	A computer program used for a particular kind of work, such as word processing.
Application icon	A graphical representation of a running application that has been minimized. Application icons appear on the desktop.
Choose	To use a mouse or key combination to pick an item that begins an action in Windows.
Click	To quickly press and release the mouse button.

Source: Adapted from *Microsoft® Windows 3.0 User's Guide,* xxii–xxiii. Reprinted with permission from Microsoft Corporation.

Some introductions introduce the introduction itself:

> This introductory section of the *Windows User's Guide* tells you about the computer equipment and software you need to run Windows, and what you'll receive when you register your copy of Windows. It also previews the Windows graphical environment and highlights its new features and enhancements. Perhaps most importantly, this section prepares you to use the guide by defining typographical conventions and important terminology.[1]

Theory of Operation/Description of Equipment

The theory of operation/description of equipment section answers these questions:

- What are the concepts or theory of operation behind the task?
- How does the equipment work?

---

1. Adapted from *Microsoft® Windows 3.0 User's Guide,* p. ix.

Your AT&T Cordless telephone works much like a regular telephone, except that no cord connects the handset to the base unit. Since you're not limited by a cord, you can move freely from room to room, and outside your home, while you're on the phone.

How Far Will It Reach?

Your AT&T Cordless telephone operates at the maximum power allowed by the Federal Communications Commission (FCC). Even so, the operating range is limited; the handset can operate only a certain distance from the base unit. Under average conditions, AT&T cordless phones will operate throughout a typical home and immediately outside it. However, the actual operating distance depends on the construction of your home, the weather and other factors. (See "Operating Range," page 21.)

You Should Know . . .

The same features that make a cordless phone convenient create some limitations. Telephone calls are transmitted between the base unit and the handset by radio waves, so radio receiving equipment within range of your cordless handset could intercept your cordless phone conversations. For this reason, you shouldn't think of cordless phone conversations as being as private as those on corded phones. . . .

Automatic Security Coding

Every time you place the handset in the base, your phone randomly selects one of 65,000 possible security codes—much like an electronic password. With this Automatic Security Coding, your handset and base can recognize each other automatically, minimizing the chance that another cordless phone will use your telephone line.

AutoSelect™

To provide the clearest possible sound quality, your phone has the advanced 10-channel **AutoSelect** feature. A microcomputer in the phone continually monitors the airwaves to determine which of the ten cordless phone channels are used the *least* in your immediate vicinity. When you use the phone, the **AutoSelect** circuit provides the channel that has been vacant the longest, minimizing the chance of interference from nearby cordless phones—such as your neighbor's. Unlike simpler "scanning" systems, the **AutoSelect** feature actually keeps track of channel activity over a long period of time, which greatly improves its accuracy. . . .

Figure 16.7 A Theory of Operation/Description of Equipment Section
Source: Adapted from *AT&T Cordless Telephone 5400 Owner's Manual.*

Readers often want or need to understand the basic theory of operation or concept governing a procedure. They also may want or need to understand how a piece of equipment operates. For example, in the user's guide for a cordless telephone (see Figure 16.7), the writers explain how cordless telephones work; this information will help readers understand how to operate the telephone properly. The writers explain not only how the telephone works but also how this type of operation affects the way readers can use the telephone. The writers describe some of the features of the telephone: Automatic Security Coding and AutoSelect. The introduction to these features helps readers to know what sections of the manual they will need to read. The brief introduction to the telephone helps them use the manual and the telephone effectively.

In sections describing the equipment or the theory of operation, use language readers can understand, and include only the details they need and expect. Generally place this information near the beginning of the instructions or manual. You can combine the theory of operation/description of equipment with the introduction, as in Figure 16.7, or you can put this information in a separate section after the introduction. For relatively simple instructions, readers generally do not need or want you to explain the concepts or theory of operation—in fact, such explanations can be quite cumbersome and distracting.

Safety Alerts

You have a legal and ethical responsibility to warn readers about possible injury to themselves or others and about possible damage to equipment and materials. You must state the seriousness of the possible injury or damage, using the correct language. The American National Standards Institute suggests specific terms for alerting readers to hazards (American Standards Institute 1989; emphasis added):

Danger: imminently hazardous situation which, if not avoided, **will** result in **death or serious injury**

Warning: potentially hazardous situation which, if not avoided, **could** result in **death or serious injury**

Caution: hazardous situation which, if not avoided, **may** result in **minor or moderate injury**

Use the word *danger* to indicate that death or serious injury will occur. Use *warning* to indicate that death or serious injury could occur. Use *caution* to indicate that a slight injury might occur. Notice these terms in the warning shown in Figure 16.8.

While preparing your instructions, consider these questions:

- Will the procedure or equipment endanger the readers, their surroundings, or their equipment?
- Is the safety alert adequate for the circumstances and severity of the hazard (Brockmann 13)?
- Is the safety alert located where readers will see it *before* they perform the task that will endanger them?

Place the safety alert before or next to the instructions for the hazardous task, not after it. If the hazard is severe, put the safety alert at the beginning of the instructions or manual, and repeat it before or next to the task where the hazard occurs.

Make safety alerts easy to see. You can use one or more of these techniques to highlight warnings:

- Use a symbol or an icon to indicate a warning, danger, or caution. The warning shown in Figure 16.8 uses an exclamation point (!) inside a triangle to indicate a hazard. The writers use this symbol because it is the international symbol for safety alert. They also use simple drawings to illustrate the potential hazard. Graphics are especially important for international readers or readers who aren't native or expert speakers of technical/business English.

Figure 16.8 A Warning

⚠ *WARNING*

Overhead doors are large, heavy objects that move with the help of springs under high tension and electric motors. Since moving objects, springs under tension, and electric motors can cause injuries, your safety and the safety of others depend on you reading the information in this manual. If you have questions or do not understand the information presented, call your nearest service representative.

POTENTIAL HAZARD	EFFECT	PREVENTION
MOVING DOOR	Can cause serious injury or death	Keep people clear of opening while the door is moving. **Do Not** allow children to play with the door operator. **Do Not** operate a door that jams or one that has a broken spring.
ELECTRICAL SHOCK	Can cause serious injury or death	Turn off the power before removing the operator cover. When replacing the cover, make sure wires are not pinched or near moving parts. Properly ground the operator.
HIGH SPRING TENSION	Can cause serious injury or death	**Do Not** try to remove, repair, or adjust springs or anything to which door spring parts are fastened, such as wood blocks, steel brackets, or cables. Follow instructions and use proper tools to repair and adjust the spring.

In the following text, the words Danger, Warning, and Caution are used to emphasize important safety information. The word:
⚠ DANGER means that severe injury or death <u>will</u> result from failure to follow instructions.
⚠ WARNING means that severe injury or death can result from failure to follow instructions.
⚠ CAUTION means that property damage or injury can result from failure to follow instructions.
The word NOTE indicates important steps or important differences in equipment.

Source: Adapted from *Genie Automatic Screw Drive Garage Door Operator System* (Alliance, OH: Genie, n.d.) 3. Used by permission of Genie.

- Use a different but consistent color for the safety alert or for at least part of it.
- Separate the safety alert from the text with white space or a border.

Step-by-Step Directions

The step-by-step directions tell readers exactly how to carry out a procedure. Before you begin writing these directions, decide how to organize them. To determine how to organize the directions, consider these questions (Brockmann 91–92):

- What action begins each task?
- What are the specific steps for performing the task? Can you group these steps into subtasks?
- What action ends each task?
- Can you perform the task in more than one way? If so, do readers need to know both ways?

Once you have considered those questions, categorize the task into major steps and then divide the steps into appropriate substeps (for more information on classification and division, see Chapter 7). For example, if you are explaining to a novice how to change the oil in an automobile, you might divide the task into four major steps—(1) drain the old oil, (2) remove the old oil filter, (3) install the new filter, and (4) refill the crankcase with oil—and then subdivide each step into substeps. When you divide the steps into substeps, you will help readers to understand the task and to follow your directions. One long list of uncategorized steps will intimidate most readers. The simple task of changing the oil could have as many as thirty steps. Most readers would prefer four major steps with substeps to a list of thirty steps.

When you write step-by-step directions, list the substeps with each major step. You can tell readers what specific materials or equipment they will need for each major step, especially if these materials or equipment vary from step to step. Give step-by-step directions in chronological order, stating any necessary safety alerts. (For more information about chronological order, see Chapter 7, "Arranging Information for Your Readers.") As you write the directions, follow these guidelines:

- Describe only one action in each step or substep.
- Number each step.
- Use a list format, so readers can follow the directions easily. Don't bury directions in paragraphs or extremely long lines of text.

The step-by-step directions shown in Figure 16.11 follow these guidelines.

Troubleshooting Guide

A troubleshooting guide helps readers solve commonly encountered problems. It often appears in a table format with the problem in the left column and the solution in the right column (see Figure 16.9). Alternatively, you could simply

Figure 16.9 A Troubleshooting Guide

Troubleshooting

If you've experienced any of the following difficulties while using your telephone, use this troubleshooting guide to help you solve the problem. If any problem continues, consult your nearest Sony dealer.

	Problem	Solution
Making calls	You hear five short error beeps when you press TALK.	• Make sure you set up the base phone correctly (see page 9). • Move the handset closer to the base phone. • Replace the handset to the base phone to recharge the battery pack (see page 12).
Making calls	You hear no dial tone.	• Make sure the telephone line cord is securely connected to the telephone outlet. • Make sure the battery is fully charged (see page 12).
Making calls	The telephone always connects with the wrong number or doesn't connect at all, even though the number you dial is correct.	• Make sure the dialing mode is set correctly (page 10).
Making calls	The phone doesn't redial correctly.	• Make sure the number you last dialed (including the tone and pause digits, if used) is fewer than 32 digits. • Make sure the last dialed number is really the one you want to dial.
Making calls	You hear interference during conversation.	• Move the handset closer to the base phone. • Press CHANNEL for a channel that gives better reception. • Place the base phone away from noise sources (see page 8).
Making calls	You hear a beep every three seconds.	• Charge the battery for more than 12 hours (see page 12). The battery is weak.
Receiving calls	The handset doesn't ring.	• Set the RING ON/BATT SAVE switch on the handset to RING ON. • Charge the battery for more than 12 hours (see page 12). The battery may be weak. • Make sure you set up the base phone correctly (see page 9). • Move the handset closer to the base phone.

Figure 16.9 (cont.)

	Problem	Solution
Speed dialing	You hear five short beeps and can't store a speed-dialing number.	• Make sure you follow the procedure in storing the number correctly (see page 19). • Make sure the number (including the tone and pause digits) is fewer than 16 digits.
	You hear five short beeps when you try to make a speed-dialing call.	• Program a phone number for the dialing key (see page 19). You entered a dialing key to which you've not stored a number.
	Speed dialing is incorrect.	• Program the correct number (see page 19).
Intercom	The handset doesn't ring when calling from the base phone.	• Set the RING ON/BATT SAVE switch to RING ON. • Charge the battery for more than 12 hours (see page 12). The battery may have little or no power. • Raise the antenna of the base phone vertically and fully extended. • Place the base phone away from noise sources (see page 8). • Move the handset closer to the base phone.

Source: Adapted from *Sony Cordless Telephone with Answering System Operating Instructions* (n.p.: Sony Corporation, 1996) 44–45. Courtesy of Sony Electronics, Inc.

use left-hanging headings for the problem and bulleted lists for the solutions. Brief, simple instructions usually don't need troubleshooting guides.

Troubleshooting guides can save you, your company, and readers time and money by helping readers to solve problems without making a service call to the company. Readers who can solve their problems without calling customer service reduce the amount of time and money that companies must spend on phone support for their products. By anticipating readers' problems, troubleshooting guides allow readers to solve common problems in less time than a trial-and-error approach would take and without expensive service calls.

Reference Aids

To help your readers find the information they need in your instructions and manuals, you can provide a variety of reference aids, depending on the needs of your readers and the length and complexity of the instructions. Common reference aids include the following:

• **Table of contents:** Include a table of contents for all manuals (see Chapter 12, "Preparing Front and End Matter").

- **Index:** Include an index for all manuals. Indexes help readers to find specific information or to solve problems quickly.
- **Headings:** Headings help readers locate specific information and provide a road map to the instructions.
- **Quick-reference cards:** Quick-reference cards provide an overview of capabilities or commands. These cards help readers who are familiar with the software and hardware and don't need the elaboration of more extensive instructions. Quick-reference cards are a separate document from the manual; they may be in the form of a brochure, a small card, or a template. Figure 16.10 shows a quick-reference card for a cordless telephone. This card includes instructions in Spanish and English.

SAMPLE INSTRUCTIONS

The sample instructions presented in Figure 16.11 (on page 430) accompany a cordless telephone that has an internal answering machine. The instructions tell readers how to set up the answering machine. The left-hanging headings help readers find the steps they want to complete. To help readers follow the instructions, the writers included a simple drawing of the telephone and labeled the keys that readers will use to set up the answering machine.

Figure 16.10
A Quick-Reference
Card

Función de control remoto	Mandato de operación		Remote control function	Command	
Para reproducir los mensajes			To play back the message		
Buzón 1	#	①	Mailbox 1	#	①
Buzón 2	#	②	Mailbox 2	#	②
Buzón 3	#	③	Mailbox 3	#	③
Para repetir el mensaje	#	④	To repeat the message	#	④
Para cesar la operación	#	⑤	To stop operation	#	⑤
Para saltar el mensaje	#	⑥	To skip the message	#	⑥
Para grabar un mensaje de contestación	*	⑦	To record a greeting	*	⑦
Para grabar un mensaje de transferencia	*	⑧	To record a transfer message	*	⑧
Para activar/desactivar la transferencia	#	⑧	To turn transferring on/off	#	⑧
Para borrar un mensaje	#	⑨	To erase individual message	#	⑨
Para activar (ANSWER ON)	*	⓪	To turn on (ANSWER ON)	*	⓪
Para desactivar (ANSWER OFF)	#	⓪	To turn off (ANSWER OFF)	#	⓪

Source: Adapted from *Sony Cordless Telephone with Answering System Operating Instructions* (n.p.: Sony Corporation, 1996). Courtesy of Sony Electronics, Inc.

WORKSHEET   for Planning and Writing Your Instructions and Manuals

Principle 1: Find Out How Much Readers Know About the Task

- Have readers performed the task, or similar tasks, before?
- Do readers have the same background or knowledge of the tasks? Will they have different purposes for using the instructions? Will their purposes for reading change?
- How much detail do readers need to complete the task? Do they want only minimal instructions?
- What are readers' attitudes toward the task and toward the equipment used for the task? (Brockmann 101)

Principle 2: Use an Accessible Design

- Is the design appropriate for the readers' environment?
- Is the typeface appropriate for the instructions and the environment?
- Does the layout allow readers to easily use the instructions?
- Are the headings task oriented?

Principle 3: Use Reader-Oriented Language

- Have you used action verbs?
- Have you used imperative sentences?
- Have you used simple and specific language?
- Have you used language readers will understand?

Principle 4: Test Your Instructions

- Have you planned for readers to test your instructions?
- Have you planned the testing early enough to allow for revising?

Principle 5: Use the Appropriate Conventional Elements of Instructions and Manuals

- Have you appropriately introduced the instructions?
- Have you included a list of all the materials and equipment?
- Have you included necessary safety alerts?
- Are the step-by-step directions complete and clear? Have you appropriately subdivided the steps?
- Have you included a troubleshooting guide?
- Have you included the appropriate reference aids?

Figure 16.11 Instructions from a Manual

The introduction tells readers that setting up the answering machine requires two steps.

Setting Up the Answering Machine

To set up your answering machine, complete these two steps:
- Set the time and day of the week
- Record the greeting

Setting the Time and the Day of the Week

To set the time and the day of the week, follow these steps:

REMOTE lamp

FLASH/REMOTE

0 – 9

#

*

RING ON/BATT SAVE

Notice that the drawing shows the various keys used in setting up the answering machine.

1 Press (FLASH/REMOTE).
   The REMOTE lamp lights up.
   You will hear day of the week, time and new message number.

2 Press (*).

3 Set the day of the week using the dialing keys.
   Sunday – (1), Monday – (2), Tuesday – (3), Wednesday – (4), Thursday – (5), Friday – (6), Saturday – (7)

4 Set the hour using the dialing keys.
   To set 3 o'clock, press (0)(3).

5 Set the minutes using the dialing keys.
   To set 8 minutes, press (0)(8).

6 Set the AM or PM.
   To set AM, press (*).
   To set PM, press (#).
   You will hear one long beep, followed by the new day and time.

7 Press (FLASH/REMOTE).
   The REMOTE lamp goes off.

Figure 16.11 (cont.)

Notice that the pages contain ample white space to highlight the headings and the step-by-step directions.

Notice the tab. Tabs help readers locate the information in manuals.

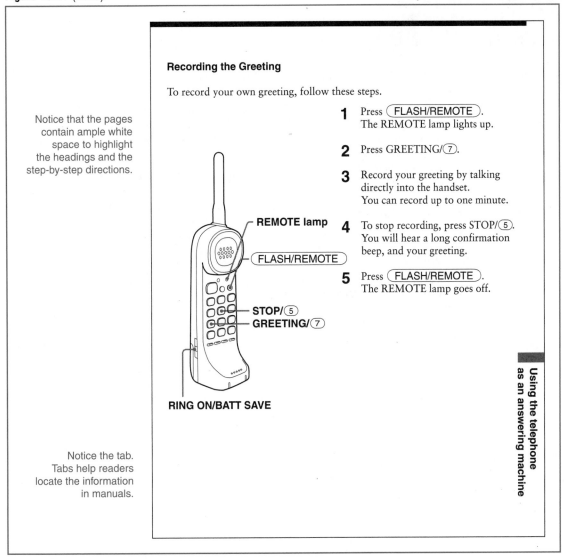

Recording the Greeting

To record your own greeting, follow these steps.

1 Press (FLASH/REMOTE).
The REMOTE lamp lights up.

2 Press GREETING/⑦.

3 Record your greeting by talking directly into the handset.
You can record up to one minute.

4 To stop recording, press STOP/⑤.
You will hear a long confirmation beep, and your greeting.

5 Press (FLASH/REMOTE).
The REMOTE lamp goes off.

REMOTE lamp

(FLASH/REMOTE)

STOP/⑤
GREETING/⑦

RING ON/BATT SAVE

Using the telephone as an answering machine

Source: Adapted from *Sony Cordless Telephone with Answering System Operating Instructions* (n.p.: Sony Corporation, 1996) 24–25. Courtesy of Sony Electronics, Inc.

EXERCISES

1. Photocopy some instructions that are hard to follow. (Your instructor may specify a length for these instructions.) Then complete these tasks:

   a. Identify the intended readers of the instructions. Analyze the content, organization, conventional elements, language, and layout to see whether they are appropriate for these readers. Using this analysis, determine why the instructions are hard to follow.

   b. Write a memo to your instructor describing the intended users of the instructions and summarizing your analysis. Attach a copy of the instructions to your memo.

   c. Rewrite the instructions (or a portion of the instructions as assigned by your instructor) so readers can follow them easily. When you give the revised instructions to your instructor, attach a copy of the original version.

2. Write instructions for a task with which you are extremely familiar.

3. Analyze the language and layout of the instructions shown in Figure 16.12. Write a memo presenting your analysis to your instructor.

4. Rewrite the instructions in Figure 16.12, eliminating the problems in language and layout that you identified in Exercise 3.

5. Examine the reference aids that accompany a manual. Then write a memo discussing the value of reference aids, using the aids in the manual that you examined to support your discussion. Be prepared to discuss your memo in class.

6. Find some outdated instructions. Update those instructions, correcting any problems with language, layout, or organization. Turn in the updated instructions with a copy of the original version to your instructor.

Figure 16.12 The Instructions for Exercises 3 and 4

Safe Food Handling for Optimum Nutrition

Shopping

Food safety in the home actually starts at the grocery store.

Plan your purchases so that perishables (meat, poultry, seafood, and dairy products) are selected last. These foods should be refrigerated within 2 hours of purchase (1 hour in hot weather) so that food poisoning bacteria do not multiply.

Bag meat and poultry products to prevent juices from dripping onto other foods and keep them separated from other foods, especially foods that will not be cooked, such as fruits and vegetables.

Buy packaged precooked foods only if packaging is sound, and buy products labeled "keep refrigerated" only if they are stored in a refrigerated case.

Storing Food

Proper storage of food prolongs its shelf-life and preserves nutrients as well as safety. Foods stored too long gradually spoil and also will lose nutritional value.

Make sure your refrigerator is kept clean and maintains a temperature no higher than 40°F.

Your frozen foods will maintain top flavor and nutritional value if the freezer is kept at 0°F or below.

Be sure to keep raw meat and poultry separate from other foods, especially those that will be eaten without further cooking. Poultry and ground meat will keep 1–2 days in the refrigerator; other meat items, 3–4 days.

Canned goods and other shelf-stable items should be stored in a cool, dry place. The temperature should stay above freezing and below 85°F.

Preparing Food

Cleanliness is the first critical step in safe food preparation. Wash hands thoroughly with soap and water before handling food. Wash hands, utensils, cutting boards, and work areas after handling raw meat or poultry products.

Frozen foods should never be thawed at room temperature. Instead, thaw them safely in the refrigerator. Thaw in the microwave only immediately before cooking.

It is essential that raw products of animal origin be cooked to an internal temperature of 160°F (180°F for poultry). Use a meat thermometer to check the temperature of meat and poultry. To check visually, juices should run clear and meat should not be pink.

Do not partially cook food. Have a constant heat source, and don't set the oven temperature under 325°F for cooking meat, poultry, seafood, or dairy-based foods. Microwave food in a covered dish and turn the dish frequently.

Serving Food

Food safety errors can be made during the serving and handling of cooked food.

When serving foods be sure to wash hands thoroughly with hot soapy water. Serve cooked products on clean plates and with clean utensils.

Foods should never sit at room temperature longer than 2 hours, 1 hour in hot weather. During serving, hot foods should be held above 140°F and cold foods should be kept cold.

Leftovers

When handling leftovers, cleanliness and temperature control are critical.

Wash hands before handling leftovers and use clean utensils and surfaces.

Refrigerate or freeze cooked leftovers in small, covered shallow containers within 2 hours after cooking. Leave airspace around containers in the refrigerator to ensure rapid, even cooling.

When reheating leftovers, cover and reheat thoroughly. Sauces, soups, and gravies should be heated to a rolling boil; all other products should be heated to 165°F.

Food spoilage bacteria will grow in the refrigerator, so discard any outdated foods. Most foods will remain safe in the refrigerator for about 4 days, but use highly perishable foods such as stuffing or gravy within 1–2 days.

When in doubt, throw it out!

Source: Dept. of Agriculture, *Nutrition: Eating for Good Health,* Publ. 685 (Washington: GPO, 1994) 184–186.

CASE STUDY   Collaborating on a Manual

Background

Every week, you encounter tasks that require you to follow instructions. These instructions might explain how to use a new software application on a personal computer to complete an assignment, how to access CD-ROM databases in your school's library to research a topic, or how to conduct a physics experiment to complete a lab report. The instructions might be for tasks as simple as cooking a microwave dinner or changing the oil in your new car. Whatever the task, you frequently need to follow written instructions.

In many companies, teams collaborate to write instructions and manuals. These teams may write instructions and manuals for a service or product that the company offers, or these teams may write instructions and manuals that employees will use inside the company.

Assignment

You and your team are to write a manual for a task for which written instructions are not available or adequate for the readers to complete the task. To write the manual, you and your team will complete these steps:

1. Select a task. Make sure that all members of your team are familiar with the task. If the task requires equipment, make sure that your team has access to the equipment to prepare and to test the manual. Your instructor may want to approve your topic before you move to step 2.

2. Prepare a detailed outline of the manual. Submit this outline to your instructor to approve.

3. Decide on the reference aids that you will include with the manual.

4. Prepare prototype pages or sample pages showing the language, headings, and layout that you plan to use in the manual.

   a. Find sample readers. Ask these readers to follow the step-by-step directions on the prototype pages. Watch these readers as they follow the instructions, noting problems. After these readers have completed the instructions, ask them whether the language, headings, and layout helped them to follow the instructions and whether you can improve any of these elements.

   b. Revise the language, headings, and layout as necessary.

5. Write the manual, dividing the writing tasks among team members.

6. Test the manual again.

7. Revise the manual based on the test.

8. Turn in the final version of the manual to your instructor.

PART IV

WRITING EFFECTIVE CORRESPONDENCE FOR YOUR READERS

Chapter 17

Writing Reader-Oriented Letters, Memos, and E-Mail

CHAPTER OUTLINE

Like most professionals in the workplace, you will use letters, memos, and e-mail to correspond with coworkers and with people outside your company. Memos, letters, and e-mail are the everyday communication tools of the workplace. You will write letters primarily to communicate with people outside your company. You might also use them inside your company to handle confidential matters such as personnel and salary issues. A letter is often more formal than a memo or e-mail. The standard elements of letters are the date, the address of the sender, the address of the reader, a salutation, a closing, and the letter writer's signature. Figure 17.1 illustrates these standard elements.

You will write memos to communicate with people within your company. You might use a memo for routine correspondence about a company picnic or for a progress report. Memos have a format that includes the date, a "to" line, a "from" line, and a "subject" line. Your company may have a preprinted form or preferred format for memos. If it does not, you can use the format illustrated in Figure 17.2.

Regardless of the format you use, create a macro or template for that format with your word-processing program. You can use macros to perform repetitive tasks such as writing memos. Macros record a series of commands that you save and then call up by entering one or two commands or pressing one or two keys. By using a macro or a template, you can call up the memo format, fill in the required information, and write the text of your memo. Macros and templates can save you time and create a consistent look for your memos.

You can use e-mail to correspond with people inside your company or outside your company. The primary communication tool for many businesses, e-mail offers several advantages:

- **E-mail is faster than traditional paper letters and memos.** You can send an e-mail message to a coworker across the globe in seconds instead of the days required for traditional mail, and the coworker can respond within seconds.

- **E-mail is often faster and more convenient than telephone communication.** When you use e-mail, you can send messages anytime. You don't have to wait for your receiver to be available by phone. With e-mail you need not leave messages and wait for someone to return your call.

- **E-mail saves companies money.** E-mail communication is cheaper than most paper and telephone communication. For example, a two-page e-mail message between any two Hewlett-Packard employees worldwide averages 22 cents, a letter averages 51 cents, and a fax averages $1.66 (Perry 25).

- **E-mail gives companies flexibility and increases productivity.** E-mail lets companies put together research and development teams by tapping the best people for a project without worrying about geographic location—eliminating stressful transfers and expensive temporary assignments (Perry 24). Team members can work in different locations, using inexpensive e-mail as their communication link.

Figure 17.1 The Standard Elements of Letters

POWER ENGINEERING, INC.

400 North Zang ▪ Shreveport, LA 75201 ▪ (318) 555-4578

June 10, 1998

Mr. John Smithson
Robinson Creek Medical Center
P.O. Box 3547
Franklin, North Dakota 57890

Subject: Unit No. 3 Boiler Thermocouple Installation—P.I.D. No. 567-4678

Dear John:

This letter reports the current status of project 567-4678, the boiler thermocouple installation on Unit No. 3. We have ordered a Pyrosonic 2000 temperature detector that will include bent tube openings for the transmitter and receiver and a remote digital display. We will install the transmitter and receiver at elevation 526' 9$^{1}/_{4}$" above the superheated tube section.

The company has approved thermocouple specification 567-4678-S401, so I have submitted a requisition to purchase the thermocouples. Please note that the contractor will install 61 thermocouples.

As we discussed, I have outlined our respective project responsibilities in the following paragraphs.

Responsibilities of Power Engineering
Power Engineering will provide the following:

- instructions for installing the equipment, the wiring diagrams, the bills of materials, and construction drawings needed for installing all thermocouples up to and including the junction boxes
- the same support for installing the Pyrosonic 2000 temperature detector up to and including the processor cabinet

The contractor then will provide all the hardware to complete the installation, except the Pyrosonic 2000, the thermocouples, and the thermocouple junction boxes.

Responsibilities of Robinson Creek Engineering Support
You and your group will be responsible for all the equipment and labor from the end devices named above up to and including the recorder located in the control room. You will also be responsible for locating and installing the remote digital display supplied with the Pyrosonic 2000.

If you have questions, please call me at (318) 555-4578 or e-mail me at mcm@pe.com.

Sincerely,

Mathew R. McCarroll

Mathew R. McCarroll

Figure 17.2
A Standard Memo
Format

Memo

November 10, 1997

To: All employees currently holding parking-garage permits
From: Deanna Jones, Parking Manager
Subject: Renewing your parking-garage permit

Many of you have not renewed your parking-garage permits. To keep your parking space in the garage for 1998, renew your permit by November 30. On December 1, we allow employees who don't currently have garage permits to purchase any remaining permits.

To renew your permit, just follow these easy steps:

1. Fill out the one-page renewal form.
2. Put your current permit number on the form next to your name.
3. Ask your manager to sign the form.
4. Attach a check for $90.00 to the form.
5. Put the form and the check in the envelope provided.
6. Put the envelope in intercompany mail, or drop it by my office.

You received a renewal form and return envelope on October 1. If you need another form and envelope or if you have questions, please contact me at extension 5678 or at jones@pon.com.

Don't miss the November 30 deadline—you could lose your parking-garage space!

The format for e-mail messages varies from writer to writer and company to company. Many e-mail messages have the same general format as a memo, even when written to readers outside a company; however, many e-mail messages include a signature line at the end of the message (see Figure 17.3). In some corporate environments, the e-mail format is less formal than a memo; and e-mail communication becomes a series of informal exchanges similar to face-to-face conversation.

PRINCIPLE 1: DETERMINE THE OBJECTIVES OF YOUR LETTER, MEMO, OR E-MAIL MESSAGE

Before writing a letter, memo, or e-mail message, decide what you want it to accomplish. Do you want readers to take a particular action after reading your correspondence? Do you want readers to give you information? Do you want to inform readers about good or perhaps bad news? As you think about writing your message, keep in mind that your correspondence may have more than just a business objective; it also may have the objective of maintaining or establishing a positive relationship with the reader.

Figure 17.3
A Formal E-Mail
Message

Date: Thu, 2 Aug 97 10:44:47 CDT
From: "Mary Gonzalez" <mmg@sw.com>
To: cosgrove@pbe.com
Subject: Proposal for Chemco

I have attached a revised outline based on our meeting yesterday. In this meeting, we agreed to the following schedule:

8/7   rough draft due to me (you can send me the draft via e-mail)
8/10   revised draft from me for you to review
8/11   suggested changes to the draft due to me
8/12   deliver final copies of proposal to you

Please verify this schedule by return e-mail.

I appreciate your help. Please call me if you have questions.

Mary M. Gonzalez
Computer Specialist
PBE, Inc.
2600 South Valley Creek Parkway
Scranton, PA 17854
(717) 678-7890
mmg@sw.com

These questions will help you to determine both the business and the human-relations objectives of your letters, memos, and e-mail messages:

- **What is the purpose of the correspondence? What do you expect it to accomplish?** Your correspondence frequently will have more than one objective. For example, the primary objective of the letter shown in Figure 17.4 is to inform the reader of the new customer comment cards. The secondary objective is to mend a damaged relationship with the reader and ensure the continued business and good will of that reader.

- **What action, if any, do you expect readers to take after reading the correspondence?** Determine what—if anything—you want readers to do after reading your correspondence. If you decide that you want readers to do something, clearly and directly state what you want them to do. Much correspondence is ineffective because the writer doesn't clearly and directly state what the writer expects the reader to do after reading the correspondence. The writer assumes that the reader will know what to do. Such assumptions will backfire if readers don't do what the writer expects.

- **What do you expect readers to know after reading the correspondence?** What, exactly, do you want your readers to know after reading your correspondence? If *you* don't know, neither will your readers. Informally list what you want your readers to know. This list can also help you to spot information that is irrelevant or that your readers won't understand.

Figure 17.4 A Message with a Primary and Secondary Objective

 **Computers on Wheels**

February 6, 1998

Mrs. Wanda Perrill
902 Indian Creek
St. Paul, Minnesota 57904

Dear Mrs. Perrill:

After our conversation last month about the quality of service in your home, we created a yellow "Customer Comment Card." To improve our service to you, your computer team will now leave this card on each visit. The purpose of the card is to solicit your comments about our service on a regular basis. These cards resulted directly from our conversation—thanks for the suggestion.

The comment cards will help us to maintain and monitor the quality of service that we provide in your home. They also are part of a new incentive program for our employees, so please take a moment after each maintenance visit to fill out the postage-paid card and drop it in the mail. Your comments will help us to provide the service you need and expect.

Thank you, Mrs. Perrill, for your comments that led to these new cards. We appreciate the confidence that you have placed in Computers on Wheels.

Sincerely,

Sherrod Segraves
Sherrod Segraves
Owner

"Serving you so you can work at home"

302 Macarthur, Suite 204
St. Paul, Minnesota 57904

PRINCIPLE 2: FIND OUT ABOUT YOUR READERS AND HOW THEY WILL PERCEIVE YOUR MESSAGE

Effective letters, memos, and e-mail are

- **Reader oriented:** Correspondence oriented toward readers contains all of the information that readers need to understand the message. It doesn't contain more than they need, and it doesn't leave them guessing about the writer's intention.
- **Helpful:** Correspondence that is helpful anticipates and provides answers to readers' questions.
- **Tactful:** Correspondence that is tactful is courteous and, when possible, positive. It maintains or gains the reader's good will by using an appropriate tone.

What can you do to ensure that your correspondence is reader oriented, helpful, and tactful? Find out as much as possible about your readers. For much of the correspondence that you write, this task will be relatively simple because you know the readers personally. However, sometimes you will be writing to readers whom you don't know and have never met. These questions will help you gather information, especially about readers you don't know:

- **Who will read the correspondence? Will more than one person read it?** If you will have more than one reader, prepare to meet the needs and expectations of all readers. If their needs and expectations vary substantially, consider writing separately to each person or group.
- **What are the readers' positions and responsibilities? How might their positions and responsibilities affect how they perceive your message?** If you know readers' positions and responsibilities in the company, you can better determine what they know about you, your responsibilities, and possibly the subject of your message. This information about your readers can also help you to anticipate how they will perceive and react to your message. Suppose the purpose of your letter is to inform readers about the company's new travel policy. Under this new policy, your readers will no longer receive a corporate credit card to pay for their travel expenses. Instead, they will use their own credit cards or cash, and the company will reimburse them. Because your readers travel extensively, you know that this information will not please them. When you know these readers' positions and responsibilities in the company, you can better address their concerns.
- **If the readers are external, what is their relationship to you and your company? How will this relationship affect how they perceive your message?** Find out as much as possible about past interactions between the readers, their company, and your company. This information will help you understand how the readers may perceive you and your company; and it will help guide you in selecting the information, language, and organization for the correspondence.

- **What do the readers know about the subject of the correspondence?** If you can find out what readers know about the subject of your correspondence, you'll be more likely to include the appropriate amount of background and detail.

After you have specifically answered these questions for several letters, memos, or e-mail messages, use them merely to guide you as you gather information about your readers and how they might perceive your messages.

PRINCIPLE 3: USE A READER-ORIENTED TONE

Create a tactful and, when possible, positive tone for your letters, memos, and e-mail. Achieving a reader-oriented tone may be most difficult when writing e-mail messages. Recipients of e-mail often complain about the bluntness or unintentional rudeness of the messages. A blunt or rude tone may be common because writers write e-mail messages quickly—rarely taking time to proofread or to consider the impact of their words on their readers. This problem may also stem from the informality of e-mail. E-mail is decidedly less formal and less inhibited in style than traditional letters and memos (Stein and Yates 101). Because of this informality, many e-mail users feel free to write what they think or feel, often without considering how their words will affect their readers.

To create a reader-oriented tone, ask yourself how readers will respond to your message. Compare the letters shown in Figures 17.5 and 17.6. The writer of the letter in Figure 17.5 didn't carefully consider the tone of his letter. He uses language focused on himself and on his company. This writer-oriented tone is evident in the pronouns that refer to him and his company (*we* and *our*). It also is evident in the way he focuses on company actions and policy instead of on the reader and her problem. In the final paragraph of his letter, he seems to be saying that the reader was negligent—not the company.

In the letter shown in Figure 17.6, the writer achieves a reader-oriented, positive tone. He focuses on the reader and her interests instead of on the company. He uses a positive tone and refers to the reader frequently by name and with second-person pronouns (*you* and *your*).

Readers want to know how a message will affect them, not how it will affect the writer or his or her company, and they want to know how a message will benefit them. When reading correspondence, most readers ask themselves, "How will this message affect me?" or "How will this message benefit me?"

Readers resist messages that point out their mistakes or messages that carry bad news. Just as you prefer to receive positive news, so will your readers. They will respond more favorably if a message concentrates on the positive, deemphasizes their mistakes, and, when possible, focuses on ways of doing better in the future. Even when you can't focus on the positive or deemphasize mistakes, try to use a positive tone that will create good will for yourself and your company.

Figure 17.5 A Letter with a Writer-Oriented Tone

colorado outfitters
1212 canyon drive
boulder, co 67899
(303) 555-4986
d r r @ c o . c o m

May 18, 1998

Mrs. Annie Shepard
1244 Fork Road
Socorro, NM 54233

Dear Mrs. Shepard:

We here at Colorado Outfitters are always pleased to hear from our customers. We try to please our customers with quality recreational gear and equipment. Our newest feature for customers is our Colorado Outfitters Catalog, a way to shop by telephone, e-mail, or fax. However, this feature does have one drawback—our mailing list for the catalog is incomplete.

Recently, we received your letter about a problem with our service: Your neighbor purchased a Flashmagic 2-person tent for $250 during our spring catalog sale, but you bought the same tent at the full price of $350 during January.

It is a shame that you weren't on our mailing list, so we could have offered you the Flashmagic 2-person tent for $250. We will put you on our mailing list today, so you won't miss any more of our sales. If we can serve you in any way, please call, write, or fax us—Colorado Outfitters is here to make your recreational activities fun and easy.

Happy camping,

David R. Rowland
Manager

Figure 17.6 A Letter with a Reader-Oriented Tone

colorado outfitters
1212 canyon drive
boulder, co 67899
(303) 555-4986
drr@co.com

May 18, 1998

Mrs. Annie Shepard
1244 Fork Road
Socorro, NM 54233

Dear Mrs. Shepard:

Your recent letter about your purchase of a Flashmagic 2-person tent in January concerned us. You explained that a neighbor had purchased the same tent during the spring catalog sale; however, you paid $100 more than your neighbor. We understand your concern, so we have enclosed a 50% discount coupon good on your next purchase from Colorado Outfitters.

Undoubtedly, you must wonder why you didn't receive a catalog. The spring catalog is the first one that we sent to our customers as part of our new shop-at-home service. Because this service is new, we are still adding long-standing customers on the mailing list. We have now entered your name on the mailing list. You will receive all future catalogs and sales notices. In the future, you—like your neighbor—can shop at home and take advantage of sales available exclusively to customers on our mailing list.

Mrs. Shepard, please let us know if we can serve you further. You are a valued customer.

Happy camping,

David R. Rowland
Manager

encl.: discount coupon

Compare the impression made by a positive and a negative tone:

Negative tone   You failed to read the instructions at the top of the form. If you had read them, you would have signed the back of the form on the appropriate line. Without this signature, your application for a patent cannot be processed.

Positive tone   We will gladly process your patent application. Please sign the back of the enclosed form on line 28 and return it to us at your convenience.

The negative example creates no good will; it points out the reader's mistake instead of offering a way to remedy that mistake. Careless, writer-oriented language may lead readers to make incorrect assumptions. Figure 17.7 gives you some tips for choosing words and phrases that will help readers to perceive your messages as you intend them.

PRINCIPLE 4: DETERMINE THE MOST EFFECTIVE APPROACH FOR YOUR READERS

Letters, memos, and e-mail present a message directly or indirectly (Dragga).

The Direct Approach

In most of your letters, memos, and e-mail, you will use the direct approach. This approach helps readers to find the purpose of your correspondence quickly:

In the First Paragraph: Present the Main Message

- Tell readers why you are writing.

In the Middle Paragraph(s): Explain the Main Message

- Explain the main message presented in the first paragraph.
- Present necessary details about the main message.

In the Final Paragraph: Close the Correspondence

- Tell readers if and when they or you will act next.
- Tell readers, if necessary, what to do.
- State where readers can call, write, or fax to ask questions, send information, and so on.

You can adapt the direct approach for most correspondence situations. The letter shown in Figure 17.8 incorporates it in the following ways:

- A subject line specifically states the subject of the letter.
- The first paragraph states the main message or purpose of the letter.
- The letter focuses on the reader's concerns by stating specific, researched facts to support the writer's request.

Figure 17.7

Tips for Choosing
Reader-Oriented
Words and Phrases in
Correspondence

Avoid words and phrases that point out readers' mistakes in a negative tone or a tone that makes readers feel inferior or ignorant.

- You neglected to read . . .
- We cannot believe that you did not observe . . .
- You failed to notify . . .
- You ignored the instructions . . .
- We fail to see how you could possibly . . .
- We cannot understand how . . .
- We are at a loss to know how you . . .

Avoid phrases that demand or insist that readers act. (Demanding or insisting that readers act often backfires, causing readers to rebel against or to ignore your demand.)

- You should . . .
- You ought to . . .
- We must insist that you . . .
- We must request that you . . .

Avoid implying that your readers are lying

- You claim that . . .
- Your letter (memo, e-mail) implies that . . .
- You insist that . . .

Avoid ambiguous words and phrases that may sound fine to you but may make readers feel inferior.

- No doubt . . .
- Obviously . . .
- You will of course . . .
- Of course, you understand . . .

Avoid impersonal and inflated words and phrases and "business-ese" that your readers may perceive as pompous, insincere, or overused.

- Your cooperation in this matter will be greatly appreciated. (Instead use "I appreciate your help.")
- We are cognizant of the fact that . . . (Instead use "We know.")
- Please endeavor to ascertain . . . (Instead use "Please try to find out.")

Avoid negative words when possible, especially when referring to readers, their actions, or their requests.

impossible	unfortunate	unable
will not	inferior	regret
misfortune	fail	neglect
wrong	overlook	deny
difficulty	complaint	inconvenient

Source: Courtesy of Elizabeth Tebeaux.

Figure 17.8 A Letter Incorporating the Direct Approach

402 Summer Court
Carrollton, TX 75007
June 11, 1998

Mrs. Norma Rowland
Denton County Appraisal District
3911 Morse Street
Denton, TX 76202-3816

Subject: Appraisal of block 5, lot 15, in Villages of Indian Creek phase 1

Dear Mrs. Rowland:

The writer tells the reader why he is writing.

I am requesting that you reconsider the 1998 appraisal of my home, 402 Summer Court in Carrollton. I have included information from the 1998 Dallas county appraisal and a market analysis by a local realtor. Based on this information, I request that you consider appraising the home between $101,300 and $105,352.

The Dallas County Appraisal

The writer explains the main message presented in the first paragraph. He also presents details about the message.

Dallas County appraised my home as follows in 1997 and 1998:

	Total Value	Improvements	Land	Sq. ft.	$ per sq. ft.
1997	$103,220	$86,220	$17,000	2,030	51
1998	$99,820	$84,820	$15,000	2,030	49

Denton County appraised my home as follows in 1997 and 1998:

	Total Value	Improvements	Land	Sq. ft.	$ per sq. ft.
1997	$106,896	$72,896	$34,000	2,170	49
1998	$122,931	$83,831	$39,100	2,170	56

As the above tables show, Denton County increased the appraisal by $16,035 while Dallas decreased the appraisal by $3,400. This increase in the appraised value is especially puzzling since similar homes in our neighborhood have not sold for more than $98,000.

The Market Analysis

A local realtor with Providence Reality, Ms. Ellen Babcock, reports that the price per square foot should be between $48.59 and $52.00 for our home. Ms. Babcock reports that similar homes in this neighborhood have not sold for more than $52.00 per square foot. As the tables in the above section show, the 1998 Denton County appraisal is $4.00 more per square foot than the upper end of the range reported by Ms. Babcock.

The writer closes the letter by offering to supply documents or to answer questions. The writer tells the reader how to contact him.

I will be happy to supply documents from Dallas or the realtor. If you would like these documents or have questions, please contact me at (972) 555-4302 or at the above address.

Sincerely,

William W. Sims

William W. Sims

The Indirect Approach

When you use the indirect approach, you delay or buffer the main message until you have graciously opened the letter and explained the message:

In the First Paragraph: Buffer the Message

- Begin with a buffer—a positive or neutral statement. A buffer may help readers to be receptive to the message, especially if the message is negative.

In the Middle Paragraph(s): Explain and Then State the Message

- Explain the message. For instance, state the reason for a refusal or rejection. By properly explaining the message, you prepare readers for the negative news.
- State the message.
- Suggest an alternative or remedy if possible when the message is negative. By suggesting an alternative or remedy, you may be able to keep the good will of your readers and show that you want to meet their needs.

In the Final Paragraph: Close the Correspondence

- End the correspondence with a gracious statement.

Most writers rarely use this approach, but it can be appropriate when the news is not urgent or doesn't require readers to respond or act. It also is good to use in correspondence with international readers who are accustomed to a less direct approach than is common in American business (Sims and Guice).

Before you use the indirect approach, consider whether it is an ethically appropriate choice for the situation. The indirect approach can inappropriately obscure information. It also can mislead some readers into thinking that the message is good because the gracious, usually positive opening delays the bad news. Readers who read no further than the opening may misinterpret the purpose of the correspondence. Thus, before using the indirect approach, carefully consider your readers and how they are likely to read the message.

The following tips will help you decide whether the indirect approach is the appropriate choice:

- If your readers expect the bad news, use the direct approach.
- If your readers may read only the first paragraph or skim the correspondence, use the direct approach (Locker 229). The indirect approach may mislead readers—they may not see the main message and may misinterpret the purpose of the correspondence.
- If you know that your readers will resist the news or "won't take no for an answer" (Locker 230), use the direct approach. In these situations, the indirect approach may mislead readers into thinking that they can persuade you or your company to change the news or the "answer."
- If the news is urgent or if you have sent the message repeatedly, use the direct approach.

The letter shown in Figure 17.9 illustrates the indirect approach:

Figure 17.9 A Letter Incorporating the Indirect Approach

Independent's Research, Incorporated
1010 West Main • Los Alamos, New Mexico 87890 • (505) 565-3000

May 16, 1998

Ms. Janice Scales
402A Summer Court
Edwardsville, IL 67843

Dear Ms. Scales:

The first paragraph includes a positive statement about the reader.

Last week, we told you that we were recommending you for a summer intern position with our Research and Development Department. Your excellent background and education would allow you and us to benefit from your interning.

The writer explains the main message in the first sentence and then presents the message in the second and third sentences. The final sentence suggests an alternative.

Last week, the board of directors announced a hiring freeze for all positions until the end of the year. We hoped this freeze would not include the internship positions, but sadly it does. Therefore, we will not be able to offer you an internship this summer. The board feels certain that these intern positions will once again be available next summer. Since you are currently a sophomore, please reapply next year.

The letter concludes with a gracious statement.

We appreciate your interest in our company and look forward to your application next year.

Sincerely,

Peggy Fagner

Peggy Fagner
Manager, Recruitment

- The first paragraph makes a positive statement.
- The second paragraph explains the main message before directly stating that message, and it offers an alternative (reapplying for the intern position next year).
- The final paragraph makes a gracious closing statement.

PRINCIPLE 5: USE AN APPROPRIATE FORMAT

Letters, memos, and most e-mail messages have basic formats that are appropriate in any business setting. If your company has its own formats for letters, memos, and e-mail, use those formats.

Letters

The three basic formats for letters are *block style* (see Figures 17.10 and 17.11), *modified block style* (Figures 17.12 and 17.13), and *AMS Simplified style* (Figure 17.14; "AMS" stands for Administrative Management Society). In letters in each of these formats, most of these elements are standard:

- **Inside address:** The address of the writer or the writer's company, usually preprinted on the letter paper
- **Date on which the letter is written**
- **Outside address:** The reader's address
- **Subject or reference line:** A subject line tells readers what the letter is about. A reference line refers readers to the date of previous correspondence or to the order or account number mentioned in the letter. Subject lines are often preceded by "subject," reference lines by "re." These lines are optional in the block and modified block styles; a subject line is required for the AMS Simplified style.
- **Salutation or greeting:** "Dear" followed by the reader's name (or official title if you don't know the reader's name) and a colon—for example,

Dear Mr. Sampson:
Dear Personnel Director:

Always use a gender-free salutation. When you don't know the reader's name, using "Dear Sir" is inappropriate. If you don't know the gender of your reader, use the AMS Simplified style and omit the salutation (see Figure 17.14), or use the reader's title in the salutation. Also, avoid "To whom it may concern"; this salutation is unprofessional.

- **Body:** The text of the letter
- **Complimentary closing:** Expressions such as "Sincerely" or "Best regards"
- **Signature of the letter writer**
- **Signature block:** The letter writer's name and title

ISSUES IN CONTEXT

E-Mail and *Netiquette*

Like face-to-face conversations, e-mail allows for spontaneous responses and feedback (Lakoff; Ong). E-mail writers who misuse this spontaneity often misspell words and inappropriately use lowercase or capital letters; they may also use emotions (faces created with type such as :-) to indicate emotions or facial expressions) when the corporate culture doesn't value such informality. When you begin working for a company, read the e-mail of others before you send your own e-mail. Determine the level of formality expected. Does the e-mail read like a letter or memo? If it does, then use a more formal tone. If the writers use a less formal tone or emotions, then use a less formal tone. Regardless of the tone, follow these guidelines of *netiquette* (etiquette on a network):

- **Include an informative subject line.** Most readers use the subject line to decide if or when to read e-mail.
- **Make messages easy to read and paragraphs short.** Use upper- and lowercase letters as you would in other documents. Skip lines between paragraphs and keep the paragraphs short.
- **Make your messages brief and put the main message in the first paragraph.** Include only the information readers need, so they don't have to scroll through irrelevant or unnecessary information to find the main message.
- **Use a polite tone—don't flame.** Flaming is sending rude or angry e-mail messages. If an e-mail message angers you or if you are angry, wait a while before writing or responding.
- **Proofread your messages.** Even when e-mail is informal, it shouldn't be sloppy and careless. Proofread to eliminate spelling, grammar, and style errors.
- **Send messages only when you have something to say—don't send "junk mail."** Unnecessary or uninformative e-mail wastes readers' time.
- **Remember that e-mail is permanent.** Most companies archive all e-mail written by its employees. In other words, companies back up the e-mail and store it on tape; so don't write anything in e-mail that you wouldn't put in print or want others to read.
- **Copy and send e-mail only when you have the writer's permission.** Before you copy and send another person's e-mail, get the writer's permission. The writer may want the message to remain private.

Figure 17.10 A Letter in Block Style on Letterhead

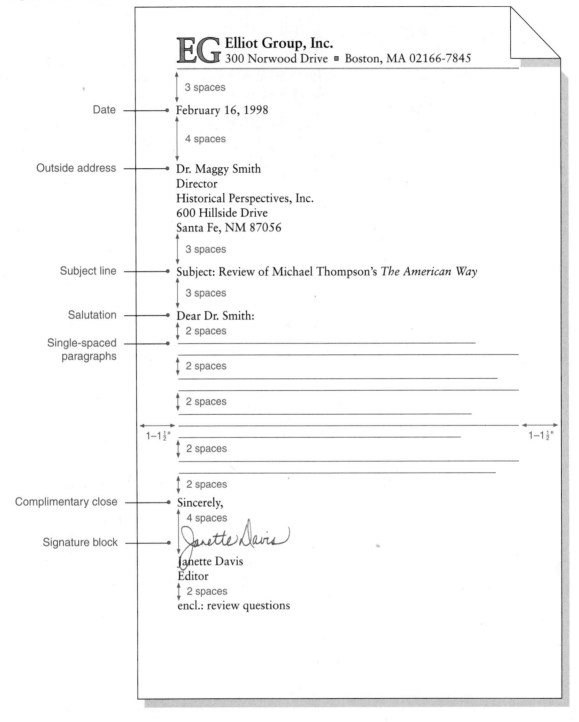

Figure 17.11 A Letter in Block Style Without Letterhead

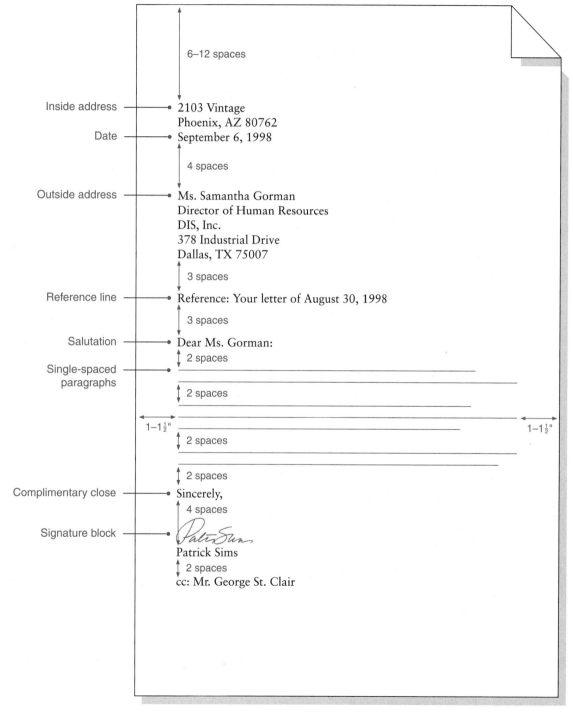

Figure 17.12 A Letter in Modified Block Style on Letterhead

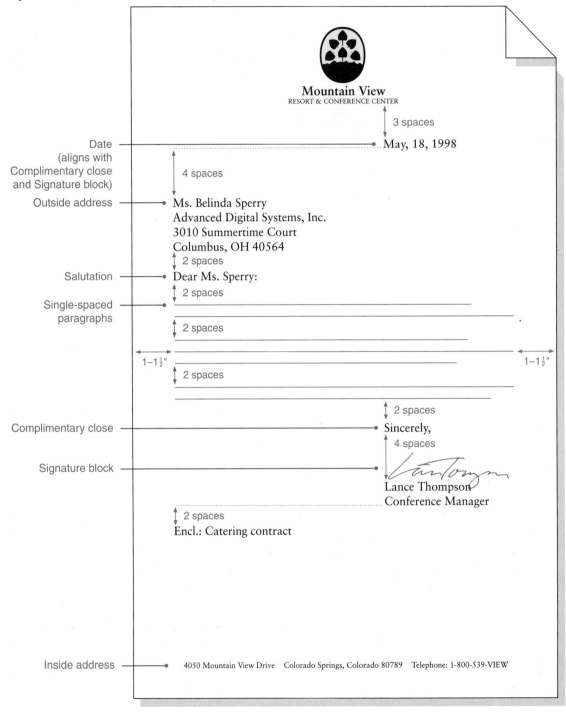

Figure 17.13 A Letter in Modified Block Style Without Letterhead

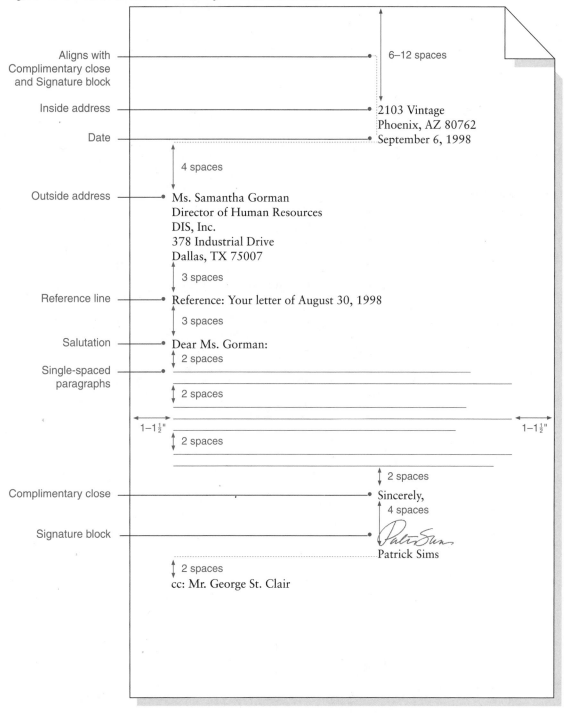

Figure 17.14 A Letter in AMS Simplified Style Without Letterhead

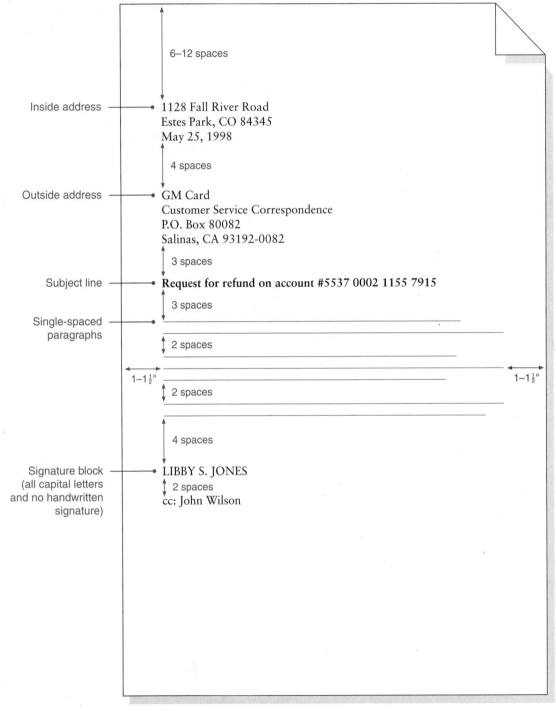

THE READER'S CORNER

Early Snail-Mail

Postal systems developed independently around the ancient world—Egypt, China, Rome, Inca, Maya—as a means of governing extensive empires. The Romans learned about the Chinese post-house relay system from Greek historians and refined this system to the point where couriers could cover 170 miles a day—a speed not duplicated until the 1800s. The uncertain political climate of the Middle Ages made extensive postal systems impossible in Western Europe. Instead, independent kings, city-states, religious orders, and universities all maintained their own private corps of messengers. The rise of international commerce during the late Middle Ages, however, spurred the growth of business correspondence. The great Italian commercial centers of Florence, Genoa, and Siena developed regular postal exchanges among themselves; Venice sent mail to Constantinople, a city considered beyond the European frontier at the time. Gutenberg's printing press (c. 1450) greatly increased the volume of this mail, the carrying of which became a profitable business, and led eventually to standardized rates and increasingly speedy and frequent deliveries. By the late nineteenth century, messengers delivered mail several times a day in some European and American cities. The increasingly commercial use of e-mail may soon transform postal systems around the world once more.

The AMS Simplified style omits the salutation, the complimentary closing, and the signature. This format is useful when you don't know the reader's name or you don't know which courtesy title (Ms., Mrs., Mr., Dr., Rev.) to use. However, the AMS Simplified style may strike some readers as impersonal. Therefore, whenever possible, take the time to find the name and title of the reader.

The three formats differ in the following ways:

- **Position of the date, the complimentary closing, and the signature block.** In letters set up in block or AMS Simplified formats, place these elements flush against the left margin. In letters set up in modified block format, indent these elements from one-half to two-thirds of the width of the page. Be sure to indent all three elements the same distance from the left margin, so that they align on the page (see Figures 17.12 and 17.13).

- **Paragraph indentation.** Indenting paragraphs is optional in the modified block format. Do not indent paragraphs in block or AMS Simplified formats.

- **Use of salutation and complimentary closing.** Omit these elements from letters in AMS Simplified style.

Once you decide which formats you will use most frequently, you can create templates or macros for these formats in your word-processing program, so you won't have to re-create the format each time you write a letter.

Memos

The primary difference between a memo and a letter is that the salutation, complimentary closing, and writer's signature do not appear in a memo. These elements are standard in memos (the order of the first four may vary):

- **Date on which the memo is written**
- **"To" line:** The name and possibly the title or department of the reader
- **"From" line:** The name, possibly the title or department of the writer, and the writer's handwritten initials
- **"Subject" line:** A phrase that tells readers what the memo is about
- **Body:** The text of the memo

Figure 17.15 presents a typical memo. The writer created the format with a template or macro in a word-processing program.

E-Mail

Because e-mail is a relatively new medium for correspondence, e-mail formats are still evolving. Because e-mail is read by people inside as well as outside an organization, writers often devise a standard format for all e-mail—both internal and external. This hybrid format is likely to incorporate elements of the letter and the memo. It also may include information added automatically by the computer—information such as the date and the environments through which the message has passed.

Many formal e-mail messages include these elements:

- **Date on which the e-mail is sent:** E-mail software automatically includes the date and usually the time that the writer sends a message.
- **Name and e-mail address of the reader**
- **Name and e-mail address of the writer:** Most e-mail software automatically includes the e-mail address of the writer.
- **Body:** The text of the e-mail message
- **Signature block:** Sometimes called a "signature" in e-mail software, this element includes the writer's name and possibly the writer's title, company or organization, mailing address, telephone number, fax number, and e-mail address.

These elements often appear with "to," "from," and "subject" lines and a complimentary closing or signature line, as in Figure 17.16.

A group of coworkers, however, may use some other—perhaps a less formal—format. The writer of the e-mail message shown in Figure 17.17

Figure 17.15 A Standard Memo Format

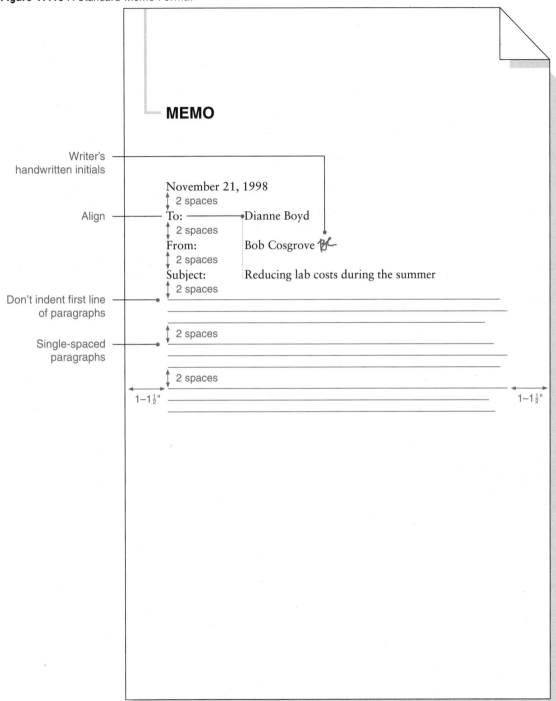

Figure 17.16

A Formal E-Mail Format with Signature Block and Optional Greeting

Subject: eaton.menu program
To: donp@txi.com (Don Price)
Date: Wed, 4 Mar 1998 15:02:51 CST
From: Debbie Botsford <dbots@txi.com>

Optional ──➤ Don,
greeting

I found a "bug" in our program. Some users found that they had documents that had been created in Qoffice, but the program did not select them. Evidently, the program didn't select them because the documents failed the file test. They test as "English text" or "ascii," but not as "data."

While talking with Jeff Seagraves, I learned that Jeff had used these files in an environment other than Qoffice. When a document is altered in another environment, it loses its document characteristics and becomes a "hybrid document" that no longer tests out as "data."

This problem could just be an isolated one, but I wanted you to be aware of it.

Signature ──➤ Debbie Botsford
block   Computer Specialist III
               TXI, Inc.
               2600 West Olive
               Phoenix, AZ 84902
               (302) 555-5409
               dbots@txi.com

Figure 17.17

An Informal E-Mail Message

From: Rebecca Kavanough
To: Tonya McKinney
Subject: Conf Rooms A and B
Priority: Normal
Date sent: 3/6/98

Hi, Gang,

I'd like to use Conf. Room A on Monday from 8:30 to 11 A.M. for Bozell proposal.

Also, IF NOBODY ELSE NEEDS IT, I'd like to have Conf. Room B one more day (Monday) for my airline time: they're begging for a place to work.

Thanks.
RBK

uses the informal salutation "Hi, Gang" and the informal complimentary closing "Thanks." She also uses only her initials for a signature line. Such informality is fine, perhaps even expected, if others in the organization are similarly informal.

CONCLUSION

Letters, memos, and e-mail messages are tools to get work done. Before you send correspondence to your reader, ask yourself these questions:

1. Is it reader oriented? Have you considered the reader's interests?
2. Is it tactful? Are you courteous? Have you put yourself in the reader's place?
3. Is it clear and concise? Do your sentences generally contain no more than one main idea? Are these ideas linked with strong transitions? Do you avoid technical terms that may not be clear to your reader?
4. Is it forceful and friendly? Do you generally use a "personal" subject ("I" or "we" as opposed to "the Company") and the active voice? Have you eliminated "negative" words?
5. Is it conversational? Do you avoid "commercialese" and "business English," and use words and phrases from your everyday speaking vocabulary?
6. Is it helpful? Have you anticipated and met the reader's needs? Have you given the reader useful information he or she may not have expected?
7. Have you affected your reader agreeably? Have you created good will for your company?

If you can answer "yes" to each of these questions, you have written an effective letter.[1]

Although these questions first appeared in 1961 and applied to letters, you can apply them to any correspondence. You also can use the "Worksheet for Writing Reader-Oriented Letters, Memos, and E-Mail" to help you as you learn to write effective correspondence.

---

1. Adapted from Effective Letters Program (n.p.: New York Life Insurance Company, 1961). Copyright 1961 New York Life Insurance Company. Used by permission.

WORKSHEET　for Writing Reader-Oriented Letters, Memos, and E-Mail

Principle 1: Determine the Objectives of Your Letter, Memo, or E-Mail Message

- What is the purpose of the correspondence? What do you expect it to accomplish?
- What action, if any, do you expect readers to take after reading the correspondence?
- What do you expect readers to know after reading the correspondence?

Principle 2: Find Out About Your Readers and How They Will Perceive Your Message

- Who will read the correspondence? Will more than one person read it?
- What are the readers' positions and responsibilities? How might their positions and responsibilities affect how they perceive your message?
- If the readers are external, what is their relationship to you and your company? How will this relationship affect how they perceive your message?
- What do the readers know about the subject of the correspondence?

Principle 3: Use a Reader-Oriented Tone

- Have you avoided words that point out readers' mistakes in a negative tone and words that may make readers feel inferior or ignorant?
- Have you avoided phrases that demand or insist that readers act?
- Have you avoided words that imply that readers are lying, and impersonal, inflated words that readers may perceive as pompous or insincere?
- Have you avoided ambiguous words and phrases that sound fine to you but may make readers feel inferior?
- Have you avoided negative words, especially when referring to readers or to their actions or requests?

Principle 4: Determine the Most Effective Approach for Your Readers

- Is the approach that you have selected appropriate?
- If you have selected the indirect approach, is the choice ethical? Is this approach likely to mislead readers?

Principle 5: Use an Appropriate Format

- For a letter, have you included all the appropriate standard elements for the readers and the chosen style? Does the letter include a complete inside and outside address and a date?

- For a letter, have you used an appropriate, gender-free salutation or greeting for the block or modified block style?

- If you've used the AMS Simplified letter style, is that style appropriate for your readers? If so, did you include an informative "subject" line?

- For a memo, have you included the date, a "to" line, a "from" line, and an informative "subject" line?

- For e-mail, have you included information in the signature block to identify you and your company or organization? Does the signature block give readers the information they need to contact you by telephone, e-mail, and traditional mail?

EXERCISES

1. Revise these sentences to improve their tone. Improve the clarity and conciseness of the sentences when necessary.

   a. We are sorry that we cannot fill your order for our product. We get so many orders for our product that we find it impossible to fill them all.

   b. You understand, of course, that we cannot credit your account for the price of the unused symphony tickets.

   c. We are searching for the faulty parts that you claim to have mailed to us on April 26.

   d. Your cooperation in this matter will be appreciated. Thank you.

   e. We cannot understand how you could have omitted your quarterly check when you mailed your copy of the statement.

   f. Since your company has defaulted on several loan payments in the past two years, we must deny you a loan for the addition to your Seattle plant.

   g. In filling out your warranty information, you failed to fill in the serial number of the new turbine.

2. Write an e-mail message or a memo to your instructor explaining how the direct and indirect approaches differ. Then suggest three specific writing situations where you would use the direct approach and three where you would use the indirect approach. Justify your suggestions.

3. You manage a large group of employees at a ring-manufacturing plant. One of your responsibilities is to evaluate the performance of your employees. Recently, Timothy Elam, your most senior employee, has been performing poorly. He reported to work late twelve times in the past month—on four days he was over two hours late. His work has severely decreased in quality and quantity. In fact, Timothy doesn't seem at all interested in his work. In recent years, he was a model employee. Just two years ago, he won the award for "Most Productive Employee." Because Timothy is popular, his coworkers picked up his share of the work for several weeks; but they are no longer willing to carry his share. They are tired of Timothy's lateness and inadequate performance.

   As you prepare to evaluate Timothy, you wonder what has caused his performance to decline. You realize that his fellow employees have legitimate complaints about having to carry his share of the load; but you also realize that until recently Timothy was a valuable employee. You decide to let your manager know about the problem. Your manager will be concerned because he likes Timothy but wants the group to be productive.

   Assignment: Write a memo to your manager describing Timothy's performance and the morale problem that his performance is creating in your group. Suggest some course of action, or ask your manager for suggestions. Remember to keep the good will and respect of your manager while specifically explaining the problems that Timothy's performance is causing.

4. Write a memo to your instructor explaining why you used the direct or indirect approach in the memo in Exercise 3.

5. You are the regional manager of a large chain of retail electronics stores. Today, you received a letter from a customer, Ms. Amy Dula (3567 Rockcreek, Tampa, FL 10067). Ms. Dula writes that she purchased a new computer and color ACR monitor from the Tampa store a month ago. Two days after she purchased the computer and monitor, the monitor quit working—it showed no images. She immediately took the monitor back to the Tampa store and asked for a replacement. The manager of the store refused to replace the monitor and instead offered to repair it. Your company doesn't offer replacements—only repairs. Ms. Dula doesn't want the monitor repaired because a clerk at the Tampa store told her that several customers had returned "repaired" ACR monitors.

Assignment: Write a letter to Ms. Dula explaining the company's policy but ensuring her good will and future business.

6. You manage several project teams for an environmental engineering firm. Recently, many members of the project teams have been charging personal expenses to their corporate charge cards. Several team members have been unable to pay for these expenses when the statements are due. When the members pick up their charge cards each year, they receive a copy of the company policy for using corporate charge cards for personal expenses. The policy reads as follows: "You can use your corporate charge card for travel and other business-related expenses during the year. You may not use your card for personal expenses such as meals, gifts, and personal travel."

Assignment: Write a memo to your project teams restating the policy and explaining that the firm will take the card away from any employees who misuse it.

7. Think of a service, procedure, or policy that your college or university should change. Write a memo or e-mail message to the appropriate official at your college or university suggesting the change. For instance, you might write a persuasive memo to the comptroller and suggest that students use bank debit cards to pay their tuition and fees.

8. Think of a service or product with which you have recently experienced problems. Write a letter to the appropriate person about the problems, and ask for an appropriate remedy. If you cannot find the name of the appropriate person, use the AMS Simplified style (see Figure 17.14).

9. Log on to the World Wide Web. Find the address of a company, government agency, or user group that may have sample materials or information that you need for a class project. Write an e-mail message to this company, agency, or user group requesting such information or materials. Print a copy of your message for your instructor.

CASE STUDY   A Tied-Up Network[2]

Background

You are the network manager of the computer network for your company. Over the past few weeks, many network users have tied up the network by failing to log off the terminals; by using the Internet to download graphics from the Library of Congress, the Oval Office, and the Walt Disney Company during peak business hours; and by "surfing" the World Wide Web for personal business during regular business hours. When users fail to log off the terminals, other users can't log on during peak hours while an open network account sits idle. The downloaded graphics and "surfing" consume enormous amounts of memory on the network server, slowing the speed of the network responses.

You have sent several e-mail messages to all network users about this problem; but the number of users failing to log off has not lessened. Yesterday, you confiscated a downloaded and printed graphic of Mickey and Minnie Mouse from Disney and of the president's cat from the White House. Today, two top-level managers were unable to log on to the World Wide Web between 11 A.M. and 1 P.M. because employees were downloading graphics and "surfing" the Web for personal business during lunch hours.

You are unusually frustrated and angry. You write an e-mail message to all network users about these problems (see Figure 17.18). The message is direct, abrupt, and writer oriented. You mean the threat humorously; however, your message offends several employees.

Assignment

This assignment has two parts:

1. Write an e-mail message to all employees retracting your "humorous" threat and explaining the company's Internet policies. Make the message reader oriented and, when possible, positive. Apologize for offending the readers. (If you don't have access to e-mail, write a memo.)

2. Write a memo to your manager explaining the problems the network users are creating and the "threatening" e-mail message that you sent to all network users. Explain to your manager how you are smoothing out the situation, and ask your manager for suggestions for solving these two network problems.

---

2. The idea for this case came from John Pollard, one of my graduate students.

Figure 17.18

The E-Mail Message for the Case Study "A Tied-Up Network"

From: Tina Martin
To: Network users
Subject: Logging off the network and using the Web for personal business
Date: Tue, 19 Dec 1997 09:12:10 CST6CDT

Today, two top-level managers could not take care of company business between 11:00 and 1:00 because the network was saturated with users surfing the Web and downloading and printing graphics for personal use. During the past week during regular business hours, I have confiscated printouts—in color—of the President's cat, Mickey and Minnie Mouse, and the Baywatch crew. I have also found at least 40 users logged on to the network when they have left the office for the day or when they are out of town.

I will say it again: IT IS AGAINST COMPANY POLICY TO USE THE NET-WORK, TO SURF THE WEB, OR TO DOWNLOAD AND PRINT GRAPH-ICS **FOR PERSONAL USE DURING REGULAR BUSINESS HOURS.** In the future, I will permanently log off all users who fail to log off when they leave the office or who download and print graphics for personal use.

Chapter 18

Writing Reader-Oriented Job Correspondence

CHAPTER OUTLINE

Nicole will graduate from college in three months. She is excited about finding a job in her chosen field and beginning her career, but first she has to find that job. Nicole realizes that all the jobs she applies for will require a résumé—even those that she learns about at her university career placement center. For jobs that she discovers for herself, she also will need to write a letter of application, or cover letter, to accompany her résumé.

Like Nicole, you soon will graduate and look for a job. This chapter presents five principles to help you locate job opportunities and then to write appropriate job correspondence before and after the interview process.

PRINCIPLE 1: CONSIDER VARIOUS METHODS FOR LOCATING JOB OPPORTUNITIES

To locate job opportunities in your field, you can use several methods:

- **Contact your college or university placement center.** Most college and universities have career-planning and placement centers that help graduating seniors and recent graduates find jobs. These placement centers link companies and their recruitment officers with qualified prospective employees. Most placement centers require that you register with them before you can interview. As part of the registration procedure, you probably will need to create a dossier (or file) that includes an information sheet about you and your job interests, your résumé, and your college or university transcripts. You also may be able to include in this file samples of your work and other information that may interest companies. After receiving your dossier, the placement center will give copies of it to the recruitment officers with whom you will interview. The recruitment officer will use the placement center to set up interviews on campus.

- **Respond to job advertisements from newspapers, trade or professional journals, or the World Wide Web.** While searching for a job, regularly check the newspapers (especially the Sunday classified sections from large cities), professional and trade journals in your field, and the Web.

- **Network with others in your field, with people who know you personally, and with your professors.** Tell people in your field that you are looking for a job. If you are a member of a professional organization, see whether the organization has a job bank to help members find jobs. If the organization doesn't have a job bank, see whether it has an electronic bulletin board or World Wide Web site where members can post messages. On such a bulletin board or Web site, you can post your résumé or at least a message describing your qualifications, your address, and the type of job you want. You can even look for job advertisements on these bulletin boards. Also, tell personal and family friends that you are looking for a job, and perhaps send them a copy of your résumé. These friends may have contacts to help you locate job opportunities.

- **Send out unsolicited letters of application.** If you are interested in working for a specific company, send an unsolicited letter of application to that company. Many companies do not advertise job opportunities, so unsolicited letters can be effective. Unsolicited letters do have an obvious disadvantage: the company may not have any openings when it receives your letter. However, if you are truly interested in working for a particular company, an unsolicited letter of application may be worth your time.

- **Use professional employment agencies.** Professional employment agencies present your résumé to potential employers. They work much like a college placement center but charge a fee paid either by potential employers or by you. The fee often is a percentage of your first-year salary once you accept a job.

PRINCIPLE 2: DETERMINE WHAT INFORMATION YOU WANT EMPLOYERS TO KNOW ABOUT YOU

Before you put together a résumé or send out any letters of application, think specifically about what information you want employers to know about you, and think generally about what information employers want to know about potential employees. The information you provide should give potential employers a positive, accurate picture of you and what you can offer their company.

You might begin by determining what information is likely to interest prospective employers. You might concentrate on these categories: education, work experience, activities, goals, and skills. After selecting your categories, brainstorm to create lists of information about yourself in each category (refer to Chapter 2 for a discussion of brainstorming). For instance, under education, list the degree you will receive when you graduate, the date when you will receive the degree, your grade-point average, and significant projects that you completed in your major field of study.

Figure 18.1 shows the brainstorming list that Nicole created. Although she may not use all the information on her list, it gives her information to work with when she begins preparing her résumé and letter of application. To create your brainstorming list, write down any information that you think will help an employer understand you and your qualifications—information that will impress an employer.

You can also consider the information that specific employers may want to know about you. At this stage of the writing process, if you are applying for several jobs at the same time, actually pulling together this information for each potential employer is not something you can do. Therefore, you probably will want to prepare a résumé first, concentrating on information that will demonstrate what you offer to employers. Later, you can customize your letter of application and your résumé for each employer, including information that will particularly interest each employer or that relates directly to a specific job opportunity.

Education
B.S. in mechanical engineering from University of Oklahoma
   expect to graduate in May 1999
Dean's list three semesters, Fall 1997, Spring 1997, and Spring 1998
GPA—3.2

Work Experience
Internship in robotics research lab (two semesters)
   helped design robotics machinery for automated assembly lines
   used CAD in refining designs
   learned to work in a dust-free environment and to work as a team member
Trinity Pharmacy—pharmacy technician since October 1997
   began as cashier and did general cleanup of store
   operate the cash register
   enter prescription information into the computer system
   help customers needing information about over-the-counter drugs and other items in the pharmacy
Lifeguard and swimming instructor—summers since high school
   know CPR
   certified Red Cross lifeguard at YMCA pool at home
   received lifeguard of the month award four times (find out year and month)
   certified Red Cross swimming instructor
   taught private, semiprivate, and group swimming to children and adults through the YMCA
   worked frequently with children with disabilities to help them learn to swim and to be comfortable in water

Skills
programming in C++ and Java
have designed Web pages for YMCA, however, not very experienced here
know computers, including statistics packages, spreadsheets, and CAD
people skills—have learned to interact with customers and to be a team player
work well with children

Activities
Mortar Board, senior year
American Society of Mechanical Engineers
Swim team all four years—won district and national honors in platform diving

My Career Goals
to find an engineering position in robotics

Figure 18.1 Nicole's Brainstorming List

PRINCIPLE 3: PREPARE AN EFFECTIVE RÉSUMÉ

Robert Greenly of Lockheed Missiles & Space Company, Inc., writes that "your résumé is the first impression you make. It should be eye-catching, clearly written, and easy to read" (47). Your résumé and letter of application generally are the first information that an employer sees about you, so you want these documents to persuade employers to interview you. To write an effective résumé,

- Organize your résumé to highlight your qualifications.
- Include specific, appropriate information about your qualifications.
- Use dynamic, persuasive language that demonstrates what you can do.
- Create an eye-catching, accessible design.

Organize Your Résumé to Highlight Your Qualifications

Once you have decided what major categories of information to include, you can determine how to organize your résumé. Think about two levels of organization:

- The overall organization of the major categories of information (education, work experience, skills, and so on)
- The local organization within these categories

For the overall organization, decide what category of information you want the employer to see first. Many recent college graduates begin with their education—possibly including college-related activities or honors—and move to work experience or skills.

After determining the overall organization, think about how you will organize the information within each category. For example, work experience is often the longest category in the résumé and, for experienced job-seekers, the most important. For this category, you can use one of two methods of organization:

- Chronological organization
- Functional organization

If you organize your résumé chronologically, you will present the information in both the work experience and the education categories in *reverse* chronological order: you will begin with your most recent or your current job or degree and end with the least recent. The résumé shown in Figure 18.2 has a chronological organization. In the education category, the writer begins with her most recent college work and ends with her least recent work. In the work experience category, she begins with her current work at the University of North Texas and Twin Eagles Restaurant and ends with her least recent work as a checker at Tom Thumb.

Most job-seekers "prefer the logical progression of a chronological résumé" (Greenly 44); and for recent college graduates or for job-seekers looking for their first career job, functional résumés generally are less effective than chronological résumés. Some job-seekers, however, need a functional résumé—one that focuses the reader's attention on the writer's marketable job skills and accomplishments rather than on a chronological listing of his or her work experience. A functional organization is especially effective in two situations. Use it when you want to present your most important accomplishments or skills early in the résumé—or at least in a lead-off position within categories (Greenly 44). Also use it later if you want to change careers, as a chronological organization might undermine your search (Greenly 44).

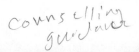
counselling
guidance

Figure 18.2 A Résumé with a Chronological Organization

Leigh Andrea Thomas
204 Oak Street
Denton, TX 76205
(817) 555-2858
lthomas@twlab.unt.edu

Objective	An entry-level corporate position in technical communication

Education	**University of North Texas, Denton, TX** Bachelor of Science in English August 1999 Grade Point Average: 3.5/4.0

Advanced Courses
Online Documentation
Designing Technical Documents
Writing Technical Proposals
Software Documentation

Baylor University, Waco, TX
Foundation Courses

Work Experience	**University of North Texas, Denton, TX** Assistant to the Director of Technical Writing October 1997 to present

- Assisted Director in writing proposal that resulted in a new Master's in Technical Communication and the potential of 50 new graduate students each year.
- Designed new brochure for the Technical Writing Program and for the Association of Teachers of Technical Writing.
- Managing Editor of Studies in Technical Communication.

SWB Telecommunications, Dallas, TX
Technical Writing Intern
May 1997 to September 1997, May 1998 to September 1998

- Developed a Web site describing wireless services offered by SWB.
- Assisted senior technical writer in designing and testing online documentation for switching equipment.
- Edited and proofread customer documentation for SWB 2000 and SWB 2020 wireless telephones.

Twin Eagles Restaurant, Denton, TX
Cashier/Server
December 1997 to May 1997

- Awarded the Silver Eagle for service in February and April 1997.

Tom Thumb, Lewisville, TX
Checker
June 1995 to December 1996

Organizations	Society for Technical Communication The Freshman Council (a leadership organization) Baylor President's Council (a leadership and service organization)

Source: Courtesy of Leigh Thomas.

The résumé in Figure 18.3 illustrates a functional organization. The major accomplishments category focuses on the job-seeker's skills and accomplishments in two areas—financial planning and financial analysis.

Include Specific, Appropriate Information About Your Qualifications

As you plan your résumé, select information that highlights your qualifications and will prompt employers to interview you. Include appropriate and effective information in these categories: career objective, education, work experience, skills and specialized training, and personal information. You may choose not to include all of these categories in your résumé.

Career Objective

A career objective states the kind of work you are seeking in the form of a brief phrase. For example, you might write, "Objective: Entry-level corporate marketing position." Views on the value of these statements vary. Many hiring managers consider these statements important because they indicate that the writer has goals. However, other managers find these statements limiting, especially if the statements are general or don't relate directly to the advertised job. For example, the following career objective could cause a manager to pass over a qualified job applicant: "An entry-level position in computer programming with the opportunity to advance into management." A broad statement like that can have unintended consequences. Reading such a statement, a potential employer might decide not to consider the applicant for a job that combines computer programming with some software documentation or for a job that will not lead to a management position. Résumés that omit the objective can give employers "greater flexibility in considering you for any number of peripheral positions that your experience and training qualify you for, perhaps even future openings that do not yet exist" (Greenly 43). If you decide to include a career objective, follow these guidelines:

- Use brief, specific statements directly related to the specific job for which you are applying.
- State only the position, goals, or tasks specifically stated in the job advertisement.
- Avoid general, broad statements such as "a position where I can use my programming and marketing skills."

Education

Identify your college or university degrees, naming the institution awarding the degree, its location, and the date you received or will receive the degree. If you haven't yet graduated, list the colleges or universities that you have

Figure 18.3 A Résumé with a Functional Organization

Katherine Diane Spence
1126 Baldpate
Chicago, IL 60637
(217) 555-4678
kdspence@aol.com

Major Accomplishments

Financial Planning
- Researched funding options that enabled company to achieve a 34% return on its investment.
- Developed long-range funding requirements to respond to government contracts that totaled over $1.6 billion.
- Developed and implemented computer software for long- and short-term financial planning that saved the company 70% in labor.

Financial Analysis and Information System Design
- Worked as a research analyst for 14 years in two different industries.
- Received three awards for innovations in information system design from the Association of Financial Planners.
- Developed computer software that applies current research to practical problems of corporate finance.

Education

University of Washington—Seattle
Master of Business Administration
May 1996

University of Colorado—Boulder
Bachelor of Science (summa cum laude)
May 1995
Major: Computer Science
Minor: Finance

Work Experience

Arthur Andersen (September 1996 to present)
Chicago, Illinois
- Senior Analyst (1998 to present)
- System Analyst (1996 to 1998)

Activities and Interests
Member, Association of Corporate Financial Planners
Amateur soccer player and coach
Gourmet cook

References available upon request

THE READER'S CORNER

Ethically Challenged Résumés

Jobs in almost every profession have become very competitive. One particularly gloomy estimate is that only 1 out of 1,470 résumés put into circulation ever actually results in a job offer. Given such odds, young professionals are often tempted to tamper with the truth on their résumés. According to one survey, fully one-third of people between the ages of 15 and 30 were willing to lie on their résumés, and experts predict that the percentage of job-hunters who actually do so may make up one-third of applicants or more.[1] Such deception occurs at the most elite levels. Jean Houston, the now infamous psychologist who counseled Hillary Rodham Clinton to imagine herself in dialogue with deceased luminaries like Eleanor Roosevelt, reported on her résumé having received a doctorate in the philosophy of religion from Columbia University. Investigations, reported in the *New York Times,* brought to light that Houston had never completed her dissertation, a requirement for the doctorate.[2] In her defense, Houston claimed that an aide had selected a résumé from the "bottom of the barrel" of résumés she kept on file. Houston's ethical lapse on her résumé, inflating her credentials, is one that résumé writers often make. Other common résumé deceits include inflating one's title or responsibilities and omitting firings or failings. Hiring managers have become more alert to the probable areas of deception and are double-checking advanced degrees, unexplained periods in employment history, and job titles.

---

1. *Working Woman* March 1996:18.
2. *New York Times* 26 June 1996: B9.

attended beyond high school, their location, and the anticipated date of your degree. For example, a senior at San Diego State University might write

San Diego State University, San Diego, California
Bachelor of Science in Mechanical Engineering
Anticipated May 1999

In addition to listing your degree (or degrees), you can include information such as

- Major and minor courses that qualify you for the type of job you are seeking
- Academic scholarships or fellowships that you received
- A high grade-point average (above 3.0 on a 4-point scale)

Figure 18.4

The Education Section
of a Résumé

> **Education**
>
> **University of New Mexico**
> Albuquerque, New Mexico
>
> Degree   Bachelor of Science
> Major   Mechanical Engineering
>   Expected in May 1999
>
> GPA   3.7/4.0
>
> Honors   Dean's List (Fall 1997, Spring 1998, Fall 1998)
>   Alpha Lambda Delta (Freshman Honor Society)
>   Tau Beta Pi (General Engineering Society)
>   Outstanding College Students of America
>
> Worked part-time to pay for my education

- Academic honors or awards that you received as a college or university student
- Any outstanding accomplishments, such as special projects or research that you did as a student

If you list courses related to the work you are seeking, include primarily upper-level courses in your major. List courses by title, not by number. For example, if you want to mention a course in advanced automated systems, write "Advanced Automated Systems," not "MECH 4302."

The education category shown in Figure 18.4 includes several of the optional items along with the writer's degree information. The writer lists his grade-point average (3.7) along with a reference point (4.0). He also mentions his academic honors. Notice that he states in this section that he worked part-time to help pay for his schooling. Achieving his high grade-point average and his honors while holding down a job is an impressive achievement, which he should highlight.

Work Experience

In the work experience category, use reverse chronological order, beginning with your most recent experience. Include this information:

- Name and location of the company where you worked
- The years (or months if less than a year) of your work with that company
- Your job or position title
- Verb phrases describing what you did (your job responsibilities)

As you describe your responsibilities, demonstrate that you can produce results. "The most qualified people don't always get the job. It goes to the person who presents himself [or herself] most persuasively in person and on

Texas Instruments, Inc. Dallas, Texas

Manufacturing Facilitator 1992–present
- Facilitated two self-directed work teams of 26 total team members performing screen printing and painting operations.
- Led screen printing team to win Gold Teaming for Excellence Award.
- Converted coating system to low VOC formulations that comply with existing air-quality standards.

Reengineering Team Leader (1992)
- Reengineered screen printing work flow to eliminate non-value added effort and reduce task handoffs from one person to another. Reduced cycle time from 5 days to 2 days, increased productivity by 25%, and saved $250,000 annually.
- Received Site Quality Improvement Award two consecutive years (1991 and 1992) for reducing cycle time and improving quality.

Process Improvement Engineer of Finish and Assembly Areas (1988–1991)
- Designed and installed custom equipment and machine upgrades that reduced manual labor required by $100,000 per year.
- Improved part racking on plating line, reducing scrap by $20,000 annually.

Figure 18.5 A Work Experience Section Written by a Job-Seeker with Experience

paper. So don't just list where you were and what you did. . . . tell *how well you did*. Were you the best salesperson? Did you cut operating costs? Give numbers, statistics, percentages, increases in sales or profits" (Simon). Describe how well you did your job.

Figures 18.5 and 18.6 illustrate how two writers approached the work experience category. In Figure 18.5, instead of using vague, unimpressive language, the writer, an experienced job-seeker, uses specific information to demonstrate how well he did his job:

Vague and unimpressive	Facilitated work teams
	Improved production
Specific and impressive	Facilitated two self-directed work teams of 26 total team members
	Reduced cycle time from 5 days to 2 days
	Saved $250,000 annually

The writer doesn't just tell prospective employers that he saved the company money or reduced the cycle time. He states the specific reduction in days and the amount saved in dollars.

University of Washington	Seattle, Washington
Computer Lab Tutor	**1996–present**

- Received Tutor of the Semester award (Fall and Spring 1998).
- Promoted to Senior Tutor. Taught new tutors the software used in the lab.
- Answered students' questions about word processing, desktop publishing, and statistics software packages
- Helped students with computer-related problems.

Shoreside Restaurant	Seattle, Washington
Server	**1997–present**

- Received the Outstanding Service Award (1998).

The experience section in Figure 18.6 is an excerpt from a college student's résumé. This student is looking for her first job in her field. She doesn't have the extensive work experience of the writer in Figure 18.5. However, she can demonstrate how well she did the jobs she held as a student at the University of Washington. She lists her award for service at Shoreside Restaurant along with the year she received the award. She also lists her "Tutor of the Semester" award. These awards and her promotion demonstrate that she did her jobs well.

Like the writer in Figure 18.6, you may not have any work experience in your field. However, you can list your summer or part-time jobs. If you were promoted or received any awards as a part of these jobs, include this information to help potential employers see that you are reliable and hard-working.

Skills and Specialized Training

Some writers include a category listing their skills or a category listing any specialized training or education they have received. These sections are most common in functional resumes. If used in a functional resume, the skills section usually appears prominently near the beginning of the resume and can have various headings such as "Major Accomplishments" or "Skills." Figure 18.7 shows the skills section from the résumé from a nontraditional student. Figure 18.8 shows a specialized training section. If you decide to use one of these categories in your résumé, include only information relevant to the type of job you are seeking.

Personal Information

You may want to include some personal information that gives readers "a glimpse of the personal you" and furthers "the image you've worked to

Figure 18.7

The Skills Section of a Résumé

Skills

Management Skills

- Hired and supervised 14 employees in a $2.3 million catering business

Communication Skills

- Trained new employees in a catering business
- Wrote performance evaluations, designed marketing brochures, and designed and programmed the Web site for a catering business

Teaching Skills

- Coach youth soccer, baseball, and basketball
- Tutored math in the McKinney Independent School District and for the Collin County Boys' and Girls' Clubs.

---

project in the preceding sections" of the résumé (Simon). You can list any of the following information if it will enhance prospective employers' picture of you:

- Community activities (such as volunteer work for charitable organizations, membership in community service organizations, or leadership or work with community youth organizations)
- College activities (such as membership in teams and organizations, offices held, and awards won)
- Professional memberships—perhaps in organizations in your field, including any leadership positions you've held with the organization
- Personal interests and hobbies, especially if they relate to your qualifications
- Sports or recreational activities that you enjoy

Perhaps you've been a Girl Scout or Boy Scout leader in your community, or you've organized a blood drive for your college or university campus, or you've won awards for your leadership abilities. These activities and awards show that you are a team player, that you care about your community, and that you are disciplined.

Figure 18.8 The Specialized Training Section of a Résumé

Special Training
- Business Process Engineering (Reengineering)
- Statistical Process Control (Design of Experiments and Six Sigma Quality)
- Structural Steel Design

Do not include information that might invite employers to discriminate—for example, information about your marital status, age, or health.

Use Dynamic, Persuasive Language That Demonstrates What You Can Do

The guideline for word choice in your résumé is simple: keep your writing style clear and uncluttered. Exclude extraneous information, and use dynamic, persuasive language. Follow these tips:

- **Keep the information and language simple and direct.** The employer reading your résumé may be reading hundreds of other résumés for the same job. Therefore, state your information or qualifications directly; omit any unnecessary information. Be brief. Give employers the information they need to know about your abilities and background—and then stop!

- **Use dynamic action verbs.** Use verbs such as *saved, created, supervised, directed,* and *designed.* Avoid words and phrases that don't describe action and demonstrate what you have achieved and can achieve. Avoid phrases such as "My responsibilities included" or "Tasks or duties were."

- **Use specific language that emphasizes your accomplishments and what you can do.** Use specific language that demonstrates what you have accomplished and what you can do. When possible, use figures as part of your specific language. Figures can effectively demonstrate your abilities.

The following examples illustrate phrases that use dynamic, persuasive language (the action verbs appear in bold type):

Not Dynamic/Persuasive	Created a computer program for students logging into the lab.
Dynamic/Persuasive	**Designed** and **programmed** software that **reduced** the number of employees needed in the student computer labs and saved the university $16,640 annually.
Not Dynamic/Persuasive	Regional sales manager for 4 years.
Dynamic/Persuasive	Regional sales manager for 4 years with a progressive telecommunications company. **Led** my region to **win** the top sales award in the company for 3 consecutive years.
Not Dynamic/Persuasive	Was responsible for designing and installing custom equipment and upgrading machines.
Dynamic/Persuasive	**Designed** and **installed** custom equipment and machine upgrades that **reduced** the manual labor required by $100,000 annually.

The language—along with the design—of your résumé gives employers their first impression of you. You want that impression to be positive.

Create an Eye-Catching, Accessible Design

Design your résumé so an employer can quickly scan it and get a good idea of your important qualifications (Greenly 42). In other words, "design résumés so that employers don't have to hunt for your qualifications"; employers should be able to quickly locate your qualifications without "playing detective" (Parker 318). If they have to play detective, they may overlook or ignore your résumé. To help employers find information, create visual categories with white space, headings, type sizes, and bulleted lists.

In the résumé shown in Figure 18.9, employers can easily spot the categories of information because of the headings and the white space surrounding those headings. These categories allow employers to quickly locate information about the writer's qualifications. The writer uses boldface type and different type sizes within the categories to highlight and prioritize information. The writer also uses bulleted lists to help employers easily read about his work.

As you design your résumé, consider these tips:

- **Use headings and subheadings to create visual categories.** Use type size to differentiate among the headings, subheadings, and text of the résumé. If you want to further differentiate the headings and subheadings from the text, use boldface type.

- **Surround the headings with enough white space for employers to easily see the headings.** Headings can't help employers to locate your qualifications if you bury the headings in text. Instead, highlight the headings with white space.

- **Use bulleted lists instead of paragraphs.** You can help employers to locate information by using bulleted lists instead of paragraphs, especially in the work experience section. The paragraph and bulleted list shown in Figure 18.10 present the same information. A prospective employer glancing at the paragraph might miss the information about the "Gold Teaming for Excellence" award. The bulleted list highlights the award.

- **Use only one typeface.** Most writers use a serif typeface such as Times Roman, but instead you could use a traditional sans-serif typeface such as Helvetica (see Chapter 10, "Designing Documents for Your Readers"). Whether you choose a serif or sans-serif typeface, select a typeface that is easily readable and professional looking.

- **Use $8^1/_2$-by-11-inch bond paper in white, off-white, light gray, or cream for readability.** Use good-quality bond paper. Because some employers will scan or copy your résumé, you may want to use white paper because even off-white paper will darken the scanned image.

- **Proofread; then proofread again!** Make sure your résumé is free of grammar, spelling, and punctuation errors. Even the smallest of punctuation errors can cost you an interview.

Figure 18.9 A Well-Designed Résumé

C. Randall Harrison
310 North Edna
Lewisville, Texas 75057
(972) 555-7893

Objective

An engineering position requiring creativity, equipment design expertise, and knowledge of manufacturing methods.

Experience

Texas Instruments, Inc. Dallas, Texas
Manufacturing Facilitator (1992–present)
- Facilitated two self-directed work teams of 26 total team members performing screen printing and painting operations.
- Led screen printing team to win Gold Teaming for Excellence Award.
- Converted coating system to low VOC formulations that comply with existing air-quality standards.

Reengineering Team Leader (1992)
- Reengineered screen printing work flow to eliminate non-value added effort and reduce task handoffs from one person to another. Reduced cycle time from 5 days to 2 days, increased productivity by 25%, and saved $250,000 annually.
- Received Site Quality Improvement Award two consecutive years (1991 and 1992) for reducing cycle time and improving quality.

Process Improvement Engineer of Finish and Assembly Areas (1988–1991)
- Designed and installed custom equipment and machine upgrades that reduced manual labor required by $100,000 per year.
- Improved part racking on plating line, reducing scrap by $20,000 annually.

Texas A&M University College Station, Texas
Research Assistant (1983–1988)
- Designed and constructed equipment and instrumentation for energy research.

Amco Manufacturing Yazoo City, Mississippi
Project Engineer (1981–1982)
- Developed agricultural tillage implements using design skills in structural steel weldments and hydraulics.

Education

- Master of Science in Agricultural Engineering (1988), Texas A&M University, College Station, Texas
- Bachelor of Science in Agricultural Engineering—Magna Cum Laude (1981), Texas A&M University, College Station, Texas

---

Special Training

- Business Process Engineering (Reengineering)
- Statistical Process Control (Design of Experiments and Six Sigma Quality)
- Structural Steel Design

Personal

- Work with local chapter of Habitat for Humanity to build homes.
- Avid "do-it-yourselfer" with my own woodworking and metalworking shop.

Source: Courtesy of C. Randall Harrison.

Figure 18.10

Comparison of
Paragraph and
Bulleted List Formats
in a Résumé

Manufacturing Facilitator
1992–present

- Facilitated two self-directed work teams of 26 total team members performing screen printing and painting operations.
- Led screen printing team to win Gold Teaming for Excellence Award.
- Converted coating system to low VOC formulations that comply with existing air-quality standards.

- -

Manufacturing Facilitator
1992–present

Facilitated two self-directed work teams of 26 total team members performing screen printing and painting operations. Led screen printing team to win Gold Teaming for Excellence Award. Converted coating system to low VOC formulations that comply with existing air-quality standards.

PRINCIPLE 4: WRITE A READER-ORIENTED LETTER OF APPLICATION

You will need a letter of application, or cover letter, to send with your résumé. A letter of application introduces your résumé and gives the employer additional information about you and your experience. Address the letter personally to the executive or manager most likely to make the hiring decision (Greenly 42; Simon). Address your letter to a specific person and spell the addressee's name correctly. If you don't know who should receive your letter, don't address it to "Dear Sir or Madam," "To Whom It May Concern," a department, or a person's job title—unless the advertisement says to address the letter to a title or a person's job title. Instead, telephone the company to find out who oversees the department. If you can't find out by telephone, address the letter to an executive such as the president or chief executive officer—and use the person's name.

Once you have found out who will read your letter of application, customize your letter for that reader and appeal directly to his or her needs (Greenly 42). For example, if you have experience or classwork especially relevant to the job you are applying for or to that employer, discuss that experience or classwork in the body of your letter.

Your customized, generally one-page letter, will have three sections:

- Your purpose for writing: the introductory paragraph
- Your qualifications: the education and experience paragraphs
- Your goal (what you want from the employer): the concluding paragraph

Figure 18.11

Sample Introductions for Three Letters of Application

Dr. Maggy Smith suggested that I contact you about the project engineer position you currently have open. My experience as a research assistant in the energy conservation lab at the University of Maine provides me with the qualifications you are seeking. Please consider me for the project engineer position.

- -

My extensive course work in computer science and my experience as an intern for Image Software qualify me for the software designer position that you advertised in the May 16 issue of the Atlanta Gazette. Please consider me for that position.

- -

My experience as a manager for Good Eats Grill and my degree in hotel and restaurant management give me a solid foundation in the restaurant business. Please consider me for a position in your management training program.

Your Purpose for Writing: The Introductory Paragraph

In the introductory paragraph, do the following:

- **Identify the position you are applying for.** Employers often receive many letters of application for several jobs at the same time, so identify the specific job you are interested in.
- **Tell the employer where you found out about the job.** Because employers may be soliciting résumés in more than one place, they often want to know where you found out about the job. This information is especially important if you learned of the job from an employee, coworker, or acquaintance of the employer. This information may lead the employer to show more interest in your résumé. If you are writing an unsolicited letter, "quickly explain why you are approaching the company," and then ask whether a job is available (Simon).

Figure 18.11 presents three sample introductory paragraphs. Each specifically identifies the job and the writer's purpose for writing. The first writer uses a personal contact (Dr. Maggy Smith) to open the paragraph and get the employer's attention. The second writer mentions a specific job advertisement. The third writer is sending an unsolicited letter. That writer is not responding to a specific job advertisement and doesn't know whether the company currently has job openings.

As these introductions illustrate, the tone of a letter of application must be positive and self-confident—not tentative or boastful. State your qualifications in a positive manner without focusing on your weaknesses, but be careful not to sound arrogant. You want to appear confident about your education, experience, and abilities while indicating that you know you have much to learn—and are eager to learn—about your profession.

Your Qualifications: The Education and Experience Paragraphs

After you have told the employer why you are writing, present information about your education and experience. Follow the order of your résumé when discussing your education and work experience. If your résumé gives information about your education first, then discuss your education first in the letter of application. If your résumé gives information about your work experience first, then discuss your experience first. When you have many years of work experience, you can eliminate the education paragraph and include two or more experience paragraphs.

In these paragraphs, highlight, add to, or expand on the information in your résumé. Do not simply repeat the information in your résumé or give the details of your education and experience in chronological order. Instead, highlight or add to information that may especially interest the employer or that is particularly relevant to the job for which you are applying.

As you develop these paragraphs, create a unified focus. Avoid the temptation to list unrelated information about your education or work experience. Instead, begin each paragraph with a topic sentence and then develop that topic in the sentences that follow. As you discuss your education, consider how it uniquely qualifies you for the job that you seek. For instance, if the job advertisement says that applicants should write well, you might discuss projects where writing was a significant component.

As you discuss your experience, consider how it uniquely qualifies you for the job. This task is especially difficult if your experience does not directly relate to the job you seek. For example, Rodney is a new college graduate looking for an engineering job. He has never worked in the field of engineering, but he worked as a tutor in a computer lab for three years and was promoted to student manager of the lab. He has several skills that will impress employers: he was promoted because of his ability to work well with others and his ability to supervise his peers. In addition, his university implemented several of his ideas, such as putting a monitor with the weekly schedule of classes outside the lab so that students will know when their classes will meet in the lab and when the lab is open for general access. This idea saved the lab $1,000 a year on paper costs. Although Rodney's experience is not directly related to engineering, he can write a paragraph focusing on his abilities to work with others and to be a team player by suggesting money-saving ideas.

Figures 18.12 and 18.13 illustrate how two writers approached the experience and education paragraphs for a letter of application. The writer of the paragraphs shown in Figure 18.12 has no work experience in her field. The writer of the paragraphs shown in Figure 18.13 has work experience. The

Figure 18.12

Education and Experience Paragraphs Written by a Job-Seeker Without Experience

At Chambers University, I have taken many courses requiring writing. In an advanced technical writing course, I used PageMaker to produce a 40-page user's manual for inventory software used by Minyards, Inc. (a regional grocery-store chain). Currently, all Minyards stores use the manual to train new employees on the inventory system and as a reference guide for employees after initial training.

For the past three years, I have worked in the Technical Writing Computer Lab at Chambers University. I began as a lab tutor, assisting students with software questions, especially related to WordPerfect, PageMaker (desktop publishing software), and Powerpoint (graphics software). After eighteen months, I was promoted to student lab manager. As manager, I work with the faculty to schedule classes in the lab, work with the lab tutors to set up their schedules, and conduct meetings each week with the lab tutors. Most recently, I set up a scheduling system that uses e-mail instead of paper. This system saved $600 in paper costs annually. As manager and tutor in the lab, I have developed interpersonal skills that would benefit Writers, Inc.

Figure 18.13

Education and Experience Paragraphs Written by a Job-Seeker with Experience

While at Texas Instruments, I worked as an innovative design engineer. I have over ten years of research, production, and manufacturing experience, especially in the areas of machine design, power transmission, and structural analysis. I began as a process improvement engineer and was promoted to reengineering team leader and finally to manufacturing facilitator. As manufacturing facilitator, I supervised two self-directed work teams of 26 total team members. I led one of these teams, the screen printing team, to win the Gold Teaming for Excellence Award. I also received the Site Quality Improvement Award in 1991 and 1992 for increasing productivity by 25% annually. Most recently, I converted the paint coating system to low VOC formulations to comply with air-quality standards not required until 2000.

Along with my experience as a design engineer for Texas Instruments, I have a Bachelor of Science and a Master of Science degree in agricultural engineering from Texas A&M University. As part of my academic experience, I worked as a research assistant in the agricultural engineering department. I designed and constructed custom equipment and instrumentation used in energy conservation research. This work along with my experience as a design engineer uniquely qualifies me for your senior design engineer position.

writer with work experience begins with this experience and moves to education because his résumé follows that order. This writer also includes his major, degrees received, and school in the education category. The tone of both writers is self-confident as they mention facts about their education and experience and state qualities and experience that are relevant to potential employers.

Your Goal: The Concluding Paragraph

In the concluding paragraph, directly state what you want from the reader: an opportunity to meet the employer and discuss your qualifications—an interview. In the paragraphs preceding the conclusion, you have provided specific, detailed information about yourself—information to convince the employer to invite you for an interview. In the concluding paragraph, do the following:

- **Refer the employer to your résumé.**
- **Request an interview.**
- **Tell the employer how to contact you by telephone and e-mail.** Give the employer your phone number, and mention the best time to call. You can encourage the employer to act by including this specific information in the concluding paragraph.

Use specific language in the concluding paragraph. Avoid vague language as in these paragraphs, in which the writer doesn't confidently state the goal of meeting the employer or encourage the employer to make contact:

Vague	I look forward to hearing from you soon. Thank you for considering my résumé.
Vague	If possible, may I meet with you or someone in your company to discuss my résumé and my qualifications?

Instead, use specific language. The writers of the next paragraphs refer the employer to their résumés and directly ask the employer to contact them for an interview. These writers also use a polite, respectful, confident tone:

Specific	My résumé provides additional information about my education and work experience. I would enjoy discussing my application with you. Please write me at raign@aol.com, or call me anytime at (307) 555-9061.
Specific	You can find more information about my education and experience on the enclosed résumé. I would appreciate the opportunity to discuss my résumé with you at your convenience. Please write to me at the above address, or call me at (505) 555-9033 weekdays or at (505) 555-0034 evenings and weekends.

ISSUES IN CONTEXT

The Electronic Job Search

The Web offers a wealth of information for the job-seeker—information about job fairs, employers, job openings, and job-hunting. Some sites, such as Monster Board, will even help you compile and post your electronic résumé. For a sampling of such sites, look at the following:

- *Career Magazine* <http://www.careermag.com/index.shtml>
- *Career Mosaic* <http://www.careermosaic.com>
- *Career Web* <http://www.occ.com>
- *Monster Board* <http://www.monsterboard.com>

Use these and other sites to gather information to enhance your job search.

Some employers search the Web for résumés while other employers scan paper résumés to create a database of applicants (Mannix). Here are guidelines for preparing a World Wide Web résumé:

- **Use a variety of internal links.** For example, you might include a link from your major to a listing of upper-level courses specific to your major or to a description of a special project that you completed.
- **Keep the design simple.** Different browsers will load a file differently, so "avoid heavy graphics or unusual or dark backgrounds" (Hansen 6).
- **Register your résumé site with the appropriate search engines.** Potential employers can locate your résumé only if you register it.
- **Use keywords that potential employers will use to search résumés.** Some search engines and employers will even provide a list of keywords that you can use in your résumés.

The following are guidelines for creating scannable résumés[3]:

- Use only one, 12-point typeface.
- Align all information on the left margin—don't indent or use double columns.
- Don't use italics, graphics, rules, or underlining.
- Use white paper.
- Don't fold or staple the résumé.
- Use keywords as suggested for the World Wide Web résumé.
- Send the original, not a copy, and include a copy of your traditional résumé.

---

3. I base these guidelines on those presented by Amy Hansen in "Teaching Techniques: Whatever Happened to the Traditional Resume: Preparing Students for an Electronic Job Search." *ATTW bulletin* 6.2(1996):4–6.

Figures 18.14 and 18.15 illustrate effective letters of application. The writers use a respectful yet confident tone and include specific information to persuade the employer to invite them for an interview.

PRINCIPLE 5: USE LETTERS TO FOLLOW UP

Follow-up letters are important to your job search. You can write a follow-up letter in several situations:

- **When you have sent a letter of application and résumé and have not received a response within three or four weeks.** If you have not received a response, write a brief, polite letter. Mention your previous letter and its date, and include another copy of your résumé. To know when to write such letters, keep copies of all the letters of application that you send; and keep a file of the responses you receive from employers. Without these copies and a detailed file, you may not know when to send follow-up letters.

- **After an interview.** Within two days of an interview, write a brief thank-you letter addressed to the manager who will decide whether to hire you. If you had extensive interviews with more than one person, write to all the people who interviewed you. In your letters, state your interest in the job and the company. Use these letters to reinforce what you offer the company—what you can bring to the job. Mention the company by name, and mention the names of people in the company with whom you talked.

- **When you accept a job.** When you accept a job, write a brief letter confirming your acceptance. In this letter, you can confirm details such as when you will begin work.

- **When you reject a job offer or no longer want an employer to consider you for a job.** When you accept a job, don't forget to write the other companies that seriously considered you for a job. You may want to work for or with one of those companies in the future, so do them the courtesy of writing a brief letter. Thank the company and the person who interviewed you for their interest in you. State that you have taken a job with another company. You don't have to identify the specific job offer that you accepted; instead, you can simply write: "I have decided to accept another offer." Include only positive comments about the company and your experiences with the interviewer. End your letter with a brief statement of good will such as "Thank you for the interest you showed in my application."

Don't forget follow-up letters, especially after an interview. Post-interview letters offer an excellent opportunity to restate your qualifications and to add any information about your application that you didn't have the opportunity to discuss during the interview (Simon). Figure 18.16 illustrates a post-interview follow-up letter.

Figure 18.14 A Letter of Application Written by a Graduating Senior

204 Oak Street
Denton, TX 76205
April 16, 1999

Dr. Brandon McCarroll
Nortel Technology
2221 Lakeside Boulevard
Richardson, TX 75082

Dear Dr. McCarroll:

I am writing in response to your advertisement in the April 12 *Dallas Morning News*.
Would you please consider me for the entry-level position in technical documentation? I
believe that my experience as an intern with SWB Telecommunications, along with my
education in technical communication from the University of North Texas, would uniquely
qualify me for the position.

My education at the University of North Texas has given me a strong background in
technical communication. I have concentrated on paper and online documentation and on
Web design. For a senior-level course, I, along with two students in computer science,
designed an intranet site for Texas Instruments employees; the site describes corporate
history and culture at Texas Instruments. For my senior project, I designed a Web site for
the technical communication program at the University of North Texas. You can view the
site at www.twlab.unt.edu.

While working as an intern for SWB Telecommunications, I applied my academic training
in a workplace environment. As one of my projects, I used my experience in designing
documents for the Internet to develop a Web site describing the wireless services offered by
SWB. Over 2,000 employees and customers use this site each week. During my second
summer with SWB, I updated this Web site. I also edited and proofread customer
documentation for SWB 2000 and SWB 2020 wireless telephones. Customers now receive
this documentation when they buy these telephones.

My résumé provides further information about my education and work experience. Dr.
McCarroll, I would enjoy the opportunity of meeting with you personally to discuss my
qualifications and résumé. You can reach me anytime at (817) 555-2858 or
lthomas@twlab.unt.edu.

Sincerely,

Leigh Thomas

Leigh Thomas

Enclosure

Figure 18.15 A Letter of Application Written by a Job-Seeker with Extensive Work Experience

310 North Edna
Lewisville, Texas 75057
February 16, 1998

Mr. Barry Boswell
AMC Engineering, Inc.
26789 Westfall Road
Portland, Oregon 97501

Dear Mr. Boswell:

Mr. John Botsford of your research and development department suggested that I contact you. He believes that my experience as a design engineer for Texas Instruments qualifies me for the manufacturing engineer position that you currently have open in your production division. My experience and education in reengineering and in supervising work teams provide me with the qualifications that you are seeking.

While at Texas Instruments, I worked as an innovative design engineer. I have over ten years of research, production, and manufacturing experience, especially in the areas of machine design, power transmission, and structural analysis. I began as a process improvement engineer and was promoted to reengineering team leader and finally to manufacturing facilitator. As manufacturing facilitator, I supervised two self-directed work teams of 26 total team members. I led one of these teams, the screen printing team, to win the Gold Teaming for Excellence Award. I also received the Site Quality Improvement Award in 1991 and 1992 for increasing productivity by 25% annually.

Along with my experience as a design engineer for Texas Instruments, I have a Bachelor of Science and a Master of Science degree in agricultural engineering from Texas A&M University. As part of my academic experience, I worked as a research assistant in the agricultural engineering department. I designed and constructed custom equipment and instrumentation used in energy conservation research.

The enclosed résumé provides further information about my experience and my education. Mr. Boswell, I would like to meet with you personally to discuss my qualifications for this position. Please call me at (972) 555-7893. I look forward to visiting with you.

Sincerely,

C. Randall Harrison
C. Randall Harrison

Encl.: résumé

Figure 18.16 A Post-Interview Follow-Up Letter

402 Spring Avenue, Apt. 6C
Alexandria, VA 23097
(703) 555-0922
cdempsey@aol.com
May 4, 1998

Mr. Dwight Wilson
Senior Production Engineer
I-2 Technology, Inc.
San Diego, CA 92093

Dear Mr. Wilson:

Thank you for taking time from your busy schedule yesterday to show me I-2 Technology's facilities and to discuss the quality control job. I especially enjoyed meeting many of your coworkers. Please thank Ms. Johnson in the quality control division.

As a result of our visit, I have a good understanding of I-2 Technology and appreciate its progressive approach to maximizing production without sacrificing quality control. I feel confident that my experience as a quality control engineer can benefit your division.

I-2 Technology's place in the semiconductor industry and your colleagues in the quality control division confirm my impression that I-2 Technology would be an exciting place to work. If I can answer further questions, please call me at (703) 555-0922.

Best regards,

Cynthia Demsey

Cynthia Demsey

CONCLUSION

Use the "Worksheet for Writing Reader-Oriented Job Correspondence" for writing résumés, letters of application, and follow-up letters. Although the job correspondence itself will not get you a job, it can be the first step toward that job.

WORKSHEET **for Writing Reader-Oriented Job Correspondence**

Principle 1: Consider Various Methods for Locating Job Opportunities

- Have you checked for job opportunities available through your college or university placement center?
- Have you looked for job advertisements in newspapers and professional or trade journals or on the World Wide Web and electronic bulletin boards?
- Have you networked with others in your field, with friends and acquaintances, and with your professors?

Principle 2: Determine What Information You Want Employers to Know About You

- Did you brainstorm about your education, work experience, activities, goals, and skills?
- Did you include information that will help employers understand you and your qualifications?
- Does the brainstorming list contain information that will impress employers?

Principle 3: Prepare an Effective Résumé

- Does your résumé include enough specific information to distinguish you from others applying for the job?
- For any chronological information, have you used reverse chronological order?
- Have you used dynamic, action verbs to begin sentences?
- Have you used specific, persuasive language?
- Have you used headings and subheadings to create visual categories? Will readers be able to find the categories in your résumé easily? Are the headings set off with enough white space?
- Is the résumé printed in only one typeface?
- Have you used bulleted lists when appropriate?
- Is the résumé free of grammar, spelling, and punctuation errors?

Principle 4: Write a Reader-Oriented Letter of Application

- Is the letter addressed to a specific person?
- Does the introductory paragraph identify the job you are applying for?
- Does the introductory paragraph identify where you found out about the job or the company?
- Does the introductory paragraph state your interest in the job or a specific type of job?
- Do the education and experience paragraphs have a unified focus and clear topic sentences?
- Do the education and experience paragraphs show how your education and experience uniquely qualify you for the job?
- Does the concluding paragraph refer the employer to your résumé?
- Does the concluding paragraph confidently and respectfully request an interview?
- Does the concluding paragraph tell the employer how to contact you?
- Does the letter have a polite yet confident tone?
- Is the letter free of grammar, spelling, style, and punctuation errors?

Principle 5: Use Letters to Follow Up

- Is the letter addressed to a specific person?
- Does the letter thank the addressee for the interview?
- Does the letter state your interest in the job and the company (if appropriate)?
- Does the letter reinforce what you have to offer the company—what you can bring to the job?
- Have you used the company name and the names of people with whom you talked?
- Is the letter brief?
- Does the letter have a controlled, professional tone?
- Is the letter free of grammar, spelling, style, and punctuation errors?

EXERCISES

1. Find a job opportunity in your field that you are qualified for or will be qualified for when you graduate. You can look for these opportunities in newspapers, in trade journals, on electronic bulletin boards, at your college placement center, or on the World Wide Web. You also can locate job opportunities by talking to acquaintances, family, and friends in business and industry. After you have located a job opportunity, complete one of these steps:

   - If you located the job through a printed advertisement or announcement, copy or cut out the advertisement.
   - If you located the job on an electronic bulletin board or the World Wide Web, print out a copy of the advertisement or announcement.
   - If you talked to someone about the job, ask for a business card from that person or a copy of the job announcement.

2. Decide on the categories of information that you might include in your résumé for the job you located in Exercise 1. Then create a list of the information that you could include in each of these categories. Your list might look like Nicole's brainstorming list in Figure 18.1. Include specific, detailed information in your list.

3. Using some or all of the information from the list that you created in Exercise 2, prepare a résumé. Use word-processing or desktop publishing soft-ware, so you can easily update or revise the résumé as necessary when you look for a job. Use the questions in the "Worksheet for Writing Reader-Oriented Job Correspondence" as you write your résumé.

4. Write a letter of application for the job you located in Exercise 1. Use the "Worksheet for Writing Reader-Oriented Job Correspondence" as you write your letter.

5. Evaluate the résumé shown in Figure 18.17 for organization, effectiveness, design, clarity, and correctness. Use the questions for résumés in the worksheet. Then write a memo to your instructor explaining your evaluation.

6. Evaluate the letters shown in Figures 18.18 and 18.19 for organization, content, and correctness. In your evaluation, answer the questions for letters of application in the worksheet.

7. Using the questions in the worksheet, evaluate your résumé and letter of application. Your instructor may also ask you to use these questions to evaluate the résumés and letters of application of two of your classmates.

8. Write a paragraph evaluating the follow-up letter shown in Figure 18.20. Use the questions for follow-up letters in the worksheet to guide you as you evaluate the letter.

9. Rewrite the follow-up letter shown in Figure 18.20.

Figure 18.17 Résumé for Exercise 5

Maureen Peterson
1713 Canadian Trail
Harrison, Arkansas 72601
(972) 555-9873

Education
University Arkansas, Fayetteville, Arkansas
B.S. in Horticulture, 1999
3.5 G.P.A.

Johnson High School
Johnson, Kansas
Graduate June 1994

Experience
Earthcare Landscaping, Johnson, Kansas
Assistant Manager. Responsible for keeping record of daily sales, deposits, inventory, and purchasing. Fill in for manager when necessary. Supervise sales clerks. Summers only 1997, 1998

White Dove Nursery, Fayetteville, Arkansas
Manager. In charge of nursery maintenance and customer service. I also ordered all plants and set up landscaping appointments with customers. In charge of six other employees. Assistance to customers looking for the right plants for their landscapes. Full responsibility for the smooth running of the nursery. 1998 to present.

A Taste of Italy, Fayetteville, Arkansas
Server. August 1997 to May 1998.

Personal
Currently active in a national sorority at University Arkansas at Fayetteville, holding a position on the pledge committee. Certified Nurseryman 1997. Volunteer as a landscaper for the city of Fayetteville Parks and Recreation Department. Awarded Harrison Mother's Club scholarship in 1997.

References available upon request.

Figure 18.18 Letter of Application for Exercise 6

425 Bernard, Apt. 1313
Ames, IA 52001

April 13, 1998

AMR, Inc.
10819 Composite Drive
Boston, MA 02116

Dear Personnel Manager:

Two years as a student in engineering and significant work as an intern uniquely qualify me for the junior engineer position with your company.

My course work in engineering and my related work experience provide me with engineering skills that you would find useful. To give you further information about my education and background, I have enclosed a copy of my résumé.

I would appreciate the opportunity to talk with you further about my qualifications. You can contact me at the above address or at (515) 555-0045. I look forward to hearing from you.

Sincerely,

Charles E. Morrison

Charles E. Morrison

enclosure

Figure 18.19 Letter of Application for Exercise 6

301 Benjamin Street
St. Petersburg, FL 30987

May 16, 1998

Mr. Don Carver
Manager
The Lotus Tree, Inc.
1408 Teasley Lane
Orlando, FL 30289

Dear Don:

Fred suggested that I apply for the open position on your sales staff. I just graduated from Central Florida University with a B.S. this May. I would be a great addition to your sales staff—Fred thinks so too.

I have a talent for sales, as Fred may have told you, and I would become a useful asset to your company. I have taken several communications and sales courses at Central Florida and most importantly enjoy the art of sales.

Enclosed is a copy of my résumé which has more on my employment background. I've also enclosed a picture of me with my dog, Scooter, so you can see what I look like. I would like to met with you soon to discuss my qualifications. I am available every day between 2 and 6 P.M. and can be reached at 555-1358. I look forward to hearing from you.

Best regards,

Janice

Janice James

Enclosures

Figure 18.20 Follow-Up Letter for Exercises 8 and 9

1717 Shoreside
Jackson, Mississippi 39216

March 30, 1998

Ms. Penny Moore
Designed Systems
307 North Central
Columbus, Ohio 43202

Dear Penny:

Meeting you and all your coworkers was great fun. The company seems to be a wonderful place to work. Thanks for showing me the facilities and for taking me to lunch. I would love to become one of your coworkers.

Again, I would enjoy working with you and your coworkers. And I believe that I have a lot to offer your company. Have a great week.

Sincerely,

Gail

Gail Spinuzzi

APPENDIXES

Appendix A

Creating Reader-Oriented Web Sites

Wendy is a technical writer for an engineering company. She will soon begin creating the external Web site for her company's products and services. Wendy feels a little intimidated by the task. Although she uses the Web for researching topics, keeping up with her professional organizations, and querying user groups for answers to computer dilemmas, Wendy has never created a Web site. Her manager thinks a Web site is like a brochure or catalog, except that it's on the computer screen. Because Wendy produces the printed version of these documents, her manager assigned the Web project to Wendy.

THE DEVELOPMENT PROCESS FOR WEB SITES

Wendy's manager has the right idea. Wendy can use all the knowledge and skill she has developed creating reader-oriented print documents to develop a user-oriented Web site. The process is the same; it's the medium that's different. Wendy just needs to discover the opportunities and limitations of the new medium through her document development process. To create a print document, Wendy follows these steps:

- Analyzes the writing situation
- Gathers information
- Structures the information
- Drafts the document
- Revises the document
- Edits and proofreads the document
- Sends the document to a printer
- Distributes the final document
- Starts preparing for the next edition or version

Wendy's process for writing print documents is part of a broader process that she can customize for creating Web pages. Some of the decisions that Wendy takes for granted when she produces printed pages (like whether to use headings, what tools to use) are not so obvious when the challenge is to create Web pages. Let's focus the writing process to accommodate the new medium of the Web. These are the steps that Wendy must take:

- **Analyze the situation for creating a web site.**
- **Choose the right tools.** This choice is also part of the print document process, but it is a foregone conclusion in most instances. However, think of the dilemma writers faced when word processors first became available.
- **Create and gather content for the Web site.** You might know where to get material for a brochure, but Web pages use sound bites, video clips, and other sources that print documents can't use.

Written by Tonya McKinney, proposal writer and Web designer for Southwestern Bell Telephone Company.

- **Design the Web site and individual Web pages.**
- **Construct the Web site.**
- **Edit and revise the Web site.**
- **Test and revise the Web site.** This step—often skipped with print documents—is essential for documents such as user manuals and Web documents.
- **Edit and proofread.**
- **Post the document.** This step corresponds to the printing process for paper documents.
- **Maintain and refine the document.** For print documents, this step would be preparing new editions of the original version.

Now let's take a detailed look at each step in developing Web sites.

Analyze the Situation for Creating a Web Site

All the other decisions about the Web site depend on what you decide in this initial stage. In this stage, you identify the purpose of the Web site and the expectations of the readers. Use the following guidelines as you analyze the purpose, readers, and situation governing your Web site:

- **Existing Web efforts:** Your company may already have a Web site. If so, you probably will have to conform to, or modify, the existing site.
- **Supervisors' expectations:** Often, many supervisors or managers who assign Web projects already have ideas about what makes a good Web site. They may even expect you to model your Web site after one of their favorite sites.
- **Technological limitations:** You may find that your company doesn't have the equipment, space, or know-how to run the Web site. In that case, you may have to post the site through an Internet Service Provider (ISP). For a fee, these providers will allow you to place your Web site on its own server. The provider will maintain and monitor the server but may limit access to the Web site for changes and updates, custom programming/scripting for interactive forms or feedback, and the amount of memory the site can use.
- **A lack of personnel or skill:** You may find people with the skills you need among existing staff. If you can't, you can ask to hire new personnel or contractors. You may have to do without some skills, such as advanced programming; without these skills, you may limit or alter the Web site design.
- **Budget limitations:** Web pages can be expensive. Expect each page to cost $150 and up to create (based on 15 to 20 lines of original text, at least one custom or altered graphic, page layout, HTML coding, some programming/scripting). Even though a Web site doesn't accrue printing costs, maintenance costs may be substantial. You may have to limit the size of the site or use fewer graphics, videos, interactive scripts, and other features.

Figure A.1 Key Business Processes and How the Web Can Support Them

Product Design	Marketing and Sales	Delivery and Installation	Customer Service	Training and Documentation
A Web site accesses the customer, collecting valuable feedback on prototypes or generating ideas for new products.	A Web site could reach new customers and become a new product "outlet." Customers could order products online.	An internet site could coordinate schedules and keep the customer informed about the order.	A Web site could take the load off customer service and give the customer a new way to provide feedback.	Internally, employees could get training online. Externally, customers could always get current product instructions.

If you are new to designing Web sites, you will have to spend more time in the discovery phase than you would with a printed document. These activities will help you analyze your Web site situation:

Familiarize Yourself with the New Medium

Browse through the Internet. Visit sites that teach you how to create Web pages (you'll find the most current information on the Web). Check out several brands of browsers. Bookmark or note the addresses of sites you like.

Study What Your Competition Does on the Web

Visit sites created by your competition or by companies in similar industries.

Survey the Technology and Skills Available in Your Company

After familiarizing yourself with the Web, you will probably have an idea of what you want to do. You can now find people in your company with the technology and skills to create what you have in mind. At the very least, you will need a writer, editor, graphic designer, and HTML coder. You may also want a programmer, a sound/video specialist, and an animator. You may find people who have several of these skills, but you probably will not find one who does them all well. Look for specialized skills in your company.

Take a Fresh Look at Your Business Through the Web

Reexamine how your company works; then try to see how a Web site could replace, enhance, or expand what your company does. Perhaps a Web site might eliminate a bottleneck in customer service. Are your customer service representatives answering the same questions over and over? Put frequently asked questions on the Web site. How do customers get forms or applications from your company? You could skip the copying, printing, mailing process if you put forms on the Web site. Figure A.1 illustrates the ways the Internet could help your company.

Build Your Team

You will need a team that brings together the skills and labor needed to complete the site. For example, if you were creating a products and services site, you might include people from several departments:

- Products and services department
- Human factors design or testing department to help build a reader-friendly site
- Marketing department
- Legal department, because the legal environment of the web is in flux, so a company attorney had best look the site over to avoid legal problems
- Information management/network services if the site will be posted on a company server

Which departments you pull from depends on your Web site's purpose. If you were designing a Web site to inform employees about employee benefits, you might involve some different departments.

Once you identify which groups have a stake in the Web site, recruit people who have the skills you require. The skills needed to create Web sites vary with the type and objectives of the site. Some common skill sets needed to develop a Web site include the following:

- Writer/researcher, to gather and write material for each page in the site
- Graphics designer, to create graphics and lay out the pages
- HTML coder, to code the pages in HTML
- Database manager, to maintain any database the Web site uses and ensure that the database and Web site can interface
- Programmer, to write short programs or scripts that perform advanced functions like downloading files or accumulating answers from a questionnaire
- Sound/video expert, to record and edit the sound and video for the site, and prepare the sound and video to run on the Web
- Animator, to create action on the site

Figure A.2 shows how you might build a Web team, given the skills you need.

After you build your team, you or the team should designate who will be the "webmaster" and "infomaster." Although these two positions are essential for developing the site, their real job begins once the site is active. The webmaster will handle the technical aspects of maintaining the Web site, such as responding to feedback e-mail. The infomaster makes decisions on content updates and changes, like posting a new product or service offer on the site.

Figure A.2
Building the Web
Team

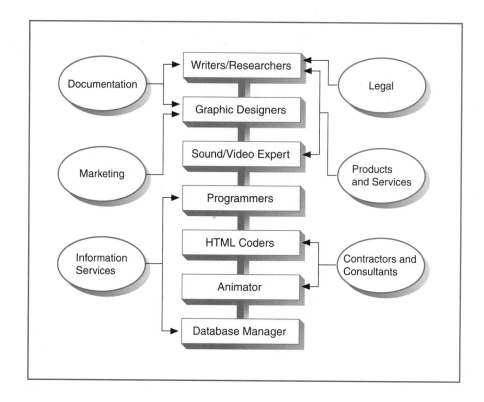

State Your Purpose and Define Objectives

Your team can now decide on the Web site's purpose, explaining the purpose in terms of what they want the user to do. Do you want the user to buy products and services directly from the Web? To learn how to use or install products on the Web? To use the Web to answer common questions instead of calling customer service representatives? To send for information? You may have several goals for your Web site. If so, rate them in order of importance to help you decide later what to include or emphasize.

Once you have your goals listed, decide how you will measure success. For instance, do you want to attract new customers through the Web and automate the order process through the Web, lessening calls to the order department? You can measure your success by charting the number of sales through the Web, while tracking the number of calls the order department receives. If sales increase but the order department has the same number of or fewer calls, you will have succeeded.

Identify Your Readers and Their Technology

Successful Web sites reflect an intimate knowledge of the readers. In fact, successful Web sites build relationships with the readers through the Web, and the readers participate in site design. Don't assume that your readers on the Web

Figure A.3
The Exponential
Growth of Web Users

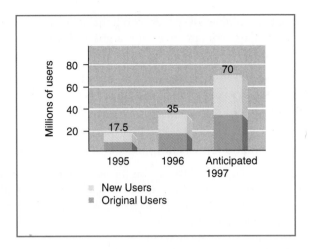

Source: Berst, Jesse. "Swami Berstananda Sees Bumps Ahead." Online. Internet. 13 Sept. 1997. Available: http://www.zdnet.com/anchordesk/story/story_323.html.

are technologically savvy. The Web is growing so quickly that 50 percent of the readers at any time may be novices (Neilsen; see Figure A.3).

Do some real reader research: survey your customers, include questionnaires with invoices, or conduct a focus group with selected customers. Go beyond reader demographics and discover

- What your readers want to know
- How your readers want information presented, how they like to learn
- How your readers search for information
- How your readers use information

Later, when the site is "up" (functioning), you can use the site itself to provide feedback on the readers.

Choose the Right Tools

You will need two types of tools to create your Web site: hardware and software.

Hardware Needed for a Web Site

The hardware needed to store and run a Web site is fairly basic. Hardware requirements include

- **A server, either your own or one provided by an Internet Service Provider (ISP):** If you plan to use a provider, select one early, because different providers have different requirements or limitations for Web sites. (Servers need special software to make them "Internet servers.")
- **Enough space to store your site:** Find some Web sites that you plan to model your site after. Check the size of the file for an average page, multiply by the

estimated number of pages you'll have in your site. Then double that amount. This estimate gives you a good idea of how much memory you'll need—for now.

You'll always need more memory, so plan for growth early. Some sites get so large and servers get so full that companies set up additional servers to handle video and sound.

Software Needed for a Web Site

To code your pages in HTML, you'll need a text editor. If you have any graphics, you'll certainly need a graphics program to create and convert graphics into formats acceptable on the Web (the Web uses graphics in GIF or JPEG format). For large sites, you'll probably want to invest in one of the many software programs that can help you create, design, code, manage, and maintain a site. Web design programs fall into three groups depending on how you design them and how you will use them:

- **Conversion programs:** These programs convert existing documents into Web documents coded in HTML. Don't expect all your current documents to magically become perfect Web pages. You'll have to refine the documents once they have been converted; conversion programs don't always produce exact matches. Fortunately, you can find conversion programs designed for a specific application. For instance, you can find conversion programs designed just for FrameMaker documents. Try out as many programs as you can, for their success depends not only on the application but on the way you've created your particular documents. One program may not convert the type of bullets you use; another may not reproduce the graphics you've created. You'll probably have to make some tradeoffs, depending on which document requires less refining. If you have an extremely large number of documents to convert, consider having a simple program written to convert your particular documents just the way you want them.

- **Page design programs:** These programs help you design and lay out your pages using a WYSIWIG (what you see is what you get) interface. They provide templates for common types of Web pages: company home pages, résumés, glossaries, order forms, search pages, and so on. You can even create and store your own templates for re-use. If you're not familiar with HTML, these programs can get you up and running quickly.

- **Site management programs:** These programs aid in maintaining large sites. They can give you the "big picture" and are especially helpful for managing links. Imagine changing a link that appears on every page in a 100-page site. With many site management programs, you can replace or move a file, and the program automatically changes all the link references throughout the site.

You might find that a couple of programs suit your needs. You may use a conversion program along with a page design program to quickly refine the converted HTML documents. If your site is a large collection of original pages, you'll probably choose a page design program to create and fill the templates; but you may keep the completed pages within a site management program. Just don't expect one program to meet all of your Web needs. Choose programs on the basis of your particular site plans and skill mix.

Another issue to consider at this stage is security. Even if you aren't putting sensitive information on the Web site, you want to minimize the risk of someone getting into your system or even harassing employees. You may need password protection, firewalls (a sort of electronic security gate), encryption, and so on, depending on the sensitivity of the information.

Create and Gather Content for the Web Site

Think of your Web site as part of your company's document set. It should work with the other documents, whether they are print, video, or multimedia. In fact, you can probably use the other documents to provide content for the Web site. You and your team will have to create any information that the existing documents cannot provide. At this stage, follow these steps:

- **Determine what existing content you can use or modify.** You may find that you already have a great deal of content for your Web pages. Some content, such as the text from online presentations, can convert almost directly to Web pages with few changes. You may have to write or edit other text, perhaps product specifications or user manuals, for online use. You can reuse graphics, if converted to JPEG or GIF (graphic formats accepted by the Web). You also can modify the text, video, animation, and sound from multimedia to Web-acceptable formats. You may even choose to let Web visitors download entire online and multimedia presentations to their own desktops.

- **Decide what content you must create, who will provide it, and what form it will take.** You'll have to create some original content. As you create Web content, remember that people are interested in other people, especially in the interactive, social environment of the Web. You may want to give real-life examples of how people use your products.

- **Help your content providers work in the new medium.** The Web may be a new medium for many of your writers. You'll find plenty of articles and books that describe what works best online and especially on the Web. You may want to provide these resources to your writers or summarize the main concepts into a tip sheet or style guide. At the very least, develop an editing checklist (see Figure A.4) to avoid common pitfalls in Web writing.

Design the Web Site and Individual Web Pages

After gathering and collecting information to include in the Web site, the Web team must decide on an overall structure for the site and for individual page layouts. Use everything you know about your readers to structure your site to meet their goals, accommodate their methods for searching, and appeal to their learning styles. Follow these guidelines to structure your site.

Figure A.4
Editing Checklist

Organization and Navigation

During your first pass, go through the entire site. Ignore the small details and make sure that the site is organized logically and that the reader can travel easily through the site. Ask these questions:

- Is the organization reader oriented?
- Are there appropriate organizations or paths for different readers?
- Are the navigation methods obvious to the readers?
- Will readers readily understand where your buttons, icons, or text links take them?
- Are readers ever trapped in a page unable to go to the next logical page or back to the previous pages?
- Are there orientation cues so that readers know where they are at all times?
- Do the screens have titles, subtitles, or numbers?
- Do all links work—and work correctly?

Layout and Design

During your second pass, take a look at the site's appearance. Ask these questions:

- Is the screen layout consistent throughout the site?
- Are too many elements crammed on the screen?
- Do the graphics appear at the right quality and load time?
- Are the graphics clear?
- Do graphics repeat and support the information in the text?
- Are page elements—heading sizes, font sizes, and font colors—consistent?
- Are the tables consistent and aligned properly?

Text Content

During this pass, edit the text for all the problems you look for in print media, plus a few other criteria for online text. Consider these questions:

- Is the text crisp and concise?
- Are sentences and paragraphs as short as possible?
- Is the text using active verbs and present tense while avoiding nominalizations?
- Is punctuation limited, especially colons, semicolons, and quotation marks?

Interactivity and Multimedia

If your site contains special programming for interactivity or multimedia, check that these elements work well within your site. Consider these questions:

- Are your background programs for screen interactivity working properly?
- Are your downloadable files actually downloading?
- Are your sound files and video files loading and intelligible?
- Does your multimedia support information already on the screen?

Organize Your Information to Suit the Readers

If you have several levels of readers, organizing the site becomes complicated. An excellent method to ensure reader-oriented design is to role-play each level of reader. Approach the site just like a reader, and ask questions that a reader would ask. In a product and services site, the team might initially list products and services alphabetically, but the team may realize that readers would search in other ways. The team might then devise several ways for readers to search: keyword search engine, product name and number, product category (entertainment, security, sound, video), reader lifestyle (student, family with children, home office).

Create a Map of Your Site

After you develop several paths for different readers and several layers of information, the site can become confusing and unwieldy. Therefore, try to story-board or map the entire site graphically, showing which pages link to each other. However, don't attempt to force the site into a hierarchical or linear organization. Organize it around the reader's task, not visual tidiness. You may have several tangential paths. Figure A.5 shows a rudimentary site map.

Figure A.5
An Example of a Site Map

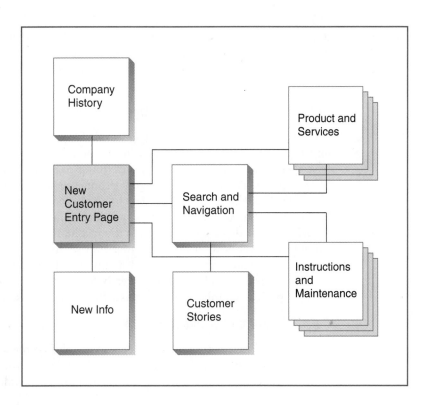

Figure A.6

The "Instruction Page" Template

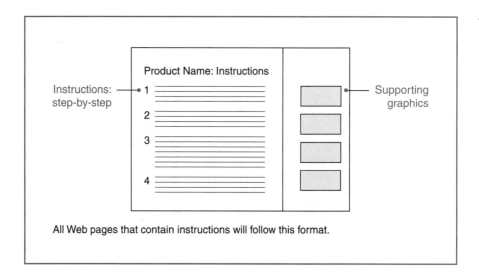

Product Name: Instructions

Instructions: step-by-step

1

2

3

4

Supporting graphics

All Web pages that contain instructions will follow this format.

Design Navigation Aids for Readers

A key to a usable Web site is good navigation aids. Take the time to create navigation buttons and orientation cues for your readers. Provide more than "back" and "home" buttons. The same principles of orientation that serve you for print can help you online. Consistent headers and footers show readers that they're still in your site. Headings and color coding make information from link to link cohesive. Navigation aids are also a design opportunity for your site.

Determine the Layout of Each Page, and Create Templates

Continue the organization at the page level. Try to group the pages of your site into types of pages. For example, in a product and services site, you might have these categories: navigation pages (jump pages that take readers to other pages), product specification pages, product installation pages, and order forms. Decide what you want readers to do at each type of page, and base your layout on that goal. For instance, on product installation pages, you might use the left two-thirds of the page to list the installation steps and the right-hand column to show how-to diagrams that follow the text (see Figure A.6). You might then create an "instruction template" in a page design program. Whenever the text and pictures are ready for a product installation page, you merely open the template, cut and paste the text, and insert the graphics.

Select the Form Your Information Will Take

After you decide what you want readers to do, choose the form of information that will best influence them—text, graphics, video, sound, animation. Don't include "space-hogging" features like video and sound unless they offer readers great value. For example, if your readers learn best visually, you might include a video clip showing the installation procedure for particularly difficult installation steps. Since readers' ability to view or download the clip depends on their browser and "plug-ins," the videos are redundant information, not essential. The site still includes graphics showing the procedure; the video clip merely offers detail on the procedure in case the readers need it.

Create a Construction Plan for Each Page

You'll want to start assigning tasks to members and setting deadlines. To keep the site development on track, create a construction plan for each page or set of pages. This plan should list the type of page, the source of content, the kinds of graphics, any required programming, the edit, and special elements like sound, video, or animation. In the construction plan include a maintenance schedule: when and what needs to be updated or changed and who will be responsible. Then assign each task to a team member with a deadline for completion.

Construct the Web Site

Once you have laid out your site and collected all the necessary information, begin constructing your Web site using these steps.

- **Prepare your text, graphics, sound, video, and animation.** Edit your text to fit the online form: Use shorter sentences and paragraphs, less punctuation, a conversational tone and style, and so on. (As mentioned before, you can find several good sources that detail the criteria for good online information.) Convert your graphics to JPEGs or GIFs. Convert sound, video, and animation into usable Web formats like WAV or MIDI files for sound, Quicktime movies for video, and Java scripts or animated GIFs for animation.

- **Start coding your content into HTML.** Supply your HTML coder with these page elements to be converted into HTML. If you set up templates, you can precode them so that the developer can just drop in text, graphics, and so on. Templates can save a great deal of time. At this stage you also can create the links to the other pages.

- **Provide programming for forms and interactivity.** The last step is to install and test any programming for advanced Web features such as interactive games, response or order forms, feedback questionnaires, and animation. You may start posting an alpha (test) site to the server and protect it with a password until you're ready for outside readers. When the site is ready, just remove the password protection.

Edit and Revise the Web Site

Once the site is complete or once you complete sections of large sites, conduct an initial edit of the site or section, screen by screen. Use these methods for an initial edit:

- Edit the site by role-playing the readers. Go through the site while role-playing each type of reader. Make sure the organization of the site reflects readers' goals.
- Edit the site using a checklist such as the one shown in Figure A.4.

Revise any problems in language, organization, navigation, layout, graphics, and performance.

Test and Revise the Web Site

Testing a Web site can be expensive, time-consuming, and invaluable. In print documents, you use many practices based on years of testing and experience. A Web site is a new medium without the research background that print media have, so the value of user testing is incalculable. If possible, test sections as you complete them. Testing in sections may save days of revision if you catch a problem early enough.

You can conduct a test of the site. In fact, your company may already have a department, such as human factors, that can conduct these tests. One of the fastest, most productive tests is a live feedback test. You can use as few as three readers to gain valuable feedback on your site. For a live feedback test, follow these steps:

- Set up a computer, video camera, microphone, and, if possible, software to record screen activity
- Give the readers a list of tasks to complete at your Web site
- Record their screen movements, comments, and actions as they complete the tasks

The user tests may indicate that you must revise your site extensively, but doing that is better than posting a flawed or ineffective site to the Web.

Edit and Proofread

Before posting, make one last pass through the entire Web site. You might want to ask people within your company to check the site.

Post the Document

If your Web site has been an alpha site already saved on the server, this step may be as simple as removing password protection. If you're posting your site onto an Internet Service Provider's server, prepare for posting to take a bit longer. As mentioned before, Internet Service Providers want to preview a site—especially any programming or scripts that a site uses—before posting it on their server.

Maintain and Refine the Document

Unlike a print document, a Web site is a dynamic document. It doesn't give rise to a "sent to the printer" sense of completion. Your team will have several post-development tasks:

- **Set up a master maintenance schedule for the Web site.** If you've already included maintenance schedules in the construction plan for each page, you can simply compile them into a spreadsheet that indicates which team member is responsible and the dates for each maintenance review.
- **Update the site regularly.** Although the infomaster will decide on adjustments to individual sections or pages, occasionally you need to review the entire site. Schedule meetings to examine the site and any feedback or data collected about the site. You may want to have such meetings monthly or even weekly after the site is first set up, and then meet each quarter.
- **Respond to reader mail.** This response is a key to any site that offers the reader a feedback or comment feature. *You must respond to reader inquiries in a timely manner.* You will anger, frustrate, and alienate visitors if you don't follow up on their communications. If you can't keep up with the responses, don't offer your readers this opportunity.
- **Incorporate user feedback into the site.** If your site does not offer and act on reader feedback, you've created one-way communication, much like a printed document. You've eliminated one of the key reasons for having a Web site if you don't allow and encourage two-way interaction.

PRINCIPLES FOR CREATING READER-ORIENTED WEB SITES

Although the Web doesn't have the base of research that print and other more familiar media have, we can already see some good standards and bad practices emerging. The following principles will help you to create usable, enduring sites while avoiding Web missteps.

Principle 1: Collaborate with Your Readers

Unlike any other media, the Web can offer you immediate access and response to your readers. Within days, even hours, of posting a site, you can start receiving communication from your readers allowing you to start customizing your pages. You can then make changes almost as fast as your readers ask for them.

Principle 2: Plan Your Site in Phases

You don't have to create a full-blown, massive Web site from the beginning. Start simple. Web sites tend to be organic, especially if you involve the readers. You can start with a few, fully developed modules, then add to them. You also can start with a simple design—maybe text and graphics only—then add search engines, interactivity, multimedia, and so on.

Principle 3: Create a Multidimensional Site

Avoid the "front-page" syndrome. Think about how you use the Web. Occasionally, you type in an address for a site and enter by the front page, but more often than not you use a search engine and access a site from an internal

Figure A.7
Designing Multiple
Approaches to Your
Web Site

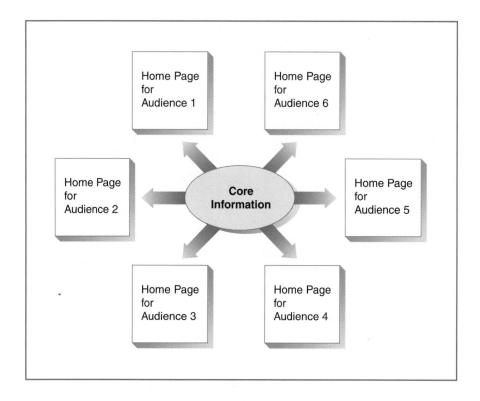

level. Try to create a three-dimensional site, with many entrances to accommodate several readers' purposes, interests, and tasks (see Figure A.7).

Principle 4: Let Function, Not Technology, Rule Content and Drive Your Site

Get past the hype, and evaluate what new technologies can really do for your objectives and readers. Just because you can produce a fancy Web feature doesn't mean you should. Site real estate, server space, load times, and download times are premium commodities. Use them for essential elements. Put multimedia in service only when it offers you great value and return.

Principle 5: Set Measurable Goals for Testing and Monitoring Your Site

Devise a way to measure whether the site is accomplishing your objectives or goals. You can even measure the effectiveness of sites designed to "increase visibility." Avoid "vanity" sites (a site with no real purpose or objective) if you can. Unfortunately, you may not have a choice if your supervisor or manager insists on a Web presence. If your Web site doesn't produce a result or offer value, get off the Web: you're wasting your time and readers' time as well. Try to push for a functional site. Convince management that the Web can save money or increase business if managed properly. At the very least, it can perform some customer-service functions.

Principle 6: Prepare to Spend More Time Maintaining and Refining Your Site Than You Did Developing It

A Web site is like an iceberg: most of the effort and cost involved are below the surface. Plan for maintaining and refining the site. Don't put all your resources into the development and end up with a static, short-lived site.

Principle 7: Meet Your Readers' Expectations for a Changing, Dynamic Site

Web readers expect a site that is dynamic, changing. Some change can be built into the site with programming, like interactive training or reader profiles that call up selective information based on the reader's responses to questions. Try to offer what readers need when they need it, or new information as it becomes available—that's the sort of change readers want. You can overdo change by making only superficial changes. You may have visited sites that offer a different "look" almost every month, although the information never really changes or improves.

Principle 8: Market Your Site Through Other Media

If your site is new to the Web, you can't expect your customer base or new customers to know it's there, and search engines won't always find your site. Start including your site URL (universal resource locator, a Web address for your pages) on all documents, marketing pieces, and advertisements. You may want to produce a special marketing mailout introducing the site to current and potential customers, or you may even want to advertise your site on the Web.

Appendix B

Creating Listener-Oriented Oral Presentations

Are you uncomfortable getting up in front of strangers or even your peers and talking? Do you enjoy making oral presentations? As a professional, you may deliver oral presentations in many settings:

- For your manager, an impromptu status report about a project
- For clients, a twenty-minute presentation of a new customized software package
- For upper-level managers, a brief presentation of proposed upgrades to the manufacturing equipment
- For colleagues at a professional meeting, a scripted speech about a research project

These situations vary in the type of preparation they require, in the use of visual aids, and in style of delivery. This appendix presents three principles to help you plan and deliver oral presentations.

PRINCIPLE 1: PLAN FOR LISTENERS AND THE SITUATION

Before you begin planning the text of your oral presentation, consider the listener and the situation. Ask yourself these questions:

- What do listeners already know about the topic?
- What is the purpose of the presentation?
- What style of presentation will listeners expect?
- How can I best meet listeners' needs and expectations?
- What information should I include? How should I order the information?

Once you have identified the purpose and ascertained what listeners already know, you can plan a presentation that will give listeners what they expect in the available time. You might give one of these styles of oral presentation:

- **Impromptu:** You do not plan an impromptu presentation in advance. You decide what you will say while you are speaking. You might give an impromptu presentation in a staff meeting when someone asks about your research or about a project. You would talk briefly and then answer questions.

- **Extemporaneous:** You plan an extemporaneous presentation in advance and deliver it in a conversational style. Most listeners prefer this type of presentation to the scripted type.

- **Scripted:** You write a scripted presentation in advance and read it (the script) to the listeners.

You can combine these styles in ways that work for you and your listeners. For example, you might begin by reading from a script to introduce a presentation and then switch to an extemporaneous style to discuss examples and visual aids. Figure B.1 presents advantages, disadvantages, and guidelines for each style.

Style of Presentation	Advantages	Disadvantages	Guidelines
Impromptu	• Delivered in a relaxed, conversational manner	• May be disorganized because the speaker can't prepare in advance • May be rambling and unfocused	• Stop and think before speaking • Ask the listeners questions to determine what they want you to speak about
Extemporaneous	• Prepared ahead of time • Delivered in a relaxed, conversational manner • Allows the speaker to adjust the presentation in response to listeners' reactions • Takes less time to create than a scripted presentation	• Can easily run over time • May cause the speaker to leave out information	• Rehearse the presentation • Use visual aids to guide you as you give the presentation (these aids will also help the listeners) • Define any new information or terminology • Use simple, not fancy language • Prepare notes or an outline
Scripted	• Prepared ahead of time • Allows the speaker to deliver complete, accurate information • Helps speaker to stay within time limit	• Often delivered in an unnatural, boring manner • Doesn't allow the speaker to adjust to listeners' reactions • Takes a long time to prepare	• Use for situations where listeners expect precision • Use visual aids and examples • Define any new information or terminology • Use simple, not fancy language

Figure B.1 Advantages, Disadvantages, and Guidelines for Three Styles of Oral Presentation

You can prepare a listener-oriented presentation—whether impromptu, extemporaneous, or scripted—by following these tips:

• Give listeners only the information they need.
• Anticipate listeners' needs and questions.

Give Listeners Only the Information They Need

Keep your presentation short and simple. Listeners want to hear only the information they need and no more. As you prepare your presentation, consider the following:

- **Listening to information takes twice as long as reading that same information.** Thus, if you can read 10 pages in 8 minutes, your listeners can comprehend the same information in about 16 minutes.
- **Condense your presentation into a few key points.** Don't try to give listeners every bit of information you have about a topic or all the tiny details. Instead, select the key points and present those. If necessary, you can refer listeners to your written research, to published articles, or to handouts that you have prepared.
- **Plan the presentation to take slightly less than the allowed time.** Look for ways to tighten your presentation, so you have time for listeners' questions. Listeners generally prefer a presentation that is a couple of minutes short rather than a presentation that exceeds the allotted time.

Anticipate Listeners' Needs and Questions

As you prepare your presentation, think about what listeners already know and what they will want to know about the topic:

- Define any terminology listeners may be unfamiliar with. If your listeners aren't experts in your field, avoid technical terminology when possible.
- Explain any information that may be new to listeners.
- Clarify and support unfamiliar information, especially if listeners may disagree with or try to reject it.

PRINCIPLE 2: USE LISTENER-ORIENTED VISUAL AIDS

Visual aids give listeners something to focus on while you're speaking. Listeners often have difficulty staying focused on an oral presentation—even when the topic is interesting. Their minds tend to wander. Visual aids will enhance your presentation because they

- Keep listeners focused on what you are saying
- Help listeners to remember key points and follow the organization of your presentation
- Help you to stay with your planned organization, to remember what you planned to talk about, and to stay within the allotted time
- Help you to explain ideas, concepts, products, or technical information concisely and briefly

Visual aids can be as simple as handouts, or they can be charts, tables, photographs, or drawings presented by means of computer slides, overhead transparencies, posters, blackboards, or television. To create effective visual aids for oral presentations, follow the guidelines presented here, and review those discussed in Chapter 11, "Creating Effective Visual Aids for Your Readers."

- **The setting is important.** Before you decide the type of visual aids you will use, find out about the room where you will give your presentation. If you plan to use computer slides such as those created by Powerpoint™ or WordPerfect Presentations™, make sure the room has a screen on which to project the slides and appropriate electrical outlets. If you plan to use a dry-erase board or blackboard, make sure the room has these boards and adequate lighting.

- **Legibility counts.** If listeners will be reading your visual aids on a screen or monitor, be sure that your visuals will be legible to all listeners, not just to those sitting up front.

- **Less is more.** Plan to use only the visual aids your listeners will need to understand your presentation. Avoid using visual aids to entertain or to demonstrate your ability to manipulate various technologies. Each visual aid should have a specific purpose and should relate directly to the key points of your presentation.

- **A storyboard might work.** To create visuals that relate directly to key points, try using a storyboard. A storyboard is a two-column format often used to create cartoons, animated films, proposals, and oral presentations (see Figure B.2). A storyboard displays the text of the presentation in one column and a description of the supporting visual in the other column. The planned visual aligns with the related text. Figure B.2 shows a storyboard for an oral presentation on designing Web sites.

- **Technology can help.** Many types of technology are available to help you visually enhance your presentation and to help listeners understand it. You can use slide presentation software such as Powerpoint™ or WordPerfect Presentations™ to create professional-looking visual aids and displays. These software programs allow you to use your laptop computer or computer disk to project slides directly from the computer to a screen. With these programs, you also can print an outline of your presentation and make thumbnail printouts of each slide in the order in which you will present them, and you can reorder the slides. You also can use hypertext and multimedia computer technology to create multidimensional visual aids. Figure B.3 gives some tips for creating listener-oriented visual aids with or without technology.

PRINCIPLE 3: USE EFFECTIVE STRATEGIES FOR DELIVERING THE PRESENTATION

To deliver smooth presentations and to put yourself and your listeners at ease, spend time getting ready:

- Prepare your talk, visual aids, and the room ahead of time.
- Be prepared for emergencies.

Creating User-Oriented Web Sites

Introduction

- To create user-oriented Web sites, follow three principles: consider the users and the purpose, select the right tools, and design the Web site and its individual pages.

Slide: List of the three principles in reverse type on blue background with yellow bullets (all lists will appear in this format)

Consider the users and the purpose

- Think about the users and their purpose for visiting the site.

Slide: List of subordinate points
Slide: Excerpts from two Web sites that meet the users' needs

- Think about the purpose of your site.

- Gather the information to write the pages.

Slide: Sample list of information from a Web site designed by our team

Select the right tools

- Hardware you'll need: a server and ample storage

Slide: List of subordinate points
Slide: List of the two hardware items needed

- Software you'll need: a text editor and possibly a graphics program

- Web design software available

Slide: Chart listing types of Web design software, their capabilities, and their advantages

---

Figure B.2 An Excerpt from a Storyboard for an Oral Presentation

- Help your listeners to enjoy your presentation.
- Provide previews, transitions, examples, and reviews to help listeners follow your presentation.

Prepare Your Talk, Visual Aids, and the Room Ahead of Time

Spend time rehearsing your talk, timing your presentation, putting your visual aids in the order in which you will present them, and checking out the room and its equipment.

- **Rehearse your presentation.** If possible, rehearse your presentation with the actual equipment you will use and in the room where you will speak. As you rehearse, practice with any visual aids that you will use.

- **Time your presentation.** Most oral presentations have an allotted time; so as you rehearse, time your presentation. If the presentation is too long, cut some of the text or some of the visual aids. Allow time for questions from your listeners, and stay within your allotted time.

Figure B.3

Tips for creating listener-oriented visual aids

- Surround the text or image with ample white space.
- Don't put too much text on the visual aid.
- Use phrases rather than sentences.
- Use simple language and images.
- Use bullets with the text when possible.
- Use 18- to 24-point sans-serif type.
- Create a consistent design for all similar visual aids.
- Give each visual aid an informative title.
- Use color to highlight, but use it consistently and sparingly.

- **Put your visual aids in order.** Before your presentation, put your visual aids in the order in which you will present them. Also, note in your outline or on your note cards where to present each visual aid. That way, you won't have to shuffle through your visual aids while your listeners sit and wait.
- **Check out the room and its equipment.** If you are speaking in an unfamiliar setting, check it out before you speak. Find the electrical outlets (if needed), look at the lighting, and determine whether you will need a microphone or a pointer.

Be Prepared for Emergencies

In case your presentation doesn't go as planned, be prepared for emergencies and be flexible. You can lessen the likelihood of some emergencies by doing the following:

- Put transparencies in a three-ring binder. (Put the transparencies in plastic sleeves made for three-ring binders.)
- Take an extra light bulb for the overhead projector or slide projector.
- Take a backup disk if you're using computer software or slides.
- Have a backup plan in case the computer, overhead projector, or slide projector doesn't work.
- Put notes on note cards and number the cards, talk from overhead transparencies, or use an outline to help yourself remember your presentation (for extemporaneous presentations).

Help Your Listeners to Enjoy Your Presentation

Use these simple guidelines to help listeners enjoy and focus on your presentation:

- Talk slowly and distinctly, making sure your listeners can understand your words.
- Look your listeners in the eye. Listeners tend to be suspicious of speakers who don't maintain eye contact.
- Speak with enthusiasm and confidence. Listeners don't want to listen to someone who seems uninterested or who lacks confidence.

- Avoid verbal tics ("um," "ah," "uh"). Rehearsing will help you to eliminate them.

These guidelines will become increasingly easy to follow the more you rehearse and the more presentations you give. If you are well prepared, these guidelines will be easy to follow because you will feel comfortable and confident.

Provide Previews, Transitions, Examples, and Reviews

To help your listeners follow your presentation, give them a road map and some examples:

- **Preview your presentation.** Tell (and possibly show) listeners how you have organized the presentation. Tell listeners what you will be telling them. In this preview, describe the organization of the presentation. Introduce the key points you will discuss (in the order in which you will discuss them). For example, you might say, "This morning, I will talk about X, Y, and Z," and support this preview with a visual aid that lists X, Y, and Z. Then you would discuss X, Y, and Z in the order in which you mentioned them.

- **Use clear transitions between topics.** Transitions tell listeners that you are changing the subject. Without transitions, listeners can misunderstand your words, get confused, or lose their focus. To alert listeners to a change, use transitions such as "My second point is" and "Next, I will discuss." You can also use visual aids to signal a change.

- **Use specific, unambiguous examples.** Examples help listeners to understand complicated or abstract concepts. You can use oral examples, or you can present examples in visual aids.

- **Summarize your presentation at the end.** In the conclusion, summarize your key points. Tell listeners what you've told them. You can use a visual aid to emphasize this summary.

- **Field questions from listeners.** Ask your listeners whether they have any questions. If they do, follow these guidelines: Repeat the question, so you can make sure that you heard it correctly and that all listeners know what question you are answering. Take a few seconds to think before you answer, so you can respond in an organized, clear manner.

CONCLUSION

As a professional, you are likely to give oral presentations in a variety of situations. You might give a presentation informally to your coworkers, or you might present your research or product to hundreds of people attending a professional meeting. In either case, the principles presented here will help you prepare the text and visual aids and deliver the presentation. Oral presentations may often begin and end your work, so be prepared to use them to your advantage. Use the "Worksheet for Creating Listener-Oriented Oral Presentations" as you prepare your oral presentations.

WORKSHEET **for Creating Listener-Oriented Oral Presentations**

Principle 1: Plan for Listeners and the Situation

- Have you given listeners only the information they need?
- Have you anticipated listeners' needs and questions?

Principle 2: Use Listener-Oriented Visual Aids

- Can listeners easily read your visual aids?
- Have you used phrases rather than sentences?
- Have you used simple language and images?
- Have you used 18- to 24-point sans-serif type?
- Have you created a consistent design for similar visual aids?
- Does each visual aid have an informative title?
- Have you used color consistently to highlight?

Principle 3: Use Effective Strategies for Delivering the Presentation

- Have you rehearsed your presentation?
- Have you timed your presentation?
- Have you put your visual aids in order?
- Have you checked out the room and its equipment?
- Have you prepared for emergencies?
- Are you prepared to help your listeners enjoy your presentation?
- Have you previewed your presentation?
- Have you used clear transitions between topics?
- Have you used specific, unambiguous examples?
- Have you reviewed and summarized your key points in the conclusion?
- Are you ready to field questions from the listeners?

Appendix C

Review of Common Sentence Errors, Punctuation, and Mechanics

Grammar, punctuation, and mechanics help a reader to understand your writing. They are like road signs that help you to get to your destination. Without them readers may become confused or may not get to the meaning you intend.

This appendix presents information about common sentence errors, punctuation, and mechanics. The topics within each section appear in alphabetical order, and an abbreviation (such as *cs* for comma splice) accompanies each topic. You can use these abbreviations as you edit your own papers or those of your peers. A complete list of these abbreviations appears at the end of this appendix on page 552. This appendix briefly reviews grammar, usage, and mechanics; it is not a substitute for a complete handbook.

COMMON SENTENCE ERRORS

This section presents common sentence errors and suggests ways to eliminate them.

Agreement Error—Pronoun and Referent

agr p

A pronoun should refer clearly to a specific noun or pronoun—its referent (also called its *antecedent*)—and should agree in number and in gender with that referent.

Correct: **Gwen** paid cash for **her** new **car** although **it** cost more than **she** was hoping to pay.

Correct: The **students** received a trophy for **their** class project.

Whenever you use a pronoun, make sure that its referent is clear.

Vague: Douglas told Bill that he should move his car.

Clear: Douglas told Bill, "I should move my car."
Douglas told Bill, "You should move your car."
Douglas told Bill, "I should move your car."

Pronoun-referent agreement becomes especially tricky with indefinite pronouns (such as *each, everyone, anybody, someone,* and *none*) and collective nouns. When an indefinite pronoun is the referent, the pronoun is singular, as in this example:

Incorrect: **Each** student will receive **their** diploma through the mail.

Correct: **Each** student will receive **his or her** diploma through the mail.

When a collective noun is the referent, determine whether the noun is singular or plural in its context. A collective noun may take a singular or a plural pronoun as its referent. Let's look at an example:

Incorrect:	The **university** will begin a new Internet service for **their** students.
Correct:	The **university** will begin a new Internet service for **its** students.

In this sentence, *university* refers to an individual unit, not to individual members of the university community. It is a singular noun, and the pronoun referring to it must also be singular.

A collective noun can also be plural, as in this example:

Incorrect:	The **company** began a new profit-sharing program for **their** employees.
Correct:	The **company** began a new profit-sharing program for **its** employees.

Here, *company* is a singular noun referring to the company as a single unit.

Agreement Error—Subject and Verb

agr sv

The subject and verb should agree in number. Often writers commit subject-verb agreement errors when the verb follows a prepositional phrase:

Incorrect:	The **consequence** of the accidents **trouble** several board members.
Correct:	The **consequence** of the accidents **troubles** several board members.

The noun *accidents* in the prepositional phrase *of the accidents* does not affect the number of the verb; only the subject of the sentence affects the number of the verb.

Comma Splice

cs

A comma splice occurs when writers incorrectly use a comma to link two independent clauses, as in this example:

Comma Splice:	We baked 10,000 pretzels, we dipped them in dark chocolate.

To correct a comma splice:

- Change the comma into a period followed by a capital letter:

  We baked 10,000 pretzels. We dipped them in dark chocolate.

- Change the comma into a semicolon:

  We baked 10,000 pretzels; we dipped them in dark chocolate.

- Leave the comma and after it add an appropriate coordinating conjunction (*and, or, nor, so, for, yet, but*):

  We baked 10,000 pretzels, and we dipped them in dark chocolate.

- Add a subordinating conjunction to create a sentence consisting of one dependent and one independent clause. A dependent clause has a subject and a verb but can't stand alone; an independent clause has a subject and a verb and can stand alone. In the following example, the dependent clause begins with *after*:

  After we baked 10,000 pretzels, we dipped them in dark chocolate.

Modification Error—Dangling Modifiers

dgl   See Chapter 9, page 178.

Modification Error—Misplaced Modifiers

mm   See Chapter 9, page 177.

Lack of Parallelism

//   Use parallel structure when you put items in a series or in a list. All the items in a series or list must have the same grammatical structure. If the first item is a verb, the remaining items must be verbs. If the first item is a noun, the remaining items must be nouns.

Not Parallel: To complete the course, you will **write a research paper, take four exams, two collaborative projects,** and **participation.**

The first two items in the series are verb phrases, the third item is a noun phrase, and the fourth item is an unmodified noun. To make items in this series parallel in structure, the writer needs to make the third and fourth items verb phrases:

Parallel: To complete the course, you will **write a research paper, take four exams, complete two collaborative projects,** and **participate in class discussions.**

For more information on parallelism, see the discussion of parallelism and headings in Chapter 7, page 143.

Run-On Sentences

ro

A run-on sentence (sometimes called a *fused sentence*) occurs when two or more independent clauses appear together without any punctuation (independent clauses have a subject and a verb and can stand alone). To correct a run-on sentence, you can use the same techniques you would use to correct a comma splice.

Run-on: We baked 10,000 pretzels we dipped them in dark chocolate.
Correct: We baked 10,000 pretzels. **We** dipped them in dark chocolate.
Correct: We baked 10,000 pretzels; **we** dipped them in dark chocolate.
Correct: We baked 10,000 pretzels, and we dipped them in dark chocolate.
Correct: After we baked 10,000 pretzels, we dipped them in dark chocolate.

Sentence Fragment

frag

A sentence fragment is an incomplete sentence. Sentence fragments usually appear because the writer has left out the subject or the verb or failed to write an independent clause, which can stand alone.

Fragments Resulting from Missing Subjects

Fragment: Detached the coupon from the statement.
Complete Sentence: Norma detached the coupon from the statement.

The fragment lacks a subject—no actor is doing the detaching. The complete sentence has a subject—*Norma*.

Fragments Resulting from Missing Verbs

Fragment: Norma detaching the coupon from the statement.
Complete Sentence: Norma is detaching the coupon from the statement.

The fragment lacks a verb; the *-ing* form requires *is, was,* or *will be* to function as a verb in a complete sentence. Let's look at another fragment:

Fragment: The power surge caused by the thunderstorm.
Complete Sentence: The power surge caused by the thunderstorm damaged my computer.

In this example *caused* functions as an adjective, not as a verb.

Fragments Resulting from Failure to Write an Independent Clause

Fragment: You can use the cellular telephone. **If you charge the battery.**

Complete Sentence: You can use the cellular telephone if you charge the battery.

If you charge the battery cannot stand alone as a sentence because it begins with the subordinating word *if*. An independent clause has a subject and a verb and can stand alone.

Verb Tense Errors

t

Writers of technical material often misuse the present and the past perfect tenses and shift tense unnecessarily.

Present Tense

Use the present tense to describe timeless principles and recurring events.

Incorrect: In 1997, the Mars *Pathfinder* scientists discovered that the climate of Mars **was** extremely cold.

Correct: In 1997, the Mars *Pathfinder* scientists discovered that the climate of Mars **is** extremely cold.

The scientists made their discovery in the past—in 1997—but the climate of Mars continues to be cold.

Past Perfect Tense

Use the past perfect tense (indicated by *had*) to indicate which of two past events occurred first.

Correct: The presentation **had started** when we found the overhead projector.

The writer uses the past perfect tense to make clear that when the presentation started, they had not found the overhead projector.

Unnecessary Shifts in Tense

Within a sentence, do not change tense unnecessarily.

| Unnecessary | He **tested** the new hardware, **loaded** the software, **adjusts** the computer settings, and **waited** for the network to respond. |

Needless shifts in tense distract readers. In this example, the tense of the four verbs should be the same:

| Correct: | He **tested** the new hardware, **loaded** the software, **adjusted** the computer settings, and **waited** for the network to respond. |
| Correct: | He **tests** the new hardware, **loads** the software, **adjusts** the computer settings, and **waits** for the network to respond. |

PUNCTUATION

Apostrophe

ap

Use the apostrophe to indicate possession, to create some plurals, and to form contractions.

Apostrophes to Indicate Possession

Use an apostrophe and *s* to create the possessive form of most singular nouns, including proper nouns:

gas's odor

Charles's calculator

student's book

If adding an apostrophe and *s* would create an *s* or *z* sound that is hard to pronounce, then add only an apostrophe, as in *Moses'*. (Try pronouncing *Moses's* and then *Charles's* to see the difference.)

When a plural noun does not end in *s,* add an apostrophe and *s.* When a plural noun does end in *s,* add only an apostrophe.

| men's | students' |
| children's | members' |

To indicate joint possession, add an apostrophe and *s* to the last noun. To indicate separate possession, add an apostrophe and *s* to each noun.

| **Joint Possession:** | John and Stephanie's multimedia presentation |
| **Separate Possession:** | John's and Stephanie's multimedia presentations |

To create the possessive form of pronouns, add an apostrophe and *s* only to indefinite pronouns. Personal pronouns and the relative pronoun *who* have special forms that indicate possession.

Possessives of Indefinite Pronouns	Possessives of Other Pronouns
anyone's	mine (my)
everybody's	his, hers (her), its
everyone's	yours (your)
nobody's	ours (our)
no one's	theirs (their)
other's (*also* others')	whose

Notice that the possessive form of *it* does not have an apostrophe. When you add an apostrophe and *s* to *it*, you create *it's*, the contraction for *it is*.

Incorrect:	The city does not believe the pollution is **it's** problem.
Correct:	The city does not believe the pollution is **its** problem.

Apostrophes to Create Plural Forms

Use an apostrophe to create the plural form of letters and numbers:

a's and b's

8's and 5's (*or* 8s and 5s)

Some companies prefer omitting the apostrophe in plural numbers. Check your company's style guidelines to determine what your company prefers.

Apostrophes to Form Contractions

Use an apostrophe to indicate the omission of a letter or letters in a contraction.

cannot	can't	who is	who's
you are	you're	let us	let's
it is	it's	they are	they're
does not	doesn't	she will	she'll

Brackets
[]/

Use brackets in the following situations:

• To indicate that you've added words to a quotation:

Correct:	The press release said, "They [Thompson and Congrove] voted against the amendment."

• To identify parenthetical information within parentheses:

Correct: (For more information, see Electronic Literacies in the Workplace: Technologies of Writing [Urbana: NCTE, 1996].)

Colon
:/

Use a colon to introduce some quotations and lists; to introduce some words, phrases, and clauses; and to observe other stylistic conventions.

Colons to Introduce Quotations

Use a colon to introduce a long or formal quotation:

Correct: In the Gettysburg Address, Lincoln began: "Fourscore and seven years ago our fathers brought forth on this continent a new nation conceived in liberty and dedicated to the proposition that all men are created equal."

Colons to Introduce Lists

Use a colon to introduce a list when the introductory text would be incomplete without the list:

Correct: For the user testing, you will need the following items: the beta version of the software, a floppy disk, and a notepad.

Colons to Introduce Words, Phrases, and Clauses

Use a colon to introduce a word, phrase, or clause that illustrates or explains a statement:

Correct: Our manager asked the following people to attend the meeting: production editor, art editor, and copy editor.

Correct: He suggested this solution: balancing the turbine to eliminate the vibration.

The text before a colon must have a subject and verb and be able to stand alone.

Incorrect: We discovered problems in: the piping system and the turbine.

Correct: We discovered problems in the piping system and the turbine.

In the incorrect example *We discovered problems in* cannot stand alone; therefore, the colon is incorrect.

Other Conventional Uses of Colons

- **Salutations.** Use a colon after the salutation in a letter:

  Dear Mr. Johnson:

- **Time.** Use a colon to separate hours and minutes:

  8:30 A.M.

- **Subtitles.** Use a colon to separate the main title from a subtitle:

  Creating Web Pages: A Handbook for Beginners

Comma

,/

You will use the comma more often than you use any other punctuation. These guidelines will help you with this most frequently misused of all punctuation marks.

Commas to Separate the Clauses of a Compound Sentence

A compound sentence has two or more independent clauses (independent clauses have a subject and verb and can stand alone). Use a comma to separate the clauses of a compound sentence when a coordinating conjunction (*and, or, for, nor, but, so, yet*) links those clauses.

Correct: We distributed 500 surveys to the shoppers, but we expect only 20 percent to return the surveys.

Often, the comma between the clauses of a compound sentence is necessary to prevent readers from at first thinking that the subject of the second clause is an object of the verb of the first clause:

Incorrect: Bob will use the test results and the survey results will help him to prepare a prototype of the software.

Correct: Bob will use the test results, and the survey results will help him to prepare a prototype of the software.

Without the comma before *and,* readers at first may think that Bob will use both the test results and the survey results. The comma signals that an independent clause, not the object of the verb *use,* follows *and.*

Commas to Separate Items in a Series

Use commas to separate items in a series composed of three or more items:

Correct: The assistant will deliver, collect, and tally the questionnaires.

The comma before the coordinating conjunction *and* is optional; however, most style manuals encourage writers to use the comma to distinguish items, to prevent ambiguity, and to prevent misreading.

Commas to Set Off Introductory Words, Phrases, or Dependent Clauses

Generally, use a comma to set off an introductory word, phrase, or dependent clause from the main clause:

Correct:	Therefore, NASA launched the shuttle two hours later. (introductory word)
Correct:	To localize documents, some companies hire translation agencies. (introductory phrase)
Correct:	Because the team lost the debate, the school will not receive the prize money. (introductory dependent clause)

A comma after an introductory clause can prevent misreading:

Incorrect:	After we completed washing the cat jumped into the tub.
Correct:	After we completed washing, the cat jumped into the tub.

Without the comma, readers at first might think that the cat was being washed.

If the introductory text is short and readers can't misunderstand what you mean, you can omit the comma.

4 -
Commas to Set Off Nonrestrictive Modifiers

A nonrestrictive modifier is not essential to the meaning of a sentence. Writers can omit a nonrestrictive modifier, and readers will still understand the sentence. In contrast, when writers omit a restrictive modifier, they change the meaning of the sentence. Consider these examples:

Restrictive:	Homeowners **who don't pay their property taxes** risk severe penalties and interest.
Nonrestrictive:	Homeowners, **whether novice or experienced,** can benefit from the seminar on home equity.

The restrictive modifier makes clear that not all homeowners, only those who don't pay their property taxes, risk severe penalties and interest. The writer restricts, or limits, the homeowners to those who don't pay their property taxes. The restrictive modifier is essential, but commas are not. The nonrestrictive modifier is not essential, but commas are.

Commas to Separate Coordinate Adjectives

Use a comma to separate coordinate adjectives—adjectives that modify the same noun equally.

Correct: The company will test this fast, powerful computer next week.
Correct: The new design incorporates a bright, rectangular screen.

When adjectives are coordinate, the sentence would still make sense if you replaced the comma with the coordinating conjunction *and*. When adjectives are not coordinate, do not separate the adjectives with a comma. Adjectives are coordinate when the noun and the adjective closest to the noun are closely associated in meaning.

Incorrect: We will begin the test after the second, special session.
Correct: We will begin the test after the second special session.

In this example, the adjective *second* modifies the combination of the adjective *special* and the noun *session*.

Other Conventional Uses of Commas

• **Dates.** Use commas to separate the parts of a date.

Correct: After Friday, January 1, 1999, you may use your corporate card to charge your tickets and meals.

Notice the comma after 1999. If you do not mention the day (January 1999), then omit the comma between the month and year. If you mention the day before the month (1 January 1999), then don't use a comma.

• **Towns, States, and Countries.** Use commas to separate the parts of an address.

Correct: The senator from Madison, Wisconsin, asked the first question.

Notice the comma after *Wisconsin*.

• **Titles of Persons.** Use commas before and after a title that follows a person's name.

Correct: Robert Stevens, Ph.D., will address the faculty on Tuesday.

- **Direct Address.** Use a comma or commas to set off nouns used in direct address.

Correct: My friends, I am happy to report the results of the second test.

Correct: If you are willing to speak, Thomas, we will select a time convenient for you.

- **Quotations.** Use a comma to introduce most quotations.

Correct: According to John Keyes, "Color grabs a reader's attention before the reader understands the surrounding informational context."

Correct: They asked, "How long will the network be down?"

- **Interjections and Transitional Adverbs.** Use a comma or commas to separate interjections and transitional adverbs from the other words in a sentence:

Correct: Well, we did not budget any money for the new generator.

Correct: Therefore, we must wait until the next budget period to purchase the generator.

Correct: The old generator, however, is still fairly reliable.

Dash
—/

Use a dash or dashes to emphasize a parenthetical statement or to indicate a sharp change in thought or tone.

Correct: The United States is a locale, China is a locale, and India is a locale—each has its own set of rules, data, and cultural experiences.

Correct: The judge found the company guilty of deceptive advertising—as I remember.

Exclamation Point
!/

Place an exclamation point at the end of an exclamatory sentence—a sentence that expresses strong emotion.

Correct: The new physics building, originally budgeted for $1.5 million, cost more than $5.5 million!

Since technical writing strives for objectivity, you will rarely use exclamation points in technical documents.

Hyphen

-/

Use hyphens to form compound words, adjectives, fractions, and numbers and to divide words at the end of a line.

Hyphens in Compound Words

A compound word is a word made up of two or more words. Not all compounds are hyphenated. If you are unsure about whether to hyphenate a compound word, check your dictionary.

Hyphenated	Not Hyphenated
up-to-date	workplace
editor-in-chief	proofread
self-image	bulletin board
vice-chancellor	case study

Hyphens to Form Compound Adjectives

A compound adjective is two or more words that serve as a single adjective before a noun.

twenty-one-inch monitor   **up-to-the-minute** news

self-induced attack   **reader-oriented** sentences

black-spotted kitten   **general-to-specific** pattern

Hyphens in Fractions and Compound Numbers

Use hyphens to connect the numerator and denominator of fractions, and to hyphenate compound numbers from twenty-one to ninety-nine, when spelling out numbers is appropriate.

three-fourths   twenty-three

one-third   seventy-seven

For more information on number conventions, see page 551.

Hyphens for End-of-Line Word Breaks

Use a hyphen to divide a word at the end of one line and continue it on the next line. Be sure to divide words only between syllables. Consult a dictionary to identify correct syllable breaks.

Correct: Technical documents can change across cultures just as body language, everyday expressions, and greetings change.

Whenever possible, avoid breaking a word at the end of a sentence. You can avoid end-of-line hyphens by using a ragged right margin. You also can instruct your word-processing software not to hyphenate any words at the ends of lines.

Parentheses
()/

Use parentheses—always in pairs—in the following situations:

• To enclose supplementary or incidental information:

Correct:	Please e-mail me (jsmith@aol.com) when you complete your section of the report.
Correct:	To readers in the United States, EPA (for Environmental Protection Agency) and IRS (for Internal Revenue Service) are common abbreviations.

• To enclose numbers and letters used to identify items listed within a sentence:

Correct:	To log on to the network, (1) type your login name, (2) press the tab key, and (3) type your password.

Parentheses are unnecessary when you display a list vertically:

Correct:	To log on to the network, complete these steps: 1. Type your login name. 2. Press the tab key. 3. Type your password.

Period
./

Use a period at the end of most sentences, after most abbreviations, and as a decimal point.

Periods to Create an End Stop

Put a period at the end of any sentence that does not ask a direct question or express strong emotion (an exclamation):

Correct:	The personal computer has changed the way companies communicate with their employees.
Correct:	Families living near the landfill are asking why the city is hauling in trash from other states.

Periods After Abbreviations

Use a period after most abbreviations. Omit periods from abbreviations for the names of organizations such as corporations and government and international agencies. Also omit periods from acronyms—pronounceable words formed from the initial letters of the words in a name—such as *NASA*.

Ph.D.	GM	WHO
etc.	NCAA	UNESCO
J.D.	FBI	NASA
U.S.	UN	DARE

For more information on abbreviations, see page 549.

Periods as Decimal Points

Use a period in decimal fractions and as a decimal point between dollars and cents:

6.079	69.8%
.05	$789.40

Question Mark

?/

Put a question mark at the end of a sentence that asks a direct question:

Correct: How many volunteers participated in the survey?

Don't put a question mark at the end of an indirect question:

Incorrect: The director asked how many volunteers participated in the survey?

Correct: The director asked how many volunteers participated in the survey.

When a question mark appears within quotation marks, don't include any other end punctuation:

Correct: The director asked, "How many volunteers participated in the survey?"

Quotation Marks

" "/

Enclose short quotations and the titles of some published works in quotation marks. Most writers know when to use quotation marks but have trouble knowing how to use other marks of punctuation with them; therefore, this section presents conventions for punctuation that accompanies quotation marks.

Quotation Marks to Enclose Short Quotations

Enclose a quotation within quotation marks when it is short enough to fit within a sentence and takes up no more than three lines of text:

Correct: According to Thompson, "Monarch butterflies have reddish-brown, black-edged wings."

When a quotation is longer than three lines, these guidelines apply:

- Indent the quotation 10 spaces from the left-hand margin.
- Omit the quotation marks. The indentation serves the same purpose as the quotation marks enclosing a short quotation.
- Introduce the quotation with a complete sentence followed by a colon.

Correct: Thompson writes the following about Monarch butterflies:

> Monarch butterflies have reddish-brown, black-edged wings. The larvae of these butterflies feed on milkweed. These butterflies migrate hundreds of miles through North America. They have been sighted as far south as Mexico and as far north as Canada.

Quotation Marks Around the Titles of Some Works

Place quotation marks around titles of articles from journals, newspapers, and other periodicals:

Correct: Tumminello and Carlshamre's article "An International Internet Collaboration"

Conventional Punctuation with Quotation Marks

If you are writing for readers in the United States, follow the conventions presented below. If you are writing for readers in other countries, consult other style guides, especially for the positioning of commas and periods with quotation marks.

- **Commas and Periods.** Put commas and periods inside the quotation marks.

Correct: Joanna Tumminello and Pär Carlshamre wrote "An International Internet Collaboration."

Correct: He cited "An International Internet Collaboration," an article by Joanna Tumminello and Pär Carlshamre.

• **Semicolons and Colons.** Put semicolons and colons outside the quotation marks.

Correct: Joanna Tumminello and Pär Carlshamre wrote "An International Internet Collaboration"; this article includes valuable information about collaborating to complete a research project.

• **Question Marks, Dashes, and Exclamation Points.** Put question marks, dashes, and exclamation points inside the quotation marks when they apply to the quoted material only and outside the quotation marks when they apply to the entire sentence.

Correct: She asked, "Have you completed the audit?" (inside)
Correct: Did she ask, "Have you completed the audit"? (outside)

Semicolon

;/

You can use semicolons in the following situations.

Semicolons to Link Independent Clauses

Place a semicolon between two independent clauses not linked by a coordinating conjunction (*and, or, nor, so, for, but, yet*):

Incorrect: The newest version of the software has more options; but it requires more memory and a faster processor.
Correct: The newest version of the software has more options; however, it requires more memory and a faster processor.

Semicolons to Separate Items in a Series

Use a semicolon to separate the items in a series when any one of the items already has internal punctuation:

Correct: The production team consists of the following people: Patrick Sims, managing editor; Norma Rowland, production editor; Gwen Chavez, copy editor; and Thomas Thompson, art editor.

MECHANICS

Abbreviations

ab

Often you can save time and improve sentence flow by using abbreviations. Use them judiciously, however, because your readers may not be familiar with them. If your readers include people who are not experts in your field, try not to use abbreviations. If you feel you can't avoid abbreviations, attach a list explaining what each one means. Whenever you are uncertain about whether or how to use an abbreviation, spell out the term.

When you use abbreviations, follow these guidelines:

- Use the singular form for most units of measure even when the word would be plural if spelled out:

  psi   means either "pound per square inch" or "pounds per square inch"

  oz   means either "ounce" or "ounces"

- Use a period after the abbreviation for clarity if readers might confuse an abbreviation for some other word. Otherwise, generally omit the period from technical abbreviations. These abbreviations are some that might require a period:

  in.   fig.   bar.

- Spell out short or common terms:

  ton

  acre

- Abbreviate units of measurement when a number precedes them:

Incorrect:	How many sq ft?
Correct:	How many square feet?
Incorrect:	10 square feet
Correct:	10 sq ft

Capitalization

cap

In technical communication, follow the capitalization conventions that apply to general writing. The conventions listed here are the most important ones; for a more complete list, consult your dictionary. Most dictionaries put the list in the end matter—after the list of words. You can also consult the style guides mentioned in Chapter 6.

- Capitalize proper nouns, such as personal names, formal titles, place-names, languages, religions, organizations, days of the week, and months:

Kathryn Sullivan (personal name)   Catholicism (religion)

Chief Counsel (formal title)   American Association of Mechanical
                                          Engineers (organization)
Europe (place-name)
                                        Monday, Tuesday (days of the week)
Chinese (language)
                                        January, February (months)

- Don't capitalize seasons, compass directions (unless the reference is to a geographic region), and areas of study (unless the area already is a proper noun):

  winter, spring, summer, fall (seasons)

  We traveled north through Wyoming. (direction)

  The storm hit the Pacific Northwest. (geographic region)

  the study of language (area of study)

  the study of the French language (area of study)

- Capitalize the first word, the last word, and every important word in titles and headings:

  Technical Writing for Readers and Writers (title)

  Research on Electronic Mail and Other Media (heading)

Italics

ital

Instead of italics, you can use underlining, although most companies and publishers prefer italics. Use italics or underlining in the following instances:

- For Latin scientific names:

  Lagerstroemia indica (crepe myrtle)

  Tryngites subruficollis (buff-breasted sandpiper)

- For the titles of books, plays, pamphlets, periodicals, manuals, radio and television programs, movies, newspapers, lengthy musical works, trains, airplanes, ships, and spacecraft:

  War and Peace (book)   *Madame Butterfly* (musical work)

  Hamlet (play)   *Titanic* (ship)

  60 Minutes (television program)   *Apollo V* (spacecraft)

  New York Times (newspaper)

- For foreign words that are not widely considered to be part of the English language:

  The county levied an *ad valorem* tax.

Your dictionary may help you decide whether italic is necessary.

- For words, letters, and numbers referred to as such:

  Use the coordinating conjuctions *and, so, nor, but, yet, for, or.*

  The child should work on writing lowercase *a* and *d* and the number *8.*

Numbers
num

Rules for using numbers vary widely and in many instances differ from one field to another. Be sure to follow the standard practices of your field or company and use numbers consistently throughout each document.

These guidelines will apply to nearly all technical documents:

- When a number is the first word of a sentence, do not use numerals. Either spell out the number or, if you can't express it in two words, rewrite the sentence.

Incorrect:	25 years ago, we began offering this degree.
Correct:	Twenty-five years ago, we began offering this degree.
Incorrect:	One thousand seventy-five of the 6,500 people we contacted returned the questionnaire.
Correct:	Of the 6,500 people we contacted, 1,075 returned the questionnaire.

- Use numerals for days and years in dates, exact sums of money, exact times, addresses, percentages, statistics, scores, and units of measurement:

  March 31, 1999 or 31 March 1999 (dates)

  $6,432.58 (money)

  6:34 P.M. (time)

  2103 Vintage Court (address)

  67 percent *or* 67% (percentage)

  a mean of 13 (statistic)

  a total score of 98.7 (score)

  37°F (unit of measurement)

- When mentioning rounded-off figures, use words:

  about five million dollars

  approximately nine o'clock

- When mentioning two sets of numbers back to back, use numerals for one and spell out the other:

  nine 2-inch screws

Correction Symbols

Common Sentence Errors

agr p	agreement error—pronoun and referent
agr sv	agreement error—subject and verb
cs	comma splice
dgl	dangling modifier
mm	misplaced modifier
ll	lack of parallelism
ro	run-on sentences
frag	sentence fragment
t	verb tense error

Punctuation

ap	apostrophe
[ ]/	brackets
:/	colon
,/	comma
—/	dash
!/	exclamation point
-/	hyphen
( )/	parentheses
./	period
?/	question mark
" "/	quotation marks
;/	semicolon

Mechanics

ab	abbreviation
cap	capitalization
ital	italics
num	numbers

Works Cited

American National Standards Institute. "American National Standards for Product Safety Signs and Labels." American National Standards Institute, 1989.

Anderson, Paul. "What Survey Research Tells Us About Writing at Work." *Writing in Nonacademic Settings*. Ed. Lee Odell and Dixie Goswami. New York: Guilford, 1985. 3–84.

Baker, William H. "How to Produce and Communicate Structured Text." *Technical Communication* 41 (1994): 456–66.

Barabas, Christine. *Technical Writing in a Corporate Culture: A Study of the Nature of Information*. Norwood: Ablex, 1990.

Barnum, C., and R. Fischer. "Engineering Technology as Writers: Results of a Survey." *Technical Communication* 31.2 (1984): 9–11.

Beason, Gary. "Redefining Written Products with WWW Documentation: A Study of the Publication Process at a Computer Company." *Technical Communication* 43 (1996): 339–48.

Beauchamp, Tom L., and Norman E. Bowie. *Ethical Theory and Business*. 2nd ed. Englewood Cliffs: Prentice Hall, 1983.

Bellis, Jack. "Information: What Should Go Online and What Should Go in Print?" *Intercom* (Nov. 1996): 20–21.

Benson, Philippa J. "Writing Visually: Design Considerations in Technical Publications." *Technical Communication* 32.4 (1985): 35–39.

Bosley, Deborah S. "International Graphics: A Search for Neutral Territory." *Intercom* (Aug./Sept. 1996): 4–7.

Brockmann, R. John. *Writing Better Computer User Documentation: From Paper to Hypertext Version 2.0*. New York: Wiley, 1990.

Caher, John M. "Technical Documentation and Legal Liability." *The Journal of Technical Writing and Communication* 25 (1995): 5–10.

Cash, J. I., Jr. "A New Farmers' Market." *InformationWeek* 26 Dec. 1994: 60.

Charney, Davida, Lynee Reder, and Gail Wells. "Studies of Elaboration in Instructional Texts." *Effective Documentation: What We Have Learned from Research*. Ed. Stephen Doheny-Farina. Cambridge: MIT, 1988. 47–72.

Cobb, Neil. Telephone interview. 30 Aug. 1997.

Dautermann, Jennie. "Writing with Electronic Tools in Midwestern Businesses." *Electronic Literacies in the Workplace: Technologies of Writing*. Ed. Patricia Sullivan and Jennie Dautermann. Urbana: NCTE, 1996.

Digital Equipment Co. *The Personal Computer Documenter's Guide*. Maynard: Digital Equipment, 1983.

Dragga, Sam. "Classifications of Correspondence: Complexity versus Simplicity." 18.1 (1991): 1–14.

Duin, Ann Hill. "How People Read: Implications for Writers." *The Technical Writing Teacher* 15 (1988): 185–93.

- - -. "Reading to Learn and Do." *Proceedings of the 35th International Technical Communication Conference, May 10–13, 1988, Philadelphia.* Washington: Society for Technical Communication, 1988.

Ede, Lisa, and Andrea Lunsford. *Singular Texts/Plural Authors: Perspectives on Collaborative Writing.* Carbondale: Southern Illinois UP, 1990.

Elbow, Peter. *Writing with Power: Techniques for Mastering the Writing Process.* Oxford: Oxford UP, 1981.

Felker, Daniel B., et al. *Guidelines for Document Designers.* Washington: American Institutes for Research, 1981.

Foy, Patricia S. "The Re-Invention of the Corporate Information Model." *IEEE Transactions on Professional Communication* 39 (1996): 23–29.

Fry, Pamela S. Informal interview. Oct. 1996.

Golen, Steven, Celeste Powers, and M. Agnes Titkemeyer. "How to Teach Ethics in a Basic Business Communication Class—Committee Report of the 1983 Teaching Methodology and Concepts Committee, Subcommittee 1." *Journal of Business Communication* 22.1 (1985): 75–83.

Gomes, Lee. "Advanced Computer Screens Have Age-Old Rival." *San Jose Mercury News* 21 February 1994.

Greenly, Robert. "How to Write a Résumé." *Technical Communication* (1993): 42–48.

Halpern, J. W. "An Electronic Odyssey." *Writing in Nonacademic Settings.* Ed. Lee Odell and Dixie Goswami. New York: Guilford, 1985. 157–201.

Hansen, Amy. "What Ever Happened to the Traditional Resume: Preparing Students for an Electronic Job Search." *ATTW Bulletin.*

Hansen, James B. "Editing Your Own Writing." *Intercom* (February 1997): 14–16.

Haramundanis, Katherine. *The Art of Technical Documentation.* Maynard: Digital Press, 1992.

Harris, Irene. "The 'Seven Commandments' of Keyboard Ergonomics." *Intercom* 43.10 (1996): 16–17.

Hayes, John R., and Linda S. Flower. "On the Structure of the Writing Process." *Topics in Language Disorders* 7 (1987): 19–30.

Holland, V. Melissa, Veda R. Charrow, and William W. Wright. "How Can Technical Writers Write Effectively for Several Audiences at Once?" *Solving Problems in Technical Writing.* Ed. Lynn Beene and Peter White. New York: Oxford UP, 1988. 27–54.

Horton, William. "The Almost Universal Language: Graphics for International Documents." *Technical Communication* 40 (1993): 682–93.

Horton, William. *Illustrating Computer Documentation.* New York: Wiley, 1991.

- - -. "Overcoming Chromophobia: A Guide to the Confident and Appropriate Use of Color." *IEEE Transactions on Professional Communication.* 34 (1991): 160–71.

Johnson-Eilola, Johndan. "Relocating the Value of Work: Technical Communication in a Post-Industrial Age." *Technical Communication Quarterly* 5.3 (1996): 245–70.

Kellogg, Ronald T. "Attentional Overload and Writing Performance: Effects of Rough Draft and Outline Strategies." *Journal of Experimental Psychology: Learning, Memory, and Cognition* 14 (1988): 355–65.

Keyes, Elizabeth. "Typography, Color, and Information Structure." *Technical Communication* 40 (1993): 638–54.

Kintsch, Eileen. "Macroprocesses and Microprocesses in the Development of Summarization Skill." ERIC Document ED305613. Washington: Educational Research Information Center, 1989.

Klein, Fred. "Beyond Technical Translation: Localization." *Intercom* (May 1997): 32–33.

Koop, W. E., and R. L. Duble. *Thatch Control in Home Lawns*. College Station: Texas Agricultural Extension Service, 1982.

Krull, Robert, and Jeanne M. Hurford. "Can Computers Increase Writing Productivity?" *Technical Communication* 34 (1987): 243–49.

Krull, Robert, and Philip Rubens. "Effects of Color Highlighting on User Performance with Online Information." 33 (1986): 268–69.

Lakoff, R. T. "Some of My Favorite Writers Are Literate: The Mingling of Oral and Literate Strategies in Written Communication." *Spoken and Written Language*. Ed. D. Tannen. Advances in Discourse Processes, Series 9 (Norwood: Ablex, 1982): 239–60.

LaQuey, Tracy. *The Internet Companion: A Beginner's Guide to Global Networking*. Reading, MA: Addison, 1994.

Lay, Mary M. "Nonrhetorical Elements of Layout and Design." *Technical Writing: Theory and Practice*. Ed. Bertie E. Fearing and W. Keats Sparrow. New York: MLA, 1989. 72–89.

Locker, Kitty O. *Business and Administrative Communication*. Homewood: Irwin, 1989.

Lorch, Robert F., and Elizabeth Pugzles Lorch. "Online Processing of Text Organization." ERIC Document ED245210. Washington: Educational Research Information Center, 1984.

Mannix, Margaret. "Writing a Computer-Friendly Resume: The Old Rules of Presenting Yourself Might Now Hurt." *U.S. News and World Report* 26 Oct. 1992: 90–93.

Martin, Cynthia J. "Individually and as Executrix of Eugene J. Martin, Deceased, v. Arthur Hacker, et al., and Chelsea Laboratories, Inc., et al." *83 NY2nd I* 23 Nov. 1993.

Martinez, Benjamin, and Jacqueline Block. *Visual Forces*. Englewood Cliffs: Prentice Hall, 1988.

Mirshafiei, Mohsen. "Culture as an Element in Teaching Technical Writing." *Technical Communication* 41.2 (1994): 276–82.

National Council of Teachers of English. *Guidelines for Nonsexist Use of Language in NCTE Publications*. Rev. ed. Urbana: NCTE, 1985.

Neilsen, Jakob. "The Web Backlash of 1996." (April 1996). Online. 18 Sept. 1997. Available html://www.useit.com/alertbox/9604.html.

Ong, W. J. "Literacy and Orality in Our Times." *The Writing Teacher's Sourcebook.* Ed. G. Tate and Edward P. J. Corbett. New York: Oxford UP, 1981. 36–48.

Parker, Roger. *Looking Good in Print.* 2nd ed. Chapel Hill: Ventana Press, 1990.

Parson, Gerald M. "A Cautionary Legal Tale: The Bose v. Consumers Union Case." *The Journal of Technical Writing and Communication* 22 (1992): 377–86.

Perl, Sondra. "The Composing Processes of Unskilled College Writers." *Research in the Teaching of English* 13 (1979): 317–36.

Perry, T. S. "E-Mail at Work." *IEEE Spectrum* Oct. 1992: 24–28.

Perry, T. S., and J. A. Adam. "E-Mail Pervasive and Persuasive." *IEEE Spectrum* Oct. 1992: 22–23.

Pugh, A. "The Development of Silent Reading." *The Road to Effective Reading.* Ed. W. Latham. London: Ward Lock, 1975.

Raign, Kathryn, and Brenda Sims. "Gender, Persuasion Techniques, and Collaboration." *Technical Communication Quarterly* 2.1 (1993): 89–104.

Reich, Robert B. *The Work of Nations: Preparing Ourselves for 21st-Century Capitalism.* New York: Knopf, 1991.

Rubens, Philip M. "Reinventing the Wheel? Ethics for Technical Communicators." *Journal of Technical Writing and Communication* 11 (1981): 329–39.

Samuels, Marilyn Schauer. "Scientific Logic: A Reader-Oriented Approach to Technical Writing." *Journal of Technical Writing and Communication* 12.4 (1982): 307–28.

Selzer, Jack. "Arranging Business Prose." *Writing in the Business Professions.* Ed. Myra Kogen. Urbana: NCTE, 1989.

Shimberg, H. Lee. "Technical Communicators and Moral Ethics." *Technical Communication* 27 (1980): 10–12.

Simon, Jerold. "How to Write a Résumé." N.p.: International Paper Company, 1981.

Sims, Brenda R. "Electronic Mail in Two Corporate Workplaces." *Electronic Literacies in the Workplace: Technologies of Writing.* Ed. Patricia Sullivan and Jennie Dautermann. Urbana: NCTE, 1996. 41–64.

- - -. "Linking Ethics and Language in the Technical Communication Classroom." *Technical Communication Quarterly* 2.3 (1993): 285–99.

Sims, Brenda R., and Stephen Guice. "Differences between Business Letters from Native and Non-Native Speakers of English." 29.1 (1992): 23–39.

Sims, William W. Personal interview. 12 Feb. 1997.

Spivey, Nancy Nelson, and James R. King. "Readers as Writers Composing from Sources." *Reading Research Quarterly* 24.1 (1989): 7–26.

Stein, Judith, and JoAnne Yates. "Electronic Mail: How Will It Change Office Communication? How Can Managers Use It Effectively?" *Information Systems and Business Communication.* Ed. Raymond W. Beswick and Alfred B. Williams. Urbana: American Business Communication Assn., 1983. 99–105.

Sticht, T. "Understanding Readers and Their Uses of Text." *Designing Usable Texts.* Orlando: Academic Press, 1985.

Sticht, T., L. Fox, R. Hauke, and D. Welty-Zapf. *The Role of Reading in the Navy.* San Diego: Navy Personnel R and D Center. Sept. 1977.

Taylor, Barbara M., and Richard W. Beach. "The Effects of Text Structure Instruction on Middle-Grade Students' Comprehension and Production of Expository Text." *Reading Research Quarterly* 19.2 (1984): 134–46.

Thomas, L. *The Self-Organized Learner and the Printed Page*. Uxbridge: Brunel University Centre for the Study of Human Learning, 1976.

Tumminello, Joanna, and Pär Carlshamre. "An International Internet Collaboration." *Technical Communication* 43.4 (1996): 413–18.

Wambeam, Cynthia A., and Robert Kramer. "Design Teams and the Web: A Collaborative Model for the Workplace." *Technical Communication* 43.4 (1996): 349–56.

Weber, Jean H. "Taming a Telecommuting Team." *Intercom* (Aug./Sept. 1996): 22–23.

White, Jan. *Visual Design for the Electronic Age*. New York: Watson-Guptill, 1988.

Wicclair, Mark R., and David K. Farkas. "Ethical Reasoning in Technical Communication: A Practical Framework." *Technical Communication* 31 (1984): 15–19.

Williams, Joseph M. *Style: Ten Lessons in Clarity and Grace*.

Winsor, Dorothy A. "The Construction of Knowledge in Organizations: Asking the Right Questions about the *Challenger*." *Journal of Business and Technical Communication* 4.2 (1990): 7–20.

Yeo, Sarah C. "Designing Web Pages That Bring Them Back." *Intercom* 43.3 (1996): 12–14.

Index